Applied Statistics (Continued)

HOEL · Elementary Statistics
KEMPTHORNE · An Introduction to Genetic Statistics
MEYER · Symposium on Monte Carlo Methods
MUDGETT · Index Numbers
RICE · Control Charts
ROMIG · 50–100 Binomial Tables
TIPPETT · Technological Applications of Statistics
WILLIAMS · Regression Analysis
WOLD and JURÉEN · Demand Analysis
YOUDEN · Statistical Methods for Chemists

Books of Related Interest

ALLEN and ELY · International Trade Statistics
ARLEY and BUCH · Introduction to the Theory of Probability and Statistics
CHERNOFF and MOSES · Elementary Decision Theory
HAUSER and LEONARD · Government Statistics for Business Use, *Second Edition*
STEPHAN and McCARTHY · Sampling Opinions—An Analysis of Survey Procedures

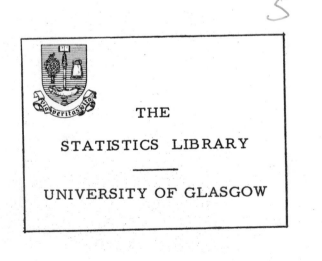

Elements of
Mathematical Statistics

A WILEY PUBLICATION IN MATHEMATICAL STATISTICS

Elements of
Mathematical Statistics

HOWARD W. ALEXANDER

Earlham College
Richmond, Indiana

John Wiley & Sons, Inc.
New York · London

Preface

Euclid, in writing his *Elements*, set himself the task of making a careful selection among the geometrical propositions extant in his time and arranging them in a logical and systematic sequence. In a science so young and so vigorously growing as mathematical statistics the task of selecting the essential is indeed difficult; it is highly unlikely that any selection of topics will receive the unanimous endorsement of teachers of the subject. Nevertheless, the topics here selected for inclusion form, in my opinion, the indispensable core of the subject. In Euclid's sense, therefore, they form the elements of statistical theory.

The form which the book has taken has been largely the product of a number of presuppositions. It is intended as an introduction to probability and mathematical statistics for students who have completed a year of calculus. No prior acquaintance with probability or statistics is assumed. The book should be completely understandable by the student who wishes to pursue the subject by himself, without the assistance of a teacher. Such ideas as are introduced from the theory of sets, from advanced calculus, and from linear algebra should be expounded in the text itself, with minimum dependence on other references. These have been the guiding aims in the writing.

Two central themes run through modern mathematical statistics: first, the notion of a sampling distribution, and the techniques of deriving sampling distributions from the distribution of the parent population; second, the concept of statistical inference, and the methodology connected therewith. These ideas lead to a structure of concepts and methods which is basically dissimilar to the structure of ideas in algebra, geometry, or analysis encountered in the undergraduate curriculum. Added to this difficulty is the necessity of repeatedly using integrals which are not usually included in calculus textbooks, as for example the large variety of integrals related to the gamma function. In this book an effort has been made to see that not too many of these difficulties are encountered at once and that as far as possible the new ideas are related to ideas with which the student may be familiar.

The approach toward abstraction in this book is very gradual. This method has been adopted in the belief that students are likely to feel insecure in their first introduction to probability theory. By expressing new ideas in terms of simple sampling devices (urn and spinner), a good intuitive preparation is provided for the abstract concepts which appear later in the book. Some students, and some classes, will wish to move rapidly over the early sections; others will find it profitable to deal thoroughly with this intuitive background material.

There is no doubt that probability theory is best erected on a foundation of set theory. The set-theoretical ideas used in this book are developed in Sections 2, 3, 5, and 6, largely in an intuitive and informal fashion. As one progresses through the book, set theory recedes into the background. It is my conviction that the presentation of set theory provided in Chapter 1 is adequate for a first course in probability and statistics and that a more sophisticated treatment can well be given in connection with a second course.

The more difficult topics will, in general, be found in the final sections of each chapter. Those that can be omitted without seriously handicapping later developments are starred. The sets of exercises have also been graded, so that the final (starred) exercises in many sets present either problems to challenge the abilities of the better student or significant extensions of the theory. It will be noted that the treatment of moment generating functions falls entirely in the starred sections. The moment generating function is judged to be a topic at the level of advanced calculus, which may well be postponed, as far as extensive treatment is concerned, until the student has developed a sound intuition in working with sampling distributions. In a first encounter the emphasis is best placed on methods of obtaining sampling distributions which focus attention on the sample space. The great beauty and economy of methods employing the moment generating function can then be better appreciated.

The structure of the book may be briefly indicated. Of the seven chapters, the fourth, on statistical inference, is pivotal. The aim in the preceding chapters has been primarily to develop enough probability and sampling theory so that a proper conceptual framework can be provided for statistical inference. Chapters 1 and 2 present the probability theory and the descriptive statistics of a single random variable. A few scattered results concerning sampling distributions are introduced where there is opportunity. Chapter 3 is devoted primarily to the simplest types of sampling distributions and to some of the simpler ways of deriving them.   This necessitates a full discussion of bivariate distributions and some mention of multivariate distributions.   After Chapter 4 the exposition divides into two main branches: sampling theory on the one hand (to which Chapter 5 is devoted) and statistical methodology on the other, represented in Chapter 6 by regression and correlation theory and in Chapter 7 by the simpler forms of analysis of variance.   The final sections of these two chapters are, however, devoted to the distribution theory associated with these methods.

A one-semester course should include Chapters 1 through 4, with or without the starred sections, supplemented if necessary by selected topics from Chapters 5 and 6.   A two-semester sequence can be based on the whole book.   Flexibility can be gained by deciding in what way the starred sections and exercises are to be used, whether as special assignments for independent study or as topics for class discussion.

An effort has been made to provide alternative paths at many points. It would be entirely possible to use all of Chapter 6, except for the final section, immediately after Chapter 3.   Or Chapters 6 and 7, omitting Sections 51 and 55, might follow Chapter 4.   Again, the book provides for a number of alternative treatments of certain topics.   For example, the normal reproductive law is treated geometrically in Section 25, by moment generating functions in Section 27, and by direct integration in Section 36.

Answers to the odd-numbered exercises are given at the end of the book.   Answers to the even-numbered exercises are given in a separate booklet which may be obtained from the publisher.

I gratefully acknowledge my deep indebtedness to all who have written earlier and to many who have given counsel and encouragement.   This debt is greatest to C. C. Craig, H. Cramér, R. A. Fisher, D. A. S. Fraser, T. C. Fry, A. Hald, P. G. Hoel, A. M. Mood, and S. S. Wilks.   Without the continuing help of Professor Wilks over a period of many years I doubt whether this book would ever have been written.

For permission to print Tables 3 and 5, I am indebted to the Trustees of *Biometrika*, to Dr. A. M. Mood, and to the McGraw-Hill Book Company; and for permission to use Table 4, I am indebted to Professor Sir Ronald A. Fisher and to Dr. Frank Yates, F.R.S., Rothamsted, as well as to Messrs. Oliver & Boyd Ltd., Edinburgh, to Dr. A. M. Mood, and to the McGraw-Hill Book Company.   These three tables are reproduced from Dr. Mood's book, *Introduction to the Theory of Statistics*, and are adapted from the sources indicated below the tables.

Criticisms and suggestions will be welcomed from the users of this book. I will also be grateful for notification of errors that remain in spite of efforts to eliminate them.

HOWARD W. ALEXANDER

Richmond, Indiana
March, 1961

Contents

CHAPTER 1

Discrete Distributions

1. POPULATIONS, SAMPLES, AND RANDOM EXPERIMENTS

The central question with which mathematical statistics is concerned may be stated as follows: given a set of data (called a *sample*) which is representative of a much larger set (called the *population* or *universe*), how may the information in the sample be used to reach dependable conclusions about the population? In order to clarify these ideas, consider Examples 1.1 through 1.6.

Example 1.1. Of great importance in industrial work is the method of inspection known as *sampling inspection*. A receiving inspector at an industrial plant receives a shipment of 10,000 pieces (let us say machine screws), identical except for such small variations as the producer could not conveniently or economically eliminate. Instead of examining every screw in the shipment, he takes a sample of 200 screws and after a careful inspection he finds seven defectives among them. From this information he wishes to draw some sort of conclusion about the number of defectives in the whole lot. More probably, he wants to know whether to accept or reject the lot on the basis of the information he has gleaned from the sample. The methods by which such a decision may be reached are presented in Chapter 4. In this example the population or universe is simply the shipment or lot consisting of 10,000 pieces. It would be possible to inspect every one of the 10,000 pieces, but experience shows that this is not economical and that entirely satisfactory results can be obtained if a suitable sampling plan is employed.

It is clear that many different samples of 200 could be obtained from the shipment of 10,000 and that the number of defective screws obtained upon inspection would vary from sample to sample. Such a sampling process is an illustration of a *random experiment*, a concept of central importance for our subject. We shall shortly be considering a variety of types of random experiments, all possessing these features: there is a set of possible results or *outcomes* of the experiment, any one of which might possibly occur on a single repetition of the experiment; nevertheless, the precise outcome of any particular trial in the experi-

1

ment cannot be known in advance. In Example 1.1 the set of possible outcomes would consist of the numbers $\{0, 1, 2, \cdots, 200\}$, each of which represents a possible number of defectives in a sample of 200.

Note that the set of outcomes of the random experiment in Example 1.1 is specified in such a way that each possible result of the experiment can be identified with one and only one member of the set. When this is the case, we say that the set of outcomes is *exhaustive* (includes all possible results) and *mutually exclusive* (no result can be identified with more than one member of the set). Such a set of outcomes is called the *sample space* of the experiment, and the individual outcomes are called *sample points*. In using these terms, we do not necessarily imply that the sample points are representable by means of geometrical points although it will frequently be convenient to use a geometrical representation when one is available. We are here using the abstract language of the theory of sets, in which it is quite immaterial whether the word "point" refers to any geometrical object. In Example 1.1 the sample space is the set $\{0, 1, \cdots, 200\}$, each of these numbers being regarded as a sample point.

Example 1.2. An interviewer visits a sample consisting of 500 Iowa farms and tabulates the number of cows on each farm. From this information he wishes to make a valid inference about the sizes of herds on all Iowa farms. Here again the whole population (all Iowa farms) could conceivably have been visited, but the expense would have been out of all proportion to the value of the results. Here the sample space would consist of the set of numbers $\{0, 1, 2, \cdots\}$.

Example 1.3. In estimating the number of white corpuscles in the blood supply of a patient, the laboratory technician smears a drop of blood on a glass plate marked with a cross-hatching of tiny ruled squares. Using a microscope, he counts the number of white blood cells in 10 of these squares, and from this information he forms an estimate of the size of the population of which these cells are a sample, namely, the totality of white cells in the patient's circulatory system. Here again the sample space will consist of the set of numbers $\{0, 1, 2, \cdots\}$.

Example 1.4. A card is drawn at random from the files in the personnel office of a large factory, and the sex and marital status of the employee is noted. The possible outcomes of this random experiment may be classified under 8 headings, for which the following table provides a numerical code:

Marital Status

Sex	Unmarried	Married	Divorced	Widowed
Male	1	2	3	4
Female	5	6	7	8

Notice that now the sample space may be specified either verbally: { Unmarried male, Married male, $\cdots$, Widowed female}, or numerically: {1, 2, 3, 4, 5, 6, 7, 8}.

When a set of numbers is associated with the sample points, as in the above example, in such a fashion that there is exactly one number for each sample point, we call the set of numbers a *random variable*. This definition is sufficiently important that we restate it formally:

(1.1)   DEFINITION.   *If $\{A_1, \cdots, A_k\}$ is the set of outcomes (sample points) defining the sample space of a random experiment and if $\{x_1, \cdots, x_k\}$ is a set of numbers such that x_i is associated with the corresponding outcome A_i for $i = 1, \cdots, k$, then the set of values $\{x_1, \cdots, x_k\}$ is called a random variable for the random experiment.*

In all examples of this section, except Example 1.4, a random variable is automatically available since the sample space is originally specified numerically.

Example 1.4 illustrates the fact that usually the sample space is *not uniquely determined* by the experiment. The cards could be classified simply {male, female} or {unmarried, married, divorced, widowed}, and either of these classifications would fulfill the requirements of a sample space.

The first three examples of random experiments involved sampling, while the fourth did not, except in the special sense that the drawing of a single card constitutes obtaining a sample of size one. In all these cases the sample must be *random* if the conclusion is to be valid. A sample is said to be random if all possible samples of the same size, similarly obtained, are equally likely. In order, for example, to obtain a list of 200 Iowa farms which would constitute a random sample of all Iowa farms, a possible method would be to number all Iowa farms, place all these numbers in identical capsules, agitate all the capsules in a container in such a manner as to mix them thoroughly, and finally draw 200 capsules, which would provide the numbers of the farms to be included in the sample. Much better and more convenient methods of obtaining random samples are available, however. The use of random numbers (to be introduced in Example 2.5) eliminates the necessity for the clumsy process of mixing capsules. There is an elaborate science of sampling, especially valuable in connection with surveys and census work.

Although in many cases it may be difficult to obtain a random sample (as in the industrial situation of Example 1.1), nevertheless a valid inference from sample to population is possible only when the sample is random since the whole mathematical theory upon which the inference depends presumes the use of random samples. This type of inference, alluded to in the opening paragraph of this section, is known as *statistical inference* and constitutes the principal theme of this book.

The examples thus far considered are all concerned with *discrete data;* in other words, the sample space in each case is representable by a set of integers, and no values between these integers may occur. Most of the data with which science deals are obtained by a process of measurement, using a scale or a dial. They are called *continuous data.* It is characteristic of continuous data that any value within an interval of the scale might conceivably be the outcome of the random experiment. For random experiments involving measurement, the sample space will thus consist of an interval of the real number scale or of a region in 2-, 3-, or higher dimensional space. These ideas are illustrated in Examples 1.5 and 1.6.

Example 1.5. A small plot is planted with several hundred seeds, say of corn. From their earliest growth the corn plants exhibit wide variations in size, presumably because of variations in heredity, soil moisture, availability of nutrients, etc. Thus, if on a certain day a single plant is chosen at random and its height is measured in inches, we may term the process a random experiment. If all possible outcomes fall in the interval $0 < x < 15$ inches, this interval constitutes the sample space of the experiment.

It is convenient, particularly in probability statements, to have different letters for the result actually obtained from a random experiment and for the possible values that may occur. When the need for the distinction arises, we shall use capital letters X, Y, $\cdots$ for actual values obtained from random experiments and small letters x, y, $\cdots$ for the numbers which specify the sample space. Thus in Example 1.5 the obtained height of a randomly selected plant would be denoted by X, while the sample space would be $0 < x < 15$. Capital letters will usually be used for sample values, but it is difficult to make this notation completely consistent, and we shall abandon it in a few places where it becomes inconvenient.

If two plants are randomly selected and measured, their heights may be designated by the number pair (X_1, X_2). Here it is convenient to conceive the sample space geometrically in the x_1, x_2 plane, as the rectangular region $(0 < x_1 < 15, 0 < x_2 < 15)$. The sample point (X_1, X_2) will be represented by the geometrical point with coordinates X_1 and X_2. If three plants are randomly selected and their heights measured, the result will be a number triple (X_1, X_2, X_3). The sample space may be taken to be the cubical region $(0 < x_1 < 15, 0 < x_2 < 15, 0 < x_3 < 15)$. Suppose now that 5 plants are randomly selected and measured. The outcome of this random experiment is the ordered set $(X_1, X_2, X_3, X_4, X_5)$, which is thus the sample point. We can no longer make use of an intuitive geometrical representation of the sample space; nevertheless, we speak of the sample space as the region $\{0 < x_1 < 15, 0 < x_2 < 15, \cdots, 0 < x_5 < 15\}$. Such higher-dimensional sample spaces are a great convenience in developing the sampling theory we shall require. We shall employ geometrical *terminology*, but all necessary concepts will be defined algebraically.

In order to select a corn plant at random, a suitable method would be to imagine the plot divided into a grid of squares by lines parallel to the sides of the plot and 1 inch apart. Then one of these squares is selected at random, and the corn plant nearest its center is measured. The selection of a square at random may be accomplished either by the "capsule" method mentioned earlier or by means of random numbers, in a manner that will be treated in Section 7.

An important characteristic of many random experiments is that of *stability*. This is conveniently illustrated by means of an industrial example.

Example 1.6. Suppose an automatic machine is producing a small screw whose length must be maintained to a certain specified dimension with an accuracy of $\pm.001$ inch. The operation of selecting at random a screw and measuring its length constitutes a random experiment. Because of wear in the cutting tool, variations in the metal stock, and the vibrations of the machine, it is impossible to be sure that a machine which now is producing parts within specification will still be doing so a few hours from now. We may say that the production process is *stable*, or *in a state of control*, if it is unaffected by the passage of time so that there is no tendency for parts produced at different times to be systematically larger or smaller. This is an informal definition of stability which will later be made precise [Definition (5.1)]. It is of utmost importance to a manufacturer that his process be kept stable. We shall consider, in Chapter 4, a simple device known as a *control chart* by means of which stability may be maintained. It should be intuitively evident that, if a random experiment is stable, its sample space will be constant, whereas for an unstable experiment the sample space may change with time.

In each of Examples 1.1 through 1.5, there was a clearly defined population and a clearly defined random experiment consisting of repeated drawings from the population. In Example 1.6, however, we have a random experiment consisting of measuring a piece drawn at random from the production process. Do we have a population? If the process is stable, we may say that the population is the indefinitely large collection of values which would be obtained if the random experiment were repeated very many times. Even if the process is unstable, we may say that the population is the collection of data that would result from many repetitions *if the process were stabilized*. Admittedly this concept is rather abstract. We introduce it in order that the terms "random experiment" and "sampling from a population" may be treated as synonyms, as they will be from this point on.

In the above discussion we have made no attempt to distinguish between the concept of a population as a collection of objects or people and the concept of a population as a set of numbers. Usually the context will make it clear which is meant.

EXERCISE 1

1.1. A student is selected at random from the student body of a university and asked, "In what state were you born?"

(a) Classify the data in this random experiment as discrete or continuous.

(b) Specify the sample space.

(c) What is the population associated with this random experiment?

(d) Set up a random variable for this random experiment, as in Example 1.4.

1.2. A die is made in the form of a prism, each end being a regular octagon, and the remaining 8 sides being congruent rectangles. The rectangles are labeled 1, 2, $\cdots$, 8. The die is then rolled in such a way that when it comes to rest a rectangle will be uppermost.

(a) Specify the sample space of this random experiment.

(b) What is the population associated with this random experiment?

(c) Are the data discrete or continuous?

1.3. A Geiger counter is held near an ore sample for 5 seconds, and an observer notes whether or not the counter has registered any radioactivity during that period.

(a) What is the sample space of this random experiment?

(b) Set up a random variable.

(c) Describe the population corresponding to this random experiment.

1.4. A Geiger counter is held near an ore sample, and the observer notes the number of "clicks" in a period of 30 seconds.

(a) Are the data discrete or continuous?

(b) What is the sample space?

(c) Describe the population corresponding to this random experiment.

1.5. A fisherman selects a certain spot and decides in advance to spend $\frac{1}{2}$ hour fishing there. He can conduct two possible random experiments:

A. Note whether or not any fish were caught.

B. Note the number of fish that were caught.

(a) Specify the sample space for each of the random experiments *A* and *B.*

(b) Are these data discrete or continuous?

(c) Define a random variable for each experiment.

1.6. A customer entering a shoe store specifies the size of shoe he wears.

(a) Can this be regarded as a random experiment? If so, what is the sample space?

(b) Are the data discrete or continuous?

1.7. In examining ore specimens, a geologist will routinely weigh them and determine their specific gravity.

(*a*) Do these measurements give rise to discrete or continuous data?

(*b*) Suggest sample spaces (they will be guesses; try to make your guesses somewhat reasonable).

1.8. An army inductee, randomly selected, is weighed.

(*a*) Are the data discrete or continuous?

(*b*) Specify the sample space.

1.9. It is desired to obtain a random sample of 50 students in a certain college. The following methods are proposed:

(*a*) Select the first 50 students emerging from a classroom building at noon.

(*b*) Take a stack of cards, one for each student in the college, shuffle them thoroughly, and use the top 50 cards in the stack.

(*c*) Use the members of an English class containing 50 students.

(*d*) Suppose the college has 1000 students. Take every twentieth name in the student directory.

Decide, in each case, whether the sample is random. If not, point out a possible form of bias that may affect the sample.

1.10. Criticize each of the following proposed methods of drawing a random sample from the specified population:

(*a*) To select 100 young men randomly, take the first 100 lining up for a physical at an induction center.

(*b*) To select 100 young men randomly, take 100 consecutive numbers assigned by the Selective Service System, and include in the sample the men whose numbers are obtained.

(*c*) To select 500 trucks at random, take the first 500 trucks on a given day on an important U. S. highway.

(*d*) To obtain a random selection of 200 U. S. manufacturers, use the directory of the National Association of Manufacturers. Take every third page and the twentieth name on the page, until 200 have been obtained.

(*e*) To select 150 corn plants from a field, assign a number to each row. Select the row randomly by means of a random number and the plant in the row using a second random number. Do this 150 times.

2. TYPES OF RANDOM EXPERIMENTS

Random experiments may conveniently be classified according to the number of outcomes (sample points) in the sample space. We first make a distinction between countably and non-countably infinite sets. The infinite set $\{2, 4, 6, \cdots\}$ consisting of all even numbers is called *countably infinite* because it is possible to number the elements $E_1 = 2, E_2 = 4, E_3 = 6, \cdots$ in such a way that there is established a one-to-one correspondence between the elements of the set and the natural numbers $1, 2, 3, \cdots$. It can be shown, on the other hand, that it is impossible to enumerate in this way the points of the interval $0 < x < 1$; such a set is therefore called non-countably infinite. The only random experiments which we shall consider with non-countably infinite sample spaces are those in which the sample spaces are continuous. The name *dichotomy* is given to a random experiment with just two outcomes. Thus we have the classification of sample spaces:

Finite sample space.
    (*a*) Two outcomes (dichotomy).
    (*b*) Many outcomes.
Infinite sample space.
    (*a*) Sample space discrete, but countably infinite.
    (*b*) Sample space continuous.

An important class of random experiments with finite sample spaces are those that are *urnlike;* i.e., their properties are similar to those of a random experiment which consists of drawing labeled balls from an urn. We shall later show that there are random experiments with finite sample spaces which are not urnlike. We shall now consider a series of examples of urnlike random experiments.

Example 2.1. *Single die.* For a single die the sample space is $\{1, 2, 3, 4, 5, 6\}$. This sample space can be represented geometrically by a line with 6 equally spaced points on it, as in Figure 2.1:

FIGURE 2.1

If the die is well made so that there is nothing in its construction to favor one side rather than another, the random experiment of throwing the die and observing the number on the uppermost side will be *equivalent* to drawing a single ball from an urn containing 6 balls labeled 1, 2, 3, 4, 5, 6. In each case we say that the 6 possible outcomes are *equally likely*. It is characteristic of urns and urnlike random experiments that the sample space may be so specified that the sample points are equally likely. Notice that another equivalent random experiment would result from drawing balls from an urn containing 12 balls, of which 2 are labeled "1," 2 labeled "2," $\cdots$, 2 labeled "6." More generally the urn could contain $6k$ balls, where k is an integer, with k each of 1's, 2's, $\cdots$, 6's. If we now let $k \to \infty$, we obtain the concept of an "infinite urn" with 1's, 2's, $\cdots$, 6's in "equal proportions."

Example 2.2. *Two dice.* Let a sample point be represented by (X_1, X_2). Then the sample space consists of the set of 36 sample points $\{(1, 1), (1, 2), \cdots, (6, 6)\}$. If X_1 and X_2 are taken as the cartesian coordinates of points in a plane, the sample space appears as a square of 36 points, as in Figure 2.2. It may be argued that the 36 sample points should be taken as equally likely in view of the fact that the 6 sample points for a single die were taken as equally likely, for the 6 sample points in any row must be equally likely since only X_1 varies from point to point of a row. Similarly the 6 sample points of any column must be equally likely. Putting these two facts together, we conclude

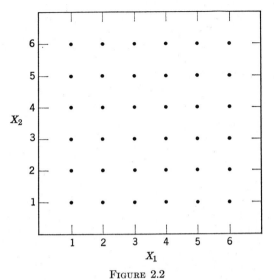

FIGURE 2.2

that the 36 sample points must be regarded as equally likely. In view of this, an equivalent urn would contain 36 balls labeled (1, 1), (1, 2), $\cdots$, (6, 6).

Remark on notation: The notation $\{A_1, \cdots, A_k\}$ will be used to indicate a *set of elements*, without regard to order. The notation $(A_1, \cdots, A_k)$ will be used to indicate an *ordered set of elements*. A set of coordinates of a point is an ordered set so that the coordinates of a point are appropriately enclosed in parentheses.

In connection with Example 1.4 a random variable was introduced by arbitrarily assigning a number to each sample point. Various

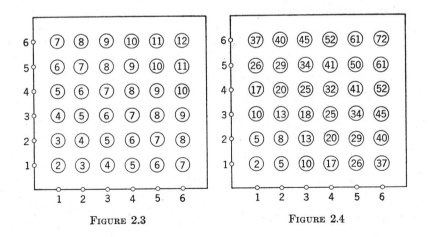

FIGURE 2.3   FIGURE 2.4

random variables can be defined for the random experiment of Example 2.2. For example, the random variable defined by $X_1 + X_2$ would attach numbers to the sample points as shown in Figure 2.3, while the random variable $X_1{}^2 + X_2{}^2$ would be represented geometrically as in Figure 2.4.

Example 2.3. Single penny. Throws of a penny form a dichotomy since there are only the two outcomes: H = heads and T = tails. The sample space is $\{H, T\}$. We may define a random variable X by letting X equal the number of heads showing when the penny is tossed. The sample space may now be described numerically: $\{1, 0\}$. The geometrical representation will consist of 2 points on a line, labeled 0 and 1. An equivalent urn will contain 2 balls labeled 0, 1.

Example 2.4. Several pennies. With 2 pennies the sample space is $\{HH, HT, TH, TT\}$. If X_1 is the number of heads showing when the first penny is tossed and X_2 is the number of heads when the second penny is tossed, then $Z = X_1 + X_2$ is the number of heads showing when both are tossed. The random variable Z may assume the set of values $\{0, 1, 2\}$, so that this set may be regarded as an alternative sample space for the experiment. With 3 pennies we have the sample space $\{HHH, HHT, HTH, HTT, THH, THT, TTH, TTT\}$. The random variable $Z = X_1 + X_2 + X_3$, defined analogously to the case of 2 pennies, will give the number of heads showing. For n pennies the sample space will contain 2^n points. The sample points may be denoted by $(X_1, X_2, \cdots, X_n)$ where X_i is 1 if the ith coin is a head and is 0 if the ith is a tail. The random variable $Z = X_1 + X_2 + \cdots + X_n$ will give the number of heads showing among the n pennies.

Example 2.5. Random numbers. Consider an urn containing 10 balls bearing the numbers 0, 1, 2, $\cdots$, 9. The drawing of balls one at a time from such an urn, replacing and mixing between drawings, constitutes a random experiment whose outcomes are known as *random numbers*. An equivalent random experiment is provided by the use of an icosahedral (20-sided) die, with 2 faces labeled "0," 2 faces labeled "1," $\cdots$, 2 faces labeled "9." A construction diagram is shown in Figure 2.5. By an argument analogous to that used in

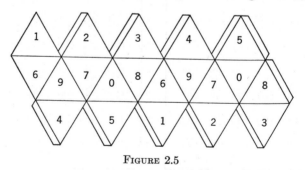

FIGURE 2.5

Example 2.2 we can demonstrate that, if random numbers are taken in pairs, the 100 combinations $\{00, 01, \cdots, 99\}$ are equally likely. These pairs denote the points of the sample space for the random experiment which consists in drawing 2 balls (with replacement) from the urn described above or in rolling 2 icosahedral dice. Extending the argument, we can show that, if n random numbers are obtained, there are 10^n equally likely combinations that might arise. Table 1 * provides a brief table of random numbers. Many large tables of random numbers are in print.

Example 2.6. *Spinner.* Consider a freely spinning pointer with a circular scale, which we shall call a *spinner*. We assume that the pointer is equally likely to come to rest in any two equal arcs of the circumference. This assumption can refer only to a mathematical idealization; any actual spinner, however well constructed, can only approximate this ideal behavior, just as the statement that the six sides of a die are equally likely to turn up can hold only for an ideal or mathematical die. A simple method of constructing a spinner, sufficiently accurate for experimentation, is described at the end of the chapter. If the circumference of the spinner scale is divided into 6 equal arcs labeled 1, 2, $\cdots$, 6, we have a random experiment equivalent to the throwing of a die. If the circumference is divided into 10 equal arcs labeled 0, 1, $\cdots$, 9, we have a random experiment yielding random numbers.

Using the spinner, we can easily construct random experiments that are not urnlike, as in the next example.

Example 2.7. Suppose we divide the circumference of the spinner scale into 2 arcs whose ratio is irrational, for example, the ratio $1 : \sqrt{2}$. Let us then label the arcs A and B. The use of such a scale with the spinner yields a random experiment which is a dichotomy since there are just 2 outcomes, but there can be no urn equivalent to such a random experiment since the spinner scale corresponding to an urn must have each of its arcs a rational fraction of the whole circumference.

In Examples 2.6 and 2.7 the sample space has been represented on the circumference of the scale in such a way that *sample points* correspond to *arcs* of the circumference. We shall now consider two examples, using the spinner, in which the sample space is continuous and sample points correspond to *points* of the circumference of the scale.

Example 2.8. *Uniform scale.* A uniform scale for the spinner is constructed by taking an arbitrary point Q on the circumference as starting point. Then with any other point P of the circumference we associate the number $u = \overset{\frown}{QP}/\text{circumference}$, where $\overset{\frown}{QP}$ indicates the clockwise arc from Q to P. A sketch of a uniform scale is shown in Figure 2.6. When this scale is used, any value in the interval $0 < u < 1$ may be obtained; this interval is thus the sample space of the experiment.

Example 2.9. In Figure 2.7 a scale has been projected from the cartesian scale on the x-axis onto a circle by joining each point P on the x-axis to the center C of the circle and labeling the two ends Q and R of this diameter with

* Table 1, and other numerical tables, will be found at the end of the book.

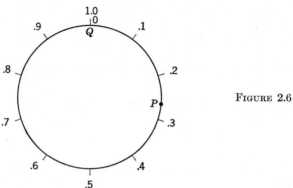

FIGURE 2.6

the x-value of the point P. It is immediately evident that the scale of Figure 2.7 is not a uniform scale. In fact values near $x = 0$ are much more likely to occur than values near, say, $x = 5$. The sample space of the random experiment arising from the use of this scale consists of the complete range of real numbers, from $-\infty$ to ∞. The sample space can be represented geometrically either on the x-axis or on one-half of the circumference of the circle.

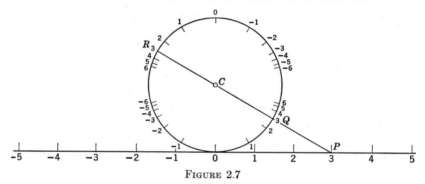

FIGURE 2.7

Let X_1 and X_2 be two random values, each obtained from the random experiment described in Example 2.8. A sample point will be specified by the number pair (X_1, X_2), and the sample space is the region $0 < x_1 < 1, 0 < x_2 < 1$, which may be represented geometrically by a square region in the x_1, x_2 plane, bounded by the lines $x_1 = 0$, $x_1 = 1$, $x_2 = 0$, $x_2 = 1$. If, on the other hand, X_1 and X_2 represent outcomes of the random experiment of Example 2.9, the random point (X_1, X_2) may range over the entire x_1, x_2 plane.

EXERCISE 2

2.1. For a throw of 2 pennies let X_1 be the number of heads showing when the first penny is tossed and X_2 be the number of heads showing when the second penny is tossed.

(a) Specify the sample space for the random experiment by giving the set of 4 possible number pairs which may result from the experiment.

(b) Represent the sample space geometrically, as in Figure 2.2.

(c) Label each sample point with the sum $X_1 + X_2$ (i.e., the total number of heads) as in Figure 2.3.

2.2. Two dice are constructed of the kind described in Exercise 1.2 and are rolled simultaneously.

(a) Specify the sample space of this experiment by means of number pairs (see Example 2.2).

(b) Represent the sample space geometrically.

(c) If X_1 represents the value showing on the first die and X_2 represents the value showing on the second, label the points of the sample space according to the random variable $Z = X_1 - X_2$.

2.3. A random experiment consists of the rolling of 2 icosahedral dice (Example 2.5) and recording the values X_1 and X_2 which are uppermost.

(a) Represent the sample space of this experiment geometrically, as in Figure 2.2.

(b) Label the points of the sample space according to the random variable $X_1 X_2$.

(c) For how many points is $X_1 X_2 > 50$?

2.4. Ten coins are tossed, and the sample points are denoted by $(X_1, X_2, \cdots, X_{10})$, where each x_i is 1 if the ith coin is a head and 0 if the ith coin is a tail.

(a) How many points in the sample space will have all coordinates equal to 1?

(b) How many points in the sample space will have a single zero among the coordinates and the rest 1's?

(c) How many points in the sample space will have 3 zeros among the coordinates and the rest 1's?

2.5. The following methods are proposed for obtaining random numbers in the sense of Example 2.5. Criticize each proposal.

(a) Remove the kings, queens, and tens from a deck, and give the jack a value of zero. Shuffle and draw a card, recording its value.

(b) Throw 10 pennies, and record the number of heads.

(c) Roll 2 dice. Discard a sum of 11 or 12, and call a sum of 10 "zero."

(d) Roll 2 dice, and use the following key:

		First Die	
		1 2 3	4 5 6
	1	1	6
Second Die	2	2	7
	3	3	8
	4	4	9
	5	5	0
	6	Discard	

(*e*) Insert a knife in a book. Record the last digit of the right-hand page number.

(*f*) Record the right-hand digits of license numbers of cars moving along a highway.

(*g*) Record the last digit of the day of birth (in whatever month) of a student selected at random from a college.

(*h*) In a large parking lot, record the right-hand digit registered on the speedometer of each car.

2.6. How would you construct a scale for a spinner so that its use would be equivalent to:

(*a*) Tossing a coin.

(*b*) Tossing 2 coins.

(*c*) Tossing 2 dice.

(*d*) Tossing 2 dice and noting their sum.

2.7. Let X_1 and X_2 be two random variables, each obtained from the random experiment described in Example 2.8. Let the sample space for X_1 be the interval $0 < x_1 < 1$ on the horizontal axis, and let the sample space for X_2 be the interval $0 < x_2 < 1$ on the vertical axis. Where do the sample points lie for which: (*a*) $X_1 - X_2 = 0$, (*b*) $X_1 - X_2 > 0$?

2.8. Describe an urn model equivalent to tossing 3 pennies.

2.9. Extend the argument of Example 2.2 to prove that, if three dice are rolled, the 216 sample points $\{(1, 1, 1), (1, 1, 2), \cdots, (6, 6, 6)\}$ are equally likely.

3. EVENTS

We frequently need to consider a certain class of outcomes of a random experiment, as, for example, "an even number shows on the top face of a die" or "a part drawn at random from a shipment is defective." Such classes of outcomes are called *events*, formally defined as follows:

(3.1) DEFINITION. *An event is any subset of the sample space.*

Example 3.1. For a single die the event "even throw" consists of the points $\{2, 4, 6\}$; the event "a throw greater than 3" is the subset $\{4, 5, 6\}$.

We say that to obtain a throw of 7 with a single die of the usual type is "impossible." This corresponds to the fact that in the sample space $\{1, 2, 3, 4, 5, 6\}$ for a single die, the set of values equal to 7 does not exist, or is *empty*. Thus an "impossible event" will correspond to the so-called *empty set*, or *null set*, denoted by 0. If A is any event, the *complement of* A, denoted by A', is the event consisting of all points in the sample space that do not belong to A. This is the event "A does not occur."

Example 3.2. For a single die, let $A = \{2, 4, 6\} =$ "an even throw," and let $B = \{1, 2, 3\} =$ "a throw of 3 or less." Then $A' = \{1, 3, 5\} =$ "an odd throw," and $B' = \{4, 5, 6\} =$ "a throw of more than 3."

Suppose, as in Examples 2.8 and 2.9, that we have a continuous sample space, represented by a finite or infinite interval. In such a situation the events we shall consider will be represented by sub-intervals of the fundamental interval rather than by isolated points. An interval is said to be *closed* if it includes its end points, *open* if it does not. Thus the interval $a \leq x \leq b$ is closed, whereas the interval $a < x < b$ is open. An interval like $a \leq x < b$ which includes one of its end points but not the other is called *half-open*. We shall adopt the following notation:

(3.2)   *Closed interval:* $[a, b]$ *represents the set* $a \leq x \leq b$
     Open interval: (a, b) *represents the set* $a < x < b$
     Half-open intervals: $[a, b)$ *represents the set* $a \leq x < b$
                       $(a, b]$ *represents the set* $a < x \leq b$

Example 3.3. Let the sample space be that of Example 2.8, namely, the open interval $(0, 1)$. Let a and b be any two values within this interval, and let $a < b$. Then the complement of (a, b) consists of the 2 half-open intervals $(0, a]$ and $[b, 1)$.

Two events may or may not have common points. The set of points common to A and B is termed their *product* or *intersection* and denoted by AB or $A \cap B$ (read "A cap B"). This is the event "A and B both occur." If A and B have no points in common, their product is the empty set, and we write $AB = 0$. In this case the sets A and B are said to be *disjoint*, and the events A and B are *mutually exclusive* or *incompatible*.

Example 3.4. With A and B defined as in Example 3.2, the event $AB = \{2\}$; that is, 2 is the only even throw of a die which is less than 4. Similarly we find $A'B = \{1, 3\}$, $AB' = \{4, 6\}$, $A'B' = \{5\}$.

The set which contains all points which belong to A or B or both is called the *union* of A and B and denoted by $A \cup B$ (read "A cup B"). This is the event "A or B occurs."

Example 3.5. With A and B defined as in Example 3.2, the event $A \cup B = \{1, 2, 3, 4, 6\}$, and $A \cup B' = \{2, 4, 5, 6\}$.

Example 3.6. Let the sample space be $(0, 1)$, and let $A = (.5, .8)$, $B = (.7, .9)$. Then $A' = (0, .5] \cup [.8, 1)$, $B' = (0, .7] \cup [.9, 1)$, $AB = (.7, .8)$, $A \cup B = (.5, .9)$, $AB' = (.5, .7]$, $A \cup B' = (0, .8) \cup [.9, 1)$.

In the preceding discussion we have made use of a number of concepts in the elementary theory of sets: the idea of a *subset*, and the three basic operations of *complementation* (i.e., forming the complement of a given set), *union*, and *intersection*. We shall not pursue set theory in a formal way, partly because our set-theoretical requirements are very simple, and partly because many excellent presentations are readily available. It is, however, worth while to list the laws of the algebra of sets (Boolean algebra), because we shall occasionally have to use this form of algebra in dealing with probability. Suppose we are given a sample space, and a set of events A, B, C, $\cdots$. In the language of set theory the sample space is the *universal set*, which we shall denote by U, and the events A, B, C, $\cdots$ are subsets of U. The algebraic system obtained by applying the operations of complementation, union, and intersection repeatedly to A, B, C, $\cdots$ is a Boolean algebra, which obeys the following laws, analogous to those governing the operations of arithmetic. These laws are here stated as in Goldberg (8),* a book which provides in its first chapter an excellent introduction to the theory of sets.

Identity laws:

1a. $A \cup 0 = A$ 　　　　　　　1b. $A \cap U = A$

2a. $A \cup U = U$ 　　　　　　　2b. $A \cap 0 = 0$

Idempotent laws:

3a. $A \cup A = A$ 　　　　　　　3b. $A \cap A = A$

Complement laws:

4a. $A \cup A' = U$ 　　　　　　　4b. $A \cap A' = 0$

5a. $(A')' = A$

Commutative laws:

6a. $A \cup B = B \cup A$ 　　　　6b. $A \cap B = B \cap A$

De Morgan's laws:

7a. $(A \cup B)' = A' \cap B'$ 　　　7b. $(A \cap B)' = A' \cup B'$

Associative laws:

8a. $A \cup (B \cup C) = (A \cup B) \cup C$

8b. $A \cap (B \cap C) = (A \cap B) \cap C$

Distributive laws:

9a. $A \cup (B \cap C) = (A \cup B) \cap (A \cup C)$

9b. $A \cap (B \cup C) = (A \cap B) \cup (A \cap C)$

Except for 5a, all the laws in the above list occur in pairs, such that the members of each pair are interchanged when we interchange $\cup$ and $\cap$ and also interchange 0 and U. This remarkable feature of Boolean algebra is known as *duality*. In the remainder of this book we shall

---

* References given in this fashion are to the bibliography on page 337.

drop the notation for intersection and shall instead indicate intersection by juxtaposition; that is, instead of $A \cap B$ we shall write AB.

The laws listed above apply, of course, whether the elements of the universal set are numbers, geometrical points, physical objects, ideas, or any other kind of element. In every case, however, we must be able to determine whether or not a given element belongs to a given set; this may be regarded as the fundamental principle of set theory.

It is often convenient to check statements in the theory of sets by geometrical means. To do this, we imagine the universal set U to be a set of points in the plane, and the sets A, B, C, $\cdots$ to be regions bounded by simple closed curves. For simplicity, we usually take the regions to be circular. The resulting diagrams are called circle diagrams, or Euler diagrams (after L. Euler, 1707–1783), or Venn diagrams (after J. Venn, 1834–1923). Their use is illustrated in the following examples.

Example 3.7. Consider the distributive law 9*a*. The Venn diagram for this law will consist of three circles representing the sets A, B, and C. In Figure 3.1 we show the two Venn diagrams, for the two members of law 9*a*.

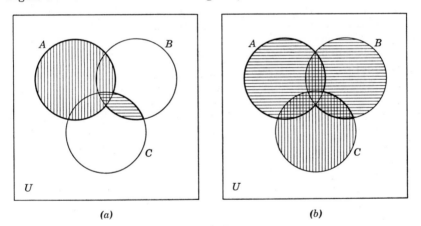

(a)   (b)

FIGURE 3.1

In each case the rectangle surrounding the circles represents the universal set, U. In Figure 3.1*a*, the set $B \cap C$, appearing on the left of the law 9*a*, is indicated by means of horizontal hatching, and the set A is shown with vertical hatching. Thus the left side of 9*a* is that area of Figure 3.1*a* which is hatched horizontally, or vertically, or both. This area is indicated by a heavy boundary. In Figure 3.1*b*, $A \cup B$ is shown by means of horizontal hatching, and $A \cup C$ by means of vertical hatching. The cross-hatched area is thus their intersection, which has again been indicated by a heavy boundary. Since the areas marked by heavy boundary in Figures 3.1*a* and *b* represent the same portion of U, we conclude that 9*a* is correct.

Example 3.8. In this example we shall use juxtaposition of symbols to denote intersection, rather than the use of the "cap" symbol $\cap$. We wish to show that $AC \cup A'C \cup BC' = B \cup C$. In Figure 3.2, AC is shown by means of

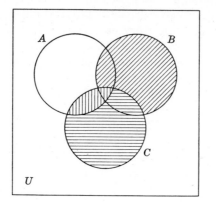

FIGURE 3.2

vertical hatching, $A'C$ by means of horizontal hatching, and BC' by means of diagonal hatching. Clearly, from the figure, these three areas together constitute the region corresponding to $B \cup C$.

Example 3.9. In Example 3.8 the equation $AC \cup A'C \cup BC' = B \cup C$ was proved by means of a Venn diagram. We now show how the laws of Boolean algebra may be used to verify this equation.

$$
\begin{aligned}
AC \cup A'C \cup BC' &= CA \cup CA' \cup BC' && \text{by } 6b \\
&= C(A \cup A') \cup BC' && \text{by } 9b \\
&= CU \cup BC' && \text{by } 4a \\
&= C(B \cup B') \cup BC' && \text{by } 4a \\
&= CB \cup CB' \cup BC' && \text{by } 9b \\
&= CB' \cup CB \cup BC' && \text{by } 6a \\
&= CB' \cup CB \cup CB \cup BC' && \text{by } 3a \\
&= C(B' \cup B) \cup CB \cup BC' && \text{by } 9b \\
&= C \cup BC \cup BC' && \text{by } 4a, 1b, \text{ and } 6b \\
&= C \cup B(C \cup C') && \text{by } 9b \\
&= C \cup B && \text{by } 4a \text{ and } 1b
\end{aligned}
$$

The Venn diagram method of verifying equations in Boolean algebra has the obvious limitation that the diagrams become very complicated when more than three sets are involved. The algebraic method of Example 3.9 has the disadvantage of being tedious, and requiring a considerable exercise of ingenuity. Another method is based on the use of a so-called set-inclusion table; it is explained in Goldberg (8).

In this section we have been laying the foundations for both the elementary theory of sets and the interpretation of these sets as events. In the following table this parallelism is made more explicit:

Theory of Sets	Events
Fundamental set	Sample space.
Subset A of fundamental set	Event A.
$A = 0$	Event A is impossible.
Complement of A	Non-occurrence of event A.
$x = AB$	Event x is the simultaneous occurrence of events A and B.
$x = A \cup B$	Event x is the occurrence of at least one of the events. A and B.
$AB = 0$	Events A and B are incompatible or mutually exclusive.

A set of events $\{A_1, A_2, \cdots, A_k\}$ which subdivides the points of the sample space into a system of classes which are mutually exclusive (i.e., $A_i A_j = 0$ for all i, j) and exhaustive (i.e., $A_1 \cup A_2 \cup \cdots \cup A_k =$ the sample space) is called a *classification* or a *decomposition* of the sample space. Then every possible outcome (sample point) of the random experiment will fall in one and only one of the classes A_1, A_2, $\cdots$, A_k. (Show that this is the case.) Usually classifications of the sample space can be set up in a variety of ways. Thus the events A and A' of Example 3.2 are associated with the classification {even, odd}, while the events B and B' are associated with the classification $\{<4, >3\}$. These two classifications cross each other and together form a *cross-classification* of the sample space, giving rise to the events AB, AB', $A'B$, $A'B'$. The subdivision of the sample space arising from this cross-classification may be represented geometrically by the overlapping of circles, as in Figure 3.3, in which the sample points are represented by small circles. Alternatively the cross-classification may be represented in the form of a two-way table, as in Table 3.1.

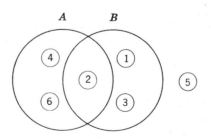

FIGURE 3.3

TABLE 3.1

	A	A'
B	$AB = \{2\}$	$A'B = \{1, 3\}$
B'	$AB' = \{4, 6\}$	$A'B' = \{5\}$

In Chapter 3 we shall return to these matters and shall provide a systematic treatment of cross-classifications and their associated probabilities.

Consider the equation $X_1 + X_2 = 5$, where X_1 and X_2 are the values showing on a pair of dice. We shall use the expression "the event $X_1 + X_2 = 5$" to mean the subset of the sample space consisting of all pairs (X_1, X_2) satisfying the given equation, which is readily found to be the set $\{(1, 4), (2, 3), (3, 2), (4, 1)\}$. Similarly, the event $X_1 + X_2 < 5$ will mean the set $\{(1, 1), (1, 2), (1, 3), (2, 1), (2, 2), (3, 1)\}$.

EXERCISE 3

3.1. Let the sample space for 2 dice be represented as in Figure 2.2. In separate diagrams, indicate the following events:

(a) $X_1 + X_2 > 5$ (b) $X_1^2 + X_2^2 = 25$
(c) $X_1/X_2 = 2$ (d) $X_1 + 2X_2 = 7$

3.2. If X_1 and X_2 are the values showing on a pair of dice, express the complement of the event $X_1 + X_2 > 5$ (a) algebraically, (b) geometrically.

3.3. For an icosahedral die (Example 2.5), let $A = \{0, 1, 3, 7, 8\}$, $B = \{2, 3, 5, 7\}$. Determine the following events:

(a) A' (b) B' (c) AB (d) $A \cup B$ (e) AB' (f) $A \cup AB'$ (g) $A \cup A'B$

3.4. For the example in Exercise 3.3, display the cross-classification of the sample space arising from the two classifications $\{A, A'\}$ and $\{B, B'\}$ in the form of a circle diagram (see Figure 3.3) and in form of a two-way table (see Table 3.1).

3.5. Suppose the sample space for a random experiment is the interval $(0, 1)$. Let A and B be intervals defined by $A = [.2, .5]$, $B = (.3, .7)$. Find

(a) A' (b) B' (c) AB (d) $A \cup B$ (e) AB'

3.6. Let X_1 and X_2 be random variables, each obtained from the random experiment described in Example 2.8. Represent geometrically the following events:

(a) $X_1 + X_2 = 1$ (b) $X_1 + X_2 > 1$
(c) $X_1^2 + X_2^2 = 1$ (d) $X_1 + X_2 > 1$ and $X_1 - X_2 < .5$

3.7. By the Venn diagram method of Example 3.7 check the following laws of Boolean algebra: 7a, 7b, 8a, 8b, 9b.

4. FREQUENCY DISTRIBUTIONS

Consider the set of values

$$2, 2, 2, 4, 4, 5, 2, 4, 7, 7, 4, 7, 5, 2, 8, 6, 7, 4, 3, 4.$$

These 20 values might be the complete description of a population (i.e., the 20 numbers on a set of balls in an urn). In this case the sample space is seen to be {2, 3, 4, 5, 6, 7, 8}. Or the 20 values may be the observations in a sample, written down in the order in which they occurred in some experiment. In either case the original set of values is rather hard to study because of its lack of organization; this difficulty would be more serious if there were several hundred values in the set. An obvious way to organize this set of numbers is in the form of a *frequency distribution*, that is, a table of the following form:

TABLE 4.1

Value, X	2	3	4	5	6	7	8	
Frequency, f	5	1	6	2	1	4	1	Total = 20

The frequency f is simply the number of repetitions of each value in the original set. The value of x corresponding to the largest frequency is called the *mode*. For the above set the mode is 4.

In Figure 4.1 are shown a *line graph* and a *histogram* for the above frequency distribution. In both graphs the frequency is shown on the vertical scale and the values of x on the horizontal scale. The histogram is somewhat more picturesque and easy to grasp, but the

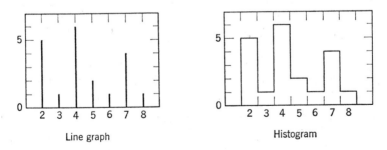

Line graph   Histogram

FIGURE 4.1

line graph is a more faithful representation of the original data since it suggests that the values are concentrated at a series of discrete values on the horizontal scale. The histogram is more appropriate for the case of continuous data because it suggests that each of the frequencies pertains to an interval of the scale of x. We shall turn to the classification of continuous data in Chapter 2.

In Table 4.2 we give the complete set of data, from which were taken the 20 values at the beginning of this section. These data were obtained by making a count of yeast cells in each of the 400 squares of a haemacytometer. The haemacytometer is a device used to count blood cells and other microscopic objects. In the present case it consisted of a square, 1 mm. by 1 mm., engraved on a glass plate. Each side of the square is divided into 20 intervals, and lines are engraved to form 400 small squares. The table gives the number of yeast cells in each of these squares. The data are from a paper by W. S. Gosset ("Student") published in 1907 in *Biometrika*, entitled "On the probable error of counting with a haemacytometer." Gosset was one of the pioneers of modern statistics. We shall encounter his work a number of times in this book.

The operation of selecting a square of the haemacytometer and observing the number of yeast cells in it is a random experiment whose sample space is, from these data, $\{1, 2, \cdots, 12\}$. Presumably, if this

TABLE 4.2

Number of Yeast Cells in Squares of the Hamacytometer

2	2	2	4	4	5	2	4	7	7	4	7	5	2	8	6	7	4	3	4	3	3	2	4	2
5	4	2	8	6	3	6	6	10	8	3	5	6	4	4	7	9	5	2	7	4	4	2	4	4
4	3	5	6	5	4	1	4	2	6	4	1	4	7	3	2	3	5	8	2	9	5	3	9	5
5	2	4	3	4	4	1	9	9	3	4	4	6	6	5	4	6	5	5	4	3	5	9	6	4
4	4	5	10	4	4	3	8	3	2	1	4	1	5	6	4	2	3	3	3	3	7	4	5	1
8	5	7	9	5	8	9	5	6	6	4	3	7	4	4	7	5	6	3	6	7	4	5	8	6
3	3	4	3	7	4	4	4	5	3	8	10	6	3	3	6	5	2	5	3	11	3	7	4	7
3	5	5	3	4	1	3	7	2	5	5	5	3	3	4	6	5	6	1	6	4	4	4	6	4
4	2	5	4	8	6	3	4	6	5	2	6	6	1	2	2	2	5	2	2	5	9	3	5	6
4	6	5	7	1	3	6	5	4	2	8	9	5	4	3	2	2	11	4	6	6	4	6	2	5
3	5	7	2	6	5	5	1	2	7	5	12	5	8	2	4	2	1	6	4	5	1	2	9	1
3	4	7	3	6	5	6	5	4	4	5	2	7	6	2	7	3	5	4	4	5	4	7	5	4
8	4	6	6	5	3	3	5	7	4	5	5	5	6	10	2	3	8	3	5	6	6	4	2	6
6	7	5	4	5	8	6	7	6	4	2	6	1	1	4	7	2	5	7	4	6	4	5	1	5
10	8	7	5	4	6	4	4	7	5	4	3	1	6	2	5	3	3	3	7	4	3	7	8	4
7	3	1	4	4	7	6	7	2	4	5	1	3	12	4	2	2	8	7	6	7	6	3	5	4

had been part of a much larger experiment under the same conditions, the sample space might need to be extended to include the value 0 and perhaps 13 or 14. In making a frequency distribution for these data, we shall group the values of x in pairs, as shown in Table 4.3. These pairs constitute a classification of the sample space, as defined in Section 3. Thus the distribution of Table 4.3 is called a *grouped* or *classi-*

TABLE 4.3

Class	1–2	3–4	5–6	7–8	9–10	11–12	
f	63	139	124	55	15	4	Total = 400

fied frequency distribution. In obtaining the frequencies for a large set of values, a *tally*, as is used in Table 13.2, may be helpful.

From a distribution such as that of Tables 4.1 and 4.3 several other useful types of distributions may be derived. The first of these is the *relative frequency distribution*, shown for the data of Table 4.1 in Table 4.4. The relative frequency f/n is obtained by dividing each of the

TABLE 4.4

Value, x	2	3	4	5	6	7	8	
Relative frequency, f/n	.25	.05	.30	.10	.05	.20	.05	Total = 1.0

frequencies by n, the sample size. When dealing with a discrete population, we shall use the letter ϕ for frequency, and $N = \Sigma\phi$[1] for the size of the population. Thus ϕ/N would be used for the relative frequencies in a population. The *cumulative frequency*, denoted by *cf*, is obtained by adding each value of f in turn to the preceding value of *cf*, starting at one side of the table (say the left side) and proceeding to the other. This process is known as *cumulation*. For the data of Table 4.1 we obtain the following table of cumulative frequencies:

TABLE 4.5

Value, x	2	3	4	5	6	7	8
Cumulative frequency, *cf*	5	6	12	14	15	19	20
Cumulative relative frequency, *crf*	.25	.30	.60	.70	.75	.95	1.00

Also shown is the *cumulative relative frequency* (*crf*) which may be obtained either by dividing each *cf* value by the sample size n or by

---

[1] In using the summation notation $\Sigma\phi$ as an abbreviation for the sum $\phi_1 + \cdots + \phi_k$, we have omitted the limits of summation. These limits will usually be omitted when there is no risk of ambiguity.

cumulating the relative frequencies of Table 4.4. The usefulness of the cumulative frequency and the cumulative relative frequency stems from the following elementary proposition:

(4.1)　*The cumulative frequency gives the number of values in the group that are less than or equal to a given value of x.　The cumulative relative frequency gives the proportion of values in the group that are less than or equal to a given value of x.*

Thus in Table 4.5 the value $cf = 14$ gives the number of values in the original table that are less than or equal to 5, while the value $crf = .70$ gives the proportion of values less than or equal to 5.

EXERCISE 4

4.1. Twenty coins were tossed 100 times. The following table gives the number of heads on each throw.

7	12	9	8	3	10	12	10	9	9
9	10	8	11	10	9	12	11	8	14
13	12	10	14	10	11	10	13	9	7
9	11	7	13	11	12	9	8	11	14
10	11	8	8	8	12	9	13	8	7
6	13	10	14	11	10	13	4	14	10
10	12	9	12	10	13	13	10	10	11
10	8	10	12	6	13	8	12	13	9
6	9	15	9	13	11	10	12	7	11
10	10	10	8	10	9	9	10	15	12

　(*a*) Using a tally, form a frequency distribution for these data.
　(*b*) Form a column of cumulative frequency (*cf*), and from it determine the proportion of the set that is less than 10, and the proportion greater than 10. (Note that 10 is the mode.)
　4.2. The following table gives 100 determinations of background radiation, using a radiation counter. Each recorded value gives the number of pulses in a 15-second interval.

7	8	14	9	4	8	12	10	6	8
9	8	11	6	11	9	13	6	12	6
8	4	9	9	5	8	6	8	11	7
5	12	15	11	7	8	7	9	10	9
11	11	10	8	18	9	17	10	7	12
11	16	14	10	9	4	7	16	8	13
14	6	15	10	3	13	6	5	12	13
10	13	7	9	7	10	11	10	8	4
9	6	11	14	8	12	7	10	10	8
13	12	8	8	6	8	12	2	6	6

(a) Using a tally, form a frequency distribution.

(b) Compute the cumulative frequency, and use it to determine the proportion of the set that is less than 8, and the proportion of the set that is greater than 8. (Note that 8 is the mode.)

4.3. (a) Make a frequency distribution of the haemacytometer data, Table 4.2, without grouping. That is, find the frequencies corresponding to individual values of x.

(b) Find also the relative frequency distribution.

4.4. Make a comparative study of word lengths of materials at two levels:

(a) 100 consecutive words from a newspaper or from a grade school or high school textbook.

(b) 100 words from a senior college or graduate school textbook. For each sample of 100 words, make a frequency distribution of word lengths.

5. PROBABILITY

In order to have a complete grasp of a particular random experiment we need to know its possible outcomes and also the likelihood of the occurrence of each outcome. The sample space, which is identical with the set of outcomes of the experiment, completely supplies the first of these needs. We must now set up the procedure for specifying, numerically, the likelihood to be associated with each sample point. These likelihoods are, for a discrete random experiment, specified by means of a set of numbers called *probabilities* associated with the sample points. The basic properties of probabilities will be derived in this section and the next for various types of random experiments. The subject of probability, in various aspects and applications, will be a continuing topic throughout the remainder of this book.

Suppose that we have an urnlike random experiment, which we may visualize as consisting of making drawings, with replacement, from an urn containing numbered balls. Suppose, further, that a fairly large sample (say 100 or more) has been obtained. We may form a frequency distribution for both the population and the sample. It then becomes natural to ask whether the two distributions are similar. In order to make the two distributions comparable, it is convenient to express both of them in terms of relative frequencies.

Example 5.1. Consider throws of a single die. An equivalent urn model for this random experiment would consist of drawings, with replacement, from an urn containing 6 balls labeled 1, 2, 3, 4, 5, 6. The population relative frequency distribution will thus be as shown in Table 5.1a. This distribution is that of an *ideal* or *mathematical* die. For a sample, 100 throws were made with a dime-store die. The resulting frequency and relative frequency distributions are shown in Table 5.1b. The comparison of these distributions is facilitated by the line graph in Figure 5.1.

TABLE 5.1

(a)							(b)					
Relative Frequency Distribution for Ideal Die							Relative Frequency Distribution for 100 Throws of an Actual Die					
x	1	2	3	4	5	6	x	1	2	3	4	5	6
ϕ	1	1	1	1	1	1	f	18	18	17	13	18	16
ϕ/N	$\frac{1}{6}$	$\frac{1}{6}$	$\frac{1}{6}$	$\frac{1}{6}$	$\frac{1}{6}$	$\frac{1}{6}$	f/n	.18	.18	.17	.13	.18	.16

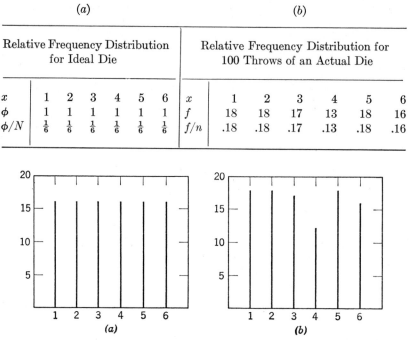

FIGURE 5.1

From the figure, we might judge that the sample distribution is "fairly close" to the population distribution. What if the sample were larger? If the sample were large enough we would probably be able to detect, with some assurance, imperfections in the dime-store die. If, for example, in 10,000 throws of the die only 1000 4's were observed, we would be inclined to say that the die had a *bias* such that "4" is less likely to occur than some of the other possible outcomes.

Example 5.2. A cardboard icosahedral die (Example 2.5) was thrown 1000 times. Table 5.2 gives the relative frequency distribution of (a) the first 100 throws, (b) the first 200 throws, (c) the first 500 throws, (d) all 1000 throws. The comparison of these relative frequencies is facilitated by Figure 5.2, in which each of the vertical lines has been subdivided into intervals representing the relative frequencies. We note two features of the graph: (a) the joining lines tend to become more parallel as we move to the right, indicating a tendency toward stability in the relative frequencies with increase of sample size; (b) the intervals, even with 1000 throws, are distinctly unequal, suggesting that the crudely made icosahedral die has a noticeable bias.

We leave to one side the moot question of whether, in actuality, it can be proved or disproved that the sample relative frequency really ap-

TABLE 5.2

RELATIVE FREQUENCY DISTRIBUTIONS OF THROWS OF A CARDBOARD
ICOSAHEDRAL DIE

Value	(a) First 100	(b) First 200	(c) First 500	(d) 1000 throws
0	.08	.050	.076	.081
1	.03	.075	.062	.048
2	.16	.140	.108	.096
3	.06	.060	.078	.085
4	.10	.070	.074	.063
5	.13	.120	.140	.144
6	.06	.115	.128	.128
7	.09	.095	.102	.088
8	.16	.155	.138	.134
9	.13	.120	.094	.133

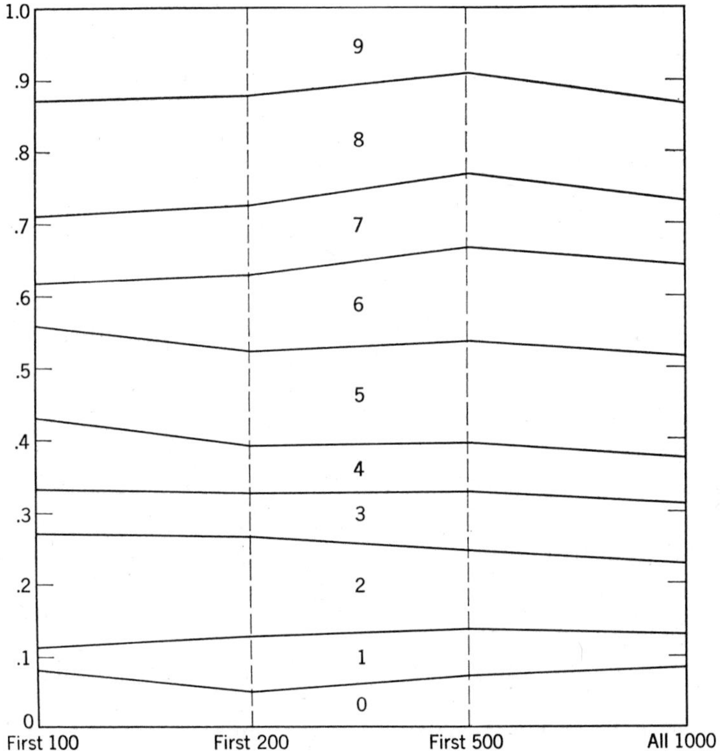

FIGURE 5.2

proaches the population relative frequency as a limit in any example where the population relative frequency is known, and content ourselves with two remarks:

(*a*) In many practical situations in which the population distribution is known, the relative frequency distribution of the sample appears to approach the population distribution as a limit, *for all practical purposes*. This would be the case, for example, for a well-made die or in various cases of sampling from a finite population in which random samples are carefully obtained.

(*b*) In many cases in which the population relative frequencies are unknown, experiments have been performed of sufficient size to make plausible the conclusion that the sample relative frequency tends to approach a limit as $n \to \infty$.

As a result we make the following definitions of *stability* and of *probability:*

(5.1)   DEFINITION.   *Let the sample space of an experiment be* $\{A_1, \cdots, A_k\}$. *Suppose that a sample of size n is obtained and that the frequencies corresponding to* $A_1, \cdots, A_k$ *are* $f_1, \cdots, f_k$, *where* $n = f_1 + \cdots + f_k$. *If each of the ratios* f_i/n *appears to approach a limit as n becomes very large, we then say that the random experiment is* stable, *and we define the limiting value* p_i *of the ratio* f_i/n *to be the* probability *that the outcome* A_i *shall occur.*

In most cases the probabilities p_i are inaccessible. From a large sample, however, we may estimate the probabilities by means of the relative frequencies f_i/n computed for the sample. Thus, for example, we assume that there is a definite probability that an individual selected at random from all men aged 25 in the United States will die within the next year. We cannot measure this probability directly, but we can calculate the *probability estimate* f_i/n from a large sample. Life insurance companies base their premium calculations on such probability estimates. Even though the probabilities are inaccessible, we can deduce some of the properties that the probabilities must possess from the properties of the corresponding estimates:

(*a*) The ratios f_i/n are non-negative. We therefore postulate that the probabilities p_i are non-negative.

(*b*) Since, for any sample, $\Sigma(f_i/n) = \Sigma f_i/n = 1$, we postulate that $\Sigma p_i = 1$.

(*c*) Let E be an event consisting of the sample points $\{A_a, A_b, A_c, \cdots\}$. In the sample, the total frequency of occurrences of the event

E is $f_a + f_b + f_c + \cdots$, and the relative frequency for E is $(f_a + f_b + f_c + \cdots)/n = f_a/n + f_b/n + f_c/n + \cdots$. We therefore *define* the probability of E to be $p_a + p_b + p_c + \cdots$. Thus:

(5.2) **DEFINITION.** *The probability of an event is the sum of the probabilities of its sample points.*

If E is an event, the probability of E will be denoted by $P(E)$. An immediate consequence of Definition 5.2 is the following theorem:

(5.3) **ADDITION THEOREM.** *If E_1 and E_2 are mutually exclusive events, then $P(E_1 \cup E_2) = P(E_1) + P(E_2)$.*

Proof. Let E_1 and E_2 be the sets $\{A_a, A_b, A_c, \cdots\}$ and $\{A_q, A_r, A_s, \cdots\}$. Then, since E_1 and E_2 are mutually exclusive, $E_1 \cup E_2 = \{A_a, A_b, A_c, \cdots, A_q, A_r, A_s, \cdots\}$, and $P(E_1 \cup E_2) = p_a + p_b + p_c + \cdots + p_q + p_r + p_s + \cdots = P(E_1) + P(E_2)$.

Theorem (5.3) may be generalized in several ways. In Theorem (5.4) it is generalized to the case of n mutually exclusive events, using mathematical induction. Then, in Theorem (5.5) we have the generalization of Theorem (5.3) for the case in which E_1 and E_2 are not necessarily mutually exclusive. In more advanced works Theorem (5.3) is further generalized to the case in which we have n events, which may or may not be mutually exclusive. (See Example 5.3 and Exercise 5.10.)

(5.4) **THEOREM.** *If $E_1, E_2, \cdots, E_n$ are mutually exclusive events, then*

$$P(E_1 \cup E_2 \cup \cdots \cup E_n) = P(E_1) + P(E_2) + \cdots + P(E_n).$$

Proof. Assume the theorem true for $n = k$, i.e., assume

$$P(E_1 \cup E_2 \cup \cdots \cup E_k) = P(E_1) + P(E_2) + \cdots + P(E_k).$$

Let E^* denote the event $E_1 \cup E_2 \cup \cdots \cup E_k$. Since the events $E_1, E_2, \cdots, E_n$ are mutually exclusive (i.e., have no points in common), it follows that E^* has no points in common with E_{k+1}. Hence, applying (5.3) to the events E^* and E_{k+1}, we find

$$P(E^* \cup E_{k+1}) = P(E^*) + P(E_{k+1})$$
$$= P(E_1) + P(E_2) + \cdots + P(E_k) + P(E_{k+1}).$$

But $E^* \cup E_{k+1} = E_1 \cup E_2 \cup \cdots \cup E_k \cup E_{k+1}$, so that

$$P(E_1 \cup E_2 \cup \cdots \cup E_k \cup E_{k+1})$$
$$= P(E_1) + P(E_2) + \cdots + P(E_k) + P(E_{k+1}).$$

We have proved that if the theorem is true when $n = k$, it is also true when $n = k + 1$. By (5.3) the theorem is true when $n = 2$. Using mathematical induction, we therefore conclude that (5.4) is true for all natural numbers n.

The reader should note carefully where, in the above proof, the laws of Boolean algebra, as listed in Section 3, are made use of. He should also be certain that he understands the use of mathematical induction in the above proof, since similar proofs by mathematical induction will occur many times in this book.

In order to derive a generalization of (5.3) to the case in which E_1 and E_2 are not mutually exclusive, let us represent the sample space as in Figure 5.3. The sample points are represented as dots in a plane, the size of each dot suggesting the probability associated with the point. The probabilities are often called weights because of the fruitful and detailed analogy between the theory of probability and that portion of mechanics which deals with systems of weights. Two events E_1 and E_2 are shown by means of closed curves, each including a number of points. The intersection E_1E_2 consists of the points in the overlapping area which lies within both closed curves; the union $E_1 \cup E_2$ consists of the points lying within either or both of the closed curves. By (5.2), $P(E_1)$ is the total probability or weight of points within the first closed curve; and $P(E_2)$ is the total probability or weight of points within the second. Thus $P(E_1) + P(E_2)$ will give the sum of the weights in either region, with the points in the overlapping region counted twice, so that $P(E_1E_2)$ is included twice. Hence we conclude

(5.5)   THEOREM. $P(E_1 \cup E_2) = P(E_1) + P(E_2) - P(E_1E_2).$

In case E_1 and E_2 are mutually exclusive, the closed curves in Figure 5.3 will not overlap, and $E_1E_2 = 0$. Thus (5.5) reduces to the simpler form of the addition theorem given in (5.3).

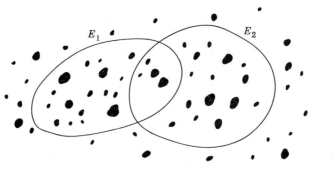

FIGURE 5.3

Example 5.3. The laws of Boolean algebra given in Section 3 permit us to generalize Theorem (5.5). We shall use (5.5), together with the Boolean algebra laws, in order to find an expression for $P(E_1 \cup E_2 \cup E_3)$ in terms of $P(E_1)$, $P(E_2)$, $P(E_3)$, $P(E_1E_2)$, $P(E_1E_3)$, $P(E_2E_3)$, and $P(E_1E_2E_3)$.

$$
\begin{aligned}
P(E_1 \cup E_2 \cup E_3) &= P(E_1 \cup (E_2 \cup E_3)) && \text{[8a]}\\
&= P(E_1) + P(E_2 \cup E_3) - P(E_1(E_2 \cup E_3)) && \text{[(5.5)]}\\
&= P(E_1) + P(E_2) + P(E_3) - P(E_2E_3) \\
&\quad - P(E_1E_2 \cup E_1E_3) && \text{[(5.5), 9b]}\\
&= P(E_1) + P(E_2) + P(E_3) - P(E_2E_3) - P(E_1E_2) \\
&\quad - P(E_1E_3) + P(E_1E_2E_1E_3) && \text{[(5.5)]}\\
&= P(E_1) + P(E_2) + P(E_3) - P(E_2E_3) - P(E_1E_2) \\
&\quad - P(E_1E_3) + P(E_1E_2E_3) && \text{[6b, 3b]}
\end{aligned}
$$

An important class of stable random experiments consists of *urnlike* random experiments. For these, the sample space may be specified as a set of N *equally likely* or *equiprobable sample points*, corresponding to the balls of an urn. The justification for the adjectives "equally likely" or "equiprobable" lies in the empirical fact attested to by many elaborate experiments that, if a large sample of size n is obtained from such a random experiment, the relative frequency for each of the sample points will approximate $1/N$ and the approximation will tend to improve as n is increased. In view of this fact we assign the probability $1/N$ to each of the sample points and conclude, using (5.2),

(5.6) THEOREM. *If the sample space of a random experiment contains N equiprobable points and if the event A comprises N_A of these points, then $P(A) = N_A/N$.*

Note that in Section 2 it was argued that the 6 sides of a well-made die are equally likely to fall uppermost because of the physical symmetry of the die. This is a second type of justification for the equiprobability of outcomes of urnlike random experiments, which will hold for a variety of examples, such as those discussed in Section 2.

Example 5.4. For a single die each sample point has a probability of 1/6. An "even" throw is the event consisting of the points $\{2, 4, 6\}$. Hence by (5.2) or (5.6) the probability of an even throw is 1/2.

Example 5.5. Two dice are rolled. What is the probability that their sum is 7? Figure 2.3 depicts the sample space of the random experiment of rolling 2 dice and observing their sum. There are 36 equally likely sample points, of which 6 belong to the event $Z = 7$, where Z is the random variable specifying the sum of the numbers showing on the dice. Hence, by (5.6), $P(Z = 7) = 6/36 = 1/6$.

Let the sample space of a random experiment be $\{A_1, \cdots, A_k\}$, with associated probabilities $p_1, \cdots, p_k$. This association between sample space and probabilities is called the *probability distribution*, or the *probability function*, or the *frequency function* of the random experiment.

More usually the terms probability function and frequency function are restricted to the case in which the sample space is specified by means of a random variable. In this case the function may be presented as a probability table:

$$\begin{array}{ll} \text{Random variable, } x & x_1 \cdots x_k \\ \text{Probability,} \quad p & p_1 \cdots p_k \end{array}$$

In order to emphasize the functional dependence of p on x, we write $p = f(x)$.

Example 5.6. Two dice are rolled. What is the frequency function of the random variable Z representing the sum of the 2 values showing on the dice? This is simply an extension of Example 5.5. Using Figure 2.3 and the method of Example 5.5, we obtain:

z	2	3	4	5	6	7	8	9	10	11	12
p	1/36	2/36	3/36	4/36	5/36	6/36	5/36	4/36	3/36	2/36	1/36

Note that in Example 5.6 we have considered *all possible samples of size* $n = 2$, as represented in Figure 2.3, and a *function* $Z = X_1 + X_2$ of the sample values. From our knowledge of the distribution of throws of a single die we were able to deduce the distribution of Z. Such a distribution of a function of the sample values is called a *sampling distribution*, a concept of central importance in mathematical statistics. Here we shall content ourselves with one additional illustration of a sampling distribution, deferring the systematic discussion of such distributions to Chapters 3 and 5.

Example 5.7. Two dice are rolled. If X_1 and X_2 are the values showing on the dice, find the sampling distribution of $Z = X_1^2 + X_2^2$. Figure 2.4 shows the sampling distribution of 2 dice, each of the 36 points being labeled with the value of $Z = X_1^2 + X_2^2$. By the method of Examples 5.5 and 5.6, and using Figure 2.4, we obtain the required distribution:

x	2	5	8	10	13	17	18	20	25	26	29
p	1/36	2/36	1/36	2/36	2/36	2/36	1/36	2/36	2/36	2/36	2/36

x	32	34	37	40	41	45	50	52	61	72
p	1/36	2/36	2/36	2/36	2/36	2/36	1/36	2/36	2/36	1/36

Most of the illustrations of this chapter have been concerned with urnlike random experiments. An important exception is the haemacytometer example of Table 4.2. The range of values in the sample was 1 to 12. But there is no a priori reason why the number of yeast cells per square should not exceed 12. In fact there are reasons for considering the random experiment of counting the yeast cells in any square to have the countably infinite sample space $\{0, 1, 2, \cdots\}$. If $f(x)$ is a frequency function for such a sample space, then we would expect $\sum_{x=0}^{\infty} f(x) = 1$. In Chapter 5 it will be shown that a reasonable frequency function for data such as those from the haemacytometer is the Poisson frequency function defined by

$$(5.7) \qquad\qquad f(x) = k^x e^{-k}/x!,$$

where k is a constant which we shall be able, in Section 35, to identify with the mean of the population, and $x!$ is the factorial function [see (7.31)]. Recalling that

$$e^y = 1 + y + \frac{y^2}{2!} + \frac{y^3}{3!} + \cdots = \sum_{i=0}^{\infty} y^i/i!,$$

it is easy to verify that $\sum_{x=0}^{\infty} f(x) = 1$. For

$$\sum_{x=0}^{\infty} f(x) = \sum_{x=0}^{\infty} k^x e^{-k}/x! = e^{-k} \sum_{x=0}^{\infty} k^x/x! = e^{-k}e^k = 1.$$

We have yet to consider the concept of probability for the case of a random experiment with continuous sample space. Examples 2.8 and 2.9 were of this kind, both based on the spinner. How shall probability be defined for the spinner? In Example 2.6 the spinner scale was divided into 6 equal arcs labeled 1, 2, $\cdots$, 6; with such a scale the spinner provides a random experiment equivalent to rolling a die. In this case the probability of obtaining, say, a "1" is simply *the proportion of the circumference which is labeled "1."* This suggests

(5.8) DEFINITION. *The probability that the pointer of a spinner shall stop in a specific arc of the circumference, of length A, is A/C, where C is the length of the circumference.*

Example 5.8. Consider a spinner with the uniform scale of Example 2.8. Let $\overset{\frown}{AB}$ be an arc of the circumference which does not include the point Q (the origin of the scale), except possibly as one of the end points A and B. Let u_A and u_B be the scale values of the ends A and B of the arc; suppose $u_B > u_A$. Then, since the whole circumference of the scale is unity, if U represents the random value indicated by the pointer,

$$P(u_A < U < u_B) = u_B - u_A$$

This is the probability that the pointer will come to rest in the arc $\overset{\frown}{AB}$. In particular, if A coincides with Q, we have $u_A = u_Q = 0$, so that

$$P(0 < U < u_B) = u_B.$$

Example 5.9. Let us attempt to construct a spinner model which will be (at least approximately) equivalent to the random experiment of Example 1.5, involving measuring the height in inches of a corn plant randomly obtained from an experimental plot. The sample space for that experiment was $0 < x < 15$, so that we shall want the spinner scale to run from 0 to 15. But it would probably be the case, in sampling and measuring the corn plants, that values in the middle of the range would be more likely to occur than extremely small or extremely large values. More specifically, if we divide the sample space into 15 intervals, each of length 1 inch, we would expect that there would be a much greater probability of obtaining a value in the intervals $(7, 8)$, than in the interval $(0, 1)$ or the interval $(14, 15)$. Thus we would not expect the scale to be a uniform one, for which each unit interval from $(0, 1)$ to $(14, 15)$ would be allotted $360°/15 = 24°$ of the circumference. The scale in Figure 5.4 was constructed arbitrarily to suggest what the scale might

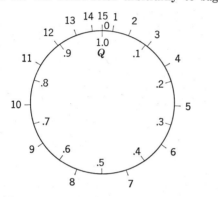

FIGURE 5.4

be like. About $36°$ of the circumference is allotted to the interval $(7, 8)$, with progressively smaller arcs given to the remaining intervals as we proceed in either direction around the circle.

In Figure 5.4 two scales are shown. The scale for the actual random experiment, with random variable x, is on the outside of the circle; while on the inside is a uniform scale whose values will be denoted by u. There is evidently a functional relationship between u and x, which we shall denote by $u = F(x)$. To find $P(x_1 < X < x_2)$, where x_1 and x_2 are arbitrary values, we need to know the proportion of the circumference lying between them. This is easily obtained by subtracting the the corresponding u-values (see Example 5.8). Thus

(5.9) $$P(x_1 < X < x_2) = F(x_2) - F(x_1).$$

This is the fundamental formula for probability in the case of a continuous random variable. These ideas will be considered in detail in Chapter 2.

In the construction of Figure 5.4 an algebraic formula (which will be

TABLE 5.3

x	$F(x)$	x	$F(x)$	x	$F(x)$	x	$F(x)$
0	0	4	.175	8	.550	12	.896
1	.013	5	.259	9	.648	13	.951
2	.049	6	.352	10	.741	14	.987
3	.104	7	.450	11	.825	15	1.000

further discussed in Example 10.2) was assumed for the function $F(x)$. Table 5.3 was derived from the algebraic formula.

Example 5.10.   To illustrate the use of (5.9), we shall use Table 5.3 to find $P(1 < X < 9)$.   We have $P(1 < X < 9) = F(9) - F(1) = .648 - .013 = .635$.   This implies that the arc in Figure 5.4 from $x = 1$ to $x = 9$ involves .635 of the circumference or subtends an angle of $.635 \times 360° = 229°$.

EXERCISE 5

5.1. If an individual is now aged 35, the probability that he will die before age 36 is, according to the Commissioners 1941 Standard Ordinary Mortality Table, .00459.   The probability that the same individual will die between ages 36 and 37 is .00484; between ages 37 and 38 is .00510; between 38 and 39 is .00538; and between 39 and 40 is .00560.   Find the probability that an individual now aged 35 will die between

(*a*) Ages 35 and 40.
(*b*) Ages 37 and 39.

5.2. A box contains 500 industrial parts, of which 50 are known to be defective.   A random sample of 10 parts is withdrawn.   The following table gives the probability of obtaining 0, 1, $\cdots$, 10 defective parts in the sample.

Number of defectives	0	1	2	3	4	5	6	7	8	9	10
Probability	.3452	.3914	.1952	.0564	.0104	.0013	.0001	0	0	0	0

Find the probability that a sample of 10 parts contains

(*a*) More than three defectives.
(*b*) Four or fewer defectives.
(*Note:* The method of computing a table such as the one given here will be introduced in Section 7.)

5.3. The probability that a worker drawn at random from a certain factory is a male is .651, that a worker is married is .701, that a worker is a married male is .472.   Find the probability that a worker drawn at random is

(*a*) A married female.
(*b*) A single female.
(*c*) A male, or married, or both.

5.4. Let X_1 and X_2 be the results of 2 throws of an icosahedral die (Example 2.5). Find the frequency functions of the following random variables:

(a) $X_1 + X_2$.

(b) $X_1 X_2$.

(c) Maximum of X_1 and X_2. (When X_1 and X_2 are equal we arbitrarily define the maximum to be their common value.)

5.5. (a) Use Table 5.3 to find, for the random experiment provided by the spinner with the scale of Figure 5.4, $P(5 < X < 11)$.

(b) Assuming that linear interpolation may be used with Table 5.3, estimate the value of $P(2 < X < 7.2)$.

5.6. Let the set $\{1, 2, 3, 4, 5\}$ constitute the sample space for a random experiment. Let x represent a variable whose range is the above set. What value must k have in order that $p = kx^2$ may constitute a frequency function for the experiment?

5.7. Consider the sample space for random drawings of a single card from a pack of 52 cards. Assume that each of the 52 points has the same probability. Let the events A, B, and C be defined as follows:

A = the card is red.

B = the card is not a Jack, Queen, or King and is even-numbered.

C = the card bears a number less than 9.

Describe in words the following events, and find the probability of each:

    (a) $A \cup B$ (b) $A \cap B$ (c) $A \cup C$ (d) $A \cap C$

    (e) $A \cup B \cup C$ (f) $A \cap (B \cup C)$ (g) $B' \cap C$.

5.8. An urn U_1 contains 3 red and 5 green balls; a second urn U_2 contains 4 white and 7 blue balls. A random experiment consists of drawing a ball from each urn. Let the sample space consist of the 88 points corresponding to the possible pairs of balls. Decide on a suitable set of probabilities for the sample space. Define events A and B as follows:

A = ball drawn from U_1 is red.

B = ball drawn from U_2 is white.

Describe in words the following events, and find the probability of each:

    (a) A' (b) B' (c) $A \cup B'$ (d) $A' \cap B$ (e) $A \cup A'B'$.

5.9. Three coins are thrown twice. Let X be the number of heads on the first throw, and Y the number of heads on the second throw. Find $P(X > Y)$.

5.10. Let E_1, E_2, E_3, E_4 be any four events. Use the method of Example 5.3 in order to express $P(E_1 \cup E_2 \cup E_3 \cup E_4)$ in terms of the probabilities of the events E_1, E_2, E_3, E_4, E_1E_2, E_1E_3, E_1E_4, E_2E_3, E_2E_4, E_3E_4, $E_1E_2E_3$, $E_1E_2E_4$, $E_1E_3E_4$, $E_2E_3E_4$, and $E_1E_2E_3E_4$.

6. INDEPENDENCE

Suppose we have two random experiments, $\mathcal{E}_x$ with sample space $\{x_1, \cdots, x_h\}$ and $\mathcal{E}_y$ with sample space $\{y_1, \cdots, y_k\}$. We shall call the random experiments $\mathcal{E}_x$ and $\mathcal{E}_y$ independent if the outcome of either one is unaffected by the outcome of the other. This is a temporary, intuitive definition of independence, which will be replaced by a more satisfactory definition in Section 20. If, for example, we toss a penny and roll a die, we expect that the result of the first of these random experiments will have no effect on the result of the second. The two experiments are, in this case, physically independent.

Consider now the *compound experiment* which consists of repeating both experiment $\mathcal{E}_x$ and experiment $\mathcal{E}_y$ and forming the ordered pair (X, Y) of outcomes of the two experiments. We shall denote the compound experiment by $(\mathcal{E}_x, \mathcal{E}_y)$. Its sample space will be the set of all pairs (x_i, y_j), where x_i is a member of the set $\{x_1, \cdots, x_h\}$, and y_j is a member of the set $\{y_1, \cdots, y_k\}$. This set, called the *Cartesian product* of the sets $\{x_1, \cdots, x_h\}$ and $\{y_1, \cdots, y_k\}$, may be conveniently presented in the form of a two-way table, as in Table 6.1.

TABLE 6.1

	x_1	$\cdots$	x_h
y_1	(x_1, y_1)	$\cdots$	(x_h, y_1)
.	.	$\cdots$	.
.	.	$\cdots$	.
.	.	$\cdots$	.
y_k	(x_1, y_k)	$\cdots$	(x_h, y_k)

Note that this is essentially a *cross-classification*, as described in Section 3.

The fundamental theorem for independent random experiments is the *multiplication theorem*, proved below for the case of urnlike experiments. The general case will be discussed in Chapter 3.

In connection with Example 2.2 it was argued that, if the 6 sides of a die are regarded as equally likely, the 36 possible outcomes for a pair of dice should be regarded as equally likely. The argument is based on the symmetry of a die. A similar argument, based on symmetry considerations, will establish the following proposition:

(6.1) THEOREM. *If a first urnlike experiment has* M *equiprobable outcomes and a second urnlike experiment, independent of the first, has* N *equiprobable outcomes, then the compound experiment consisting of a pair of outcomes, one from the first experiment and one from the second, has* MN *equiprobable outcomes.*

Proof. Consider the array of MN sample points of Figure 6.1. The points of each row are equiprobable because in any row only the outcome of the first experiment varies, and we have assumed that the M

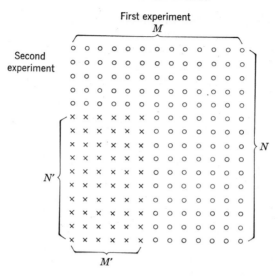

FIGURE 6.1

outcomes of the first experiment are equiprobable. Similarly the N outcomes in any column are equiprobable. Hence all MN points must be equiprobable.

We recall from Section 3 that, if A and B are events, the notation AB stands for the simultaneous occurrence of both events.

(6.2) MULTIPLICATION THEOREM. *Let A and B be two events, associated with independent urnlike random experiments. Then $P(AB) = P(A)P(B)$.*

Proof. Suppose that the event A comprises M' of the M equiprobable points of the first experiment and that the event B comprises N' of the N equiprobable points of the second experiment. Then $P(A) = M'/M$ and $P(B) = N'/N$. On the other hand, the event AB includes $M'N'$ of the MN equiprobable outcomes of the compound experiment. Hence $P(AB) = M'N'/MN = (M'/M)(N'/N) = P(A)P(B)$ (see Figure 6.1, in which the points of AB are marked "$\times$").

Theorem (6.2) may be extended in several ways:

(a) The requirement of independence may be dropped. This is done in Chapter 3.

(*b*) The theorem may be extended to 3 or more events, as is done below:

(6.3)   MULTIPLICATION THEOREM.   *Let A, B, C, $\cdots$ be a sequence of events, associated with independent urnlike random experiments.*   Then
$$P(ABC) \cdots) = P(A)P(B)P(C) \cdots.$$

The proof, which can be carried out by mathematical induction, will be omitted.

(*c*) The theorem may be stated for frequency functions, rather than for individual probabilities.   In order to do this we make the following definition:

(6.4)   DEFINITION.   *Let $\mathcal{E}_x$ and $\mathcal{E}_y$ be random experiments with sample spaces $\{x_1, \cdots, x_h\}$ and $\{y_1, \cdots, y_k\}$.   Then the function $f(x, y)$ defined by $f(x, y) = P(X = x, Y = y)$ is called the frequency function of the compound random experiment $(\mathcal{E}_x, \mathcal{E}_y)$ whose sample space is given in Table* 6.1.

It is now an immediate corollary of (6.2) that the following theorem holds:

(6.5)   THEOREM.   *Let $\mathcal{E}_x$ and $\mathcal{E}_y$ be independent random experiments with sample spaces $\{x_1, \cdots, x_h\}$ and $\{y_1, \cdots, y_k\}$, and with frequency functions $f(x)$ and $g(y)$.   The frequency function of the compound experiment $(\mathcal{E}_x, \mathcal{E}_y)$ is $f(x) \, g(y)$.*

Example 6.1.   Let X and Y be independent urnlike random variables with the distributions shown:

x	1	2	3	4	5
p	.1	.2	.4	.2	.1

y	0	1	2	3
p'	.2	.1	.4	.3

Find the distribution of (*a*) $X + Y$, (*b*) XY, (*c*) Y/X.

Solution.   The joint distribution of X and Y may be presented in the form of a two-way table (see Table 6.2).   Each cell in the body of the table represents a point of the sample space of the compound random experiment.   In the upper right of each cell is the pair of values (x, y), and in the lower left is the probability for that pair, obtained by multiplying the corresponding probabilities in the margin.

(*a*) To find the distribution of $X + Y$, we note that $X + Y = $ const. for diagonal rows of cells.   For example, $X + Y = 4$ in a row of cells extending from the lower left corner upward and to the right.   To find $P(X + Y = 4)$, we simply add the probabilities of these cells:

$$P(X + Y = 4) = .03 + .08 + .04 + .04 = .19.$$

TABLE 6.2

x		1	2	3	4	5
y	p	.1	.2	.4	.2	.1
0	.2	(1, 0) .02	(2, 0) .04	(3, 0) .08	(4, 0) .04	(5, 0) .02
1	.1	(1, 1) .01	(2, 1) .02	(3, 1) .04	(4, 1) .02	(5, 1) .01
2	.4	(1, 2) .04	(2, 2) .08	(3, 2) .16	(4, 2) .08	(5, 2) .04
3	.3	(1, 3) .03	(2, 3) .06	(3, 3) .12	(4, 3) .06	(5, 3) .03

Proceeding in this way we obtain the distribution:

$x + y$	1	2	3	4	5	6	7	8
p	.02	.05	.14	.19	.26	.21	.10	.03

(b) To find the distribution of XY, consider the following table:

```
0  0  0   0   0
1  2  3   4   5
2  4  6   8  10
3  6  9  12  15
```

The values of the product XY have been arranged in the same rectangular form as that of Table 6.2. To find, for example, $P(XY = 6)$, we note the 2 positions in the above table where "6" occurs and add the corresponding probabilities in Table 6.2, obtaining .22. In this way we find

xy	0	1	2	3	4	5	6	8	9	10	12	15
p	.20	.01	.06	.07	.10	.01	.22	.08	.12	.04	.06	.03

(c) To find the distribution of Y/X, we form the auxiliary table

```
0    0    0    0    0
1   1/2  1/3  1/4  1/5
2    1   2/3  1/2  2/5
3   3/2   1   3/4  3/5
```

Proceeding as before, we find the distribution

y/x	0	1/5	1/4	1/3	2/5	1/2	3/5	2/3	3/4	1	3/2	2	3
p	.20	.01	.02	.04	.04	.10	.03	.16	.06	.21	.06	.04	.03

EXERCISE 6

6.1. Let X and Y be random variables with the following distributions:

x	1	2	3
p	.3	.4	.3

y	1	2	3
p	.2	.5	.3

Form a two-way table of the joint distribution of X and Y, and use it to determine the distribution of

(a) $X + Y$ (b) $X^2 + Y^2$

6.2. Let X and Y be random variables with the following distributions:

x	-2	-1	0	1	2
p	.1	.3	.2	.3	.1

y	-2	-1	0	1	2
p	.1	.3	.2	.3	.1

Form a two-way table of the joint distribution of X and Y, and use it to determine the distribution of

(a) $X + Y$ (b) $X - Y$ (c) $|X| + |Y|$

6.3. For which of the following bivariate distributions are the random variables X and Y independent?

(a)

y \ x	1	2	3
1	.2	0	.2
2	0	.2	0
3	.2	0	.2

(b)

y \ x	1	2	3
1	.16	.08	.16
2	.08	.16	.08
3	.16	.08	.16

(c)

y \ x	1	2	3
1	.02	.10	.08
2	.04	.20	.16
3	.04	.20	.16

7. SAMPLING FROM A FINITE POPULATION

In Section 1 an informal definition of random sampling was given. We now provide a suitable formal definition:

(7.1) DEFINITION. *A process of drawing samples in which every possible sample of the same size has the same probability of being drawn is called simple random sampling.*

Simple random sampling is a special case of *probability sampling*, which is said to take place when the sample is selected in such a way that the probability associated with every obtainable sample may be computed.

A possible method of drawing a random sample from a finite population would consist of two steps: first, list all possible samples of the given size (as is done in Exercise 8.8); second, number the possible samples consecutively and use a table of random numbers to make the actual selection. However the number of possible samples may get very large. For example, the number of possible samples of size $n = 10$ from a population of size $N = 20$ is 184,756, as may be shown by methods discussed later in this section.

Random numbers are often employed to obtain random samples from a finite population, as illustrated in the following example:

Example 7.1. A factory employing 1500 workers wishes to obtain interviews with a random sample of 50 workers. Assume that each worker is assigned a number from 1 to 1500. A sequence of four-figure random numbers is examined, obtained from four adjacent columns of a table of random numbers. Those from 0001 to 1500 are retained, and others rejected. The process of selection is continued until 50 different numbers are obtained; these numbers determine the sample.

In the above example it is tacitly assumed that a simple random sample is obtained if the drawings are made in succession, instead of simultaneously, with each of the remaining members of the population regarded as equally likely to be drawn, at each stage. That this is indeed the case may be proved by means of the general "multiplication theorem" of Section 20. However just as we have argued that the six sides of a die are equally likely to appear uppermost because of the symmetry of the die, so we may here conclude that each possible sample of 50 employees is equally likely to be drawn because the set of all possible samples of size 50 possesses a kind of symmetry analogous to the symmetry of a well-made die. These considerations suggest the following alternative definition of a random sample:

(7.2) DEFINITION. *A sample is random if every individual in the population has an equal and independent chance of being included in the sample.*

Example 7.2. Let us assume that in Example 7.1 a card file is available with the names of the 1500 employees, arranged alphabetically. A process frequently used in order to obtain a sample of 50 from such a population is to draw every 30th card in the card file. Obviously there is no element of randomness unless the first card is chosen randomly. Hence a two-digit random number between 01 and 30, inclusive, is used to determine the first card. Such a process is called *systematic sampling*. Note carefully in what way such a sample fails to be random, in the sense of (7.1).

Let us now recall the fundamentals of the theory of permutations and combinations:

(7.3)   *The factorial function n! is defined by*

$$n! = n(n - 1) \cdots 2.1, n \geqq 1$$

$$0! = 1$$

(7.4)   *The number of permutations (arrangements) of n things taken r at a time is*

$$_nP_r = n!/(n - r)! = n(n - 1) \cdots (n - r + 1).$$

(7.5)   *The number of combinations of n different things taken r at a time is*

$$\binom{n}{r} = \binom{n}{n - r} = \frac{n!}{r!(n - r)!} \quad (Note\ that\ \binom{n}{0} = \binom{n}{n} = 1)$$

(7.6)   *The number of permutations of n things, of which n_1 are alike of one kind, n_2 alike of another, $\cdots$, n_k alike of another, where $n_1 + \cdots + n_k = n$, is*

$$\frac{n!}{n_1!n_2! \cdots n_k!}$$

The same formula gives the number of ways in which n distinguishable objects can be distributed among k groups, with n_1 in the first group, n_2 in the second group, $\cdots$, n_k in the kth group, where $n_1 + \cdots = n_k = n$.

The binomial theorem and its generalization in the form of the multinomial theorem will be used from time to time in subsequent work. Combinatorial proofs are given here for both of these theorems.

(7.7)   BINOMIAL THEOREM.

$$(a + b)^n$$

$$= a^n + na^{n-1}b + \binom{n}{2} a^{n-2}b^2 + \cdots + \binom{n}{r} a^{n-r}b^r + \cdots + b^n.$$

Proof. We note that, if in the expansion of $(a + b)^n$ similar terms were not collected and combined, there would be 2^n individual terms, each of degree n. Each of the factors in each of these individual terms is drawn from one of the n binomial factors of $(a + b)^n$. Thus, in the term $a^{n-r}b^r$, a "b" is drawn from r of the binomial factors, and an "a" from the remaining $n - r$ factors. The selection of the r factors from which "b" is to be drawn may be carried out in $\binom{n}{r}$ ways. Thus the total number of such terms as $a^{n-r}b^r$ is $\binom{n}{r}$, and when combined their value is $\binom{n}{r} a^{n-r}b^r$. This is a typical term in the expansion (7.7).

(7.8) MULTINOMIAL THEOREM.

$$(a_1 + a_2 + \cdots + a_k)^n = \sum \frac{n!}{n_1! n_2! \cdots n_k!} a_1{}^{n_1} a_2{}^{n_2} \cdots a_k{}^{n_k},$$

where the summation is over all possible partitions of n into component parts $n_1, n_2, \cdots, n_k$, such that $n = n_1 + n_2 + \cdots + n_k$.

The proof is entirely analogous to that for the binomial theorem. A term such as $a_1{}^{n_1} a_2{}^{n_2} \cdots a_k{}^{n_k}$ is formed by selecting one letter from each of the n multinomial factors $(a_1 + \cdots + a_k)$. We must select a_1 from n_1 of these factors, a_2 from n_2 of them, and so on. The number of ways in which this can be done is the same as the number of ways of arranging n distinguishable objects into k groups, containing $n_1, \cdots, n_k$ objects. By (7.6) this yields precisely the coefficient specified by (7.8).

Example 7.3. The coefficient of $a^2 b^2 c$ in the expansion of $(a + b + c + d)^5$ is $5!/2!2! = 30$.

Consider, now, a simple example of an urnlike random experiment, in which drawings are without replacement. All the probabilities which we shall derive in the next few illustrations will be based on Theorem (5.6).

Example 7.4. What is the probability of drawing a heart in a single drawing from a pack of cards? The sample space consists of $N = 52$ equiprobable points, corresponding to the cards in a pack. The event $A = \{heart\}$ comprises $N_A = 13$ of the sample points. Thus $P(A) = 13/52 = 1/4$.

Example 7.5. What is the probability that 3 cards drawn at random from a pack will all be hearts? We take for our sample space all possible drawings of 3 cards from a pack of 52. Thus there are $N = \binom{52}{3}$ sample points. The subset A consisting of all triples of hearts contains $N_A = \binom{13}{3}$ points. Hence $P(A) = \binom{13}{3} \Big/ \binom{52}{3} = 11/850$.

Example 7.6. If 5 cards are drawn from a pack, what is the probability of obtaining exactly 3 hearts among the 5? The sample space will consist of $\binom{52}{5}$ equiprobable points corresponding to the ways in which 5 cards may be selected from 52. The event A in which we are interested will consist of the subset of points each of which combines 3 hearts with 2 non-hearts. The 3 hearts may be selected from 13 in $\binom{13}{3}$ ways, and the 2 non-hearts may be selected from 39 in $\binom{39}{2}$ ways. The required combination may be selected in $N_A = \binom{13}{3} \binom{39}{2}$ ways, which is the number of points of the sample space belonging to the event A. Thus $P(A) = \binom{13}{3} \binom{39}{2} \Big/ \binom{52}{5}$.

Suppose X is a random variable which ranges over the set $\{x_1, \cdots, x_k\}$; this set may be taken to be the sample space of the random experiment. Let $\{p_1, \cdots, p_k\}$ be the set of probabilities associated with the sample points, so that $P(X = x_i) = p_i$. As pointed out in Section 5, we regard the relation between the set $\{x_i\}$ and the set $\{p_i\}$ as determining a function, known as the frequency function of the random experiment, and we write $p_i = f(x_i)$, or simply $p = f(x)$. Given an arbitrary set of real numbers $\{x_1, \cdots, x_k\}$, any set of non-negative numbers $\{p_1, \cdots, p_k\}$ for which $\Sigma p_i = 1$ may be regarded as specifying a frequency function.

Certain important frequency functions may be specified analytically, that is, by means of an algebraic formula for $f(x)$. We shall consider in the remainder of this section a number of such algebraic frequency functions, all based on the concept of sampling from a finite population, with or without replacement. Several of the frequency functions to be considered are functions of several random variables. They are known as *joint frequency functions*.

Generalizing from Example 7.6, consider an urn containing N balls, of which Np are black, Nq are white, so that p and q are the proportions of black and white and $p + q = 1$. What is the probability that, if n balls are withdrawn (without replacement), exactly x will be black? The sample space has $\binom{N}{n}$ equiprobable points, corresponding to the ways in which n balls may be drawn from N. The event A whose probability we seek consists of all combinations of x black with $n - x$ white balls, so that $N_A = \binom{Np}{x}\binom{Nq}{n-x}$. Thus the probability is

$$(7.9) \qquad f(x) = \binom{Np}{x}\binom{Nq}{n-x} \bigg/ \binom{N}{n}.$$

This is the *hypergeometric frequency function* (probability distribution), of considerable importance in industrial quality control, especially in sampling inspection. Let us note the restrictions on the variable x in (7.9) imposed by the fact that the lower number in the symbol $\binom{n}{m}$ cannot be negative and cannot be greater than the upper number. We find the conditions $0 \leq x \leq Np$, $0 \leq n - x \leq Nq$. The latter may be written $n \geq x \geq n - Nq$. These conditions may be summarized in the following form: x ranges from the larger of 0 and Nq to the smaller of n and Np.

Example 7.7. If 5 cards are drawn from a pack, what is the probability of obtaining $x = 0, 1, \cdots, 5$ hearts? What is the probability of obtaining 3 or more hearts? We must use (7.9) with $Np = 13$, $Nq = 39$, $N = 52$, $n = 5$, and $x = 0, 1, \cdots, 5$. Logarithms of factorials (Table 6) may be employed, or a short table of logarithms of binomial coefficients, such as that in *Statistical Tables and Formulas*, by A. Hald (John Wiley & Sons, 1952). We find

x	0	1	2	3	4	5
$f(x)$	.2215	.4113	.2743	.0816	.0107	.0005

A line graph of this distribution is shown in Figure 7.1. If X denotes the random variable which represents the number of hearts obtained in a drawing of 5 cards, the probability $P(X > 2) = .0816 + .0107 + .0005 = .0928$. This is the probability of obtaining 3 or more hearts.

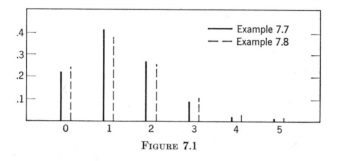

FIGURE 7.1

From the frequency function (7.9) we may now derive the frequency function for drawings with replacement. Suppose that the number N of balls in the urn is increased while the proportions p and q, and also the numbers n and x, are held fixed. If the drawings are with replacement, the increase in N has no effect on the probabilities since the proportions are preserved. On the other hand, when the drawings are without replacement, the larger N becomes, the less the proportions are altered by successive drawings. These two facts imply that, as $N \to \infty$, drawings without replacement will become indistinguishable from drawings with replacement. Sometimes the term "sampling from an infinite discrete population" is used; such sampling may always be regarded as equivalent to sampling from a finite population, with replacement.

In order to investigate the effect of increase of N on the expression $\binom{Np}{x}\binom{Nq}{n-x} \Big/ \binom{N}{n}$, we write it as follows:

$$\frac{\binom{Np}{x}\binom{Nq}{n-x}}{\binom{N}{n}}$$

$$= \frac{(Np)!}{x!(Np-x)!} \frac{(Nq)!}{(n-x)!(Nq-n+x)!} \frac{n!\,(N-n)!}{N!}$$

$$= \binom{n}{x}\frac{Np(Np-1)\,\cdots\,(Np-x+1)Nq(Nq-1)\,\cdots\,(Nq-n+x+1)}{N(N-1)\,\cdots\,(N-n+1)}.$$

In the fraction that follows $\binom{n}{x}$ there are n factors in both numerator and denominator. If we divide each of these by N, we find

$$\frac{\binom{Np}{x}\binom{Nq}{n-x}}{\binom{N}{n}}$$

$$= \binom{n}{x}\frac{p\left(p-\dfrac{1}{N}\right)\cdots\left(p-\dfrac{x-1}{N}\right)q\left(q-\dfrac{1}{N}\right)\cdots\left(q-\dfrac{n-x-1}{N}\right)}{1\left(1-\dfrac{1}{N}\right)\cdots\left(1-\dfrac{n-1}{N}\right)}.$$

If we now hold p, q, n, and x fixed and permit N to approach ∞, we find

$$\lim_{N\to\infty}\frac{\binom{Np}{x}\binom{Nq}{n-x}}{\binom{N}{n}} = \binom{n}{x}p^x q^{n-x},$$

which is the frequency function for drawings with replacement. This is the *binomial frequency function*, which will be discussed further in Chapters 3 and 5. For comparison with Example 7.6 we give here the corresponding binomial distribution:

Example 7.8. If 5 cards are drawn from a pack, with replacement, what is the probability of obtaining $x = 0, 1, \cdots, 5$ hearts? The frequency function is $f(x) = \binom{5}{x}\left(\dfrac{1}{4}\right)^x\left(\dfrac{3}{4}\right)^{5-x} = \binom{5}{x}\dfrac{3^{5-x}}{1024}.$ We readily find the values shown below:

x	0	1	2	3	4	5
$f(x)$	.2373	.3955	.2637	.0879	.0146	.0010

These values are also shown in Figure 7.1, for comparison with the corresponding hypergeometric probabilities.

It is worth while to give a direct derivation of the binomial frequency function. Let Y be a random variable which takes the values 0 or 1 in a single trial of the dichotomous random experiment, and let the corresponding probabilities be q and p. In a sample of n repetitions we obtain the n values $(Y_1, \cdots, Y_n)$; for example, we might obtain the set $(0, 1, 1, 0, 0, 0, 1, 1, 0, \cdots)$. All possible samples of this type will form the sample space of the experiment, containing 2^n sample points (see Example 2.4). Let X denote the random variable $X = Y_1 + \cdots + Y_n$. Consider the event: $X = x$, i.e., the sample point has x 1's and $n - x$ 0's. There will be $\binom{n}{x}$ such points since there are $\binom{n}{x}$ ways of arranging a sequence of x 1's and $n - x$ 0's. By (6.3), each sample point in the event will have probability $p^x q^{n-x}$, so that the probability of the event $X = x$ is $\binom{n}{x} p^x q^{n-x}$, by (5.2).

The results we have obtained are summarized below:

THEOREM. *An urn contains N balls, of which Np are black, Nq white, where $p + q = 1$. If n balls are withdrawn, the probability of getting x black balls is*

$$(7.10) \qquad f(x) = \frac{\binom{Np}{x} \binom{Nq}{n-x}}{\binom{N}{n}},$$

if the drawings are without replacement (hypergeometric frequency function),

$$(7.11) \qquad f(x) = \binom{n}{x} p^x q^{n-x},$$

if the drawings are with replacement (binomial frequency function).

The following example suggests a graphical approach to problems involving the binomial distribution.

Example 7.9. Mr. Adams moves into a house located at A on the corner of a north-south street AB and an east-west street AH. Assume all north-south streets are .1 mile apart and that the same is true for all east-west streets. A highway cuts through the lattice of streets at 45°. Mr. Adams discovers there are drugstores at the 7 corners B, C, D, E, F, G, and H. He also discovers that he can reach any one of the drugstores by traveling exactly 6 blocks, provided that he always proceeds either east or north at each corner. Mr. Adams wishes to distribute his patronage impartially among the drugstores and decides to flip a coin at each corner, going east if the coin falls "heads," north if

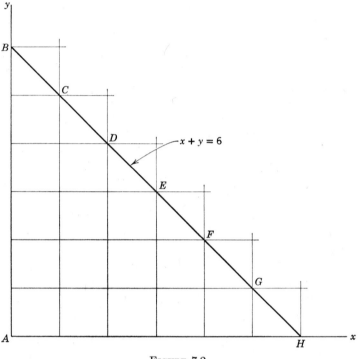

FIGURE 7.2

it falls "tails." Does he succeed in distributing his patronage evenly, that is, is the probability for each of the seven drugstores the same?

Solution. Each drugstore can be labeled $(x, 6\text{-}x)$, where x is the number of blocks to the east. Thus drugstore F has coordinates $(4, 2)$, which implies that Mr. Adams can reach this point by traversing 4 blocks east and 2 blocks north in any order. In fact, there are as many possible paths to F as there are permutations of the letters $EEEENN$, and by (7.6) this number is 15. Each succession of 6 blocks has a probability of $2^{-6} = 1/64$ that it will be selected. Hence the probability is 15/64 that he will reach F. This is, of course, simply the probability that 6 throws of a coin will yield 4 heads, 2 tails, and (7.11) shows this to be $\binom{6}{2}\left(\frac{1}{2}\right)^6 = 15/64$. The probabilities of reaching each of the seven stores are as given below:

Store	B	C	D	E	F	G	H
Probability	1/64	6/64	15/64	20/64	15/64	6/64	1/64

Mr. Adams has failed miserably in his commendable effort to act impartially.

A sequence of n Bernoullian trials, considered as resulting in success or failure, can always be represented on a diagram of the kind just considered.

The diagram related to Example 7.9 need not be regarded as a map of a portion of a city. It becomes more useful if we regard it as an abstract representation of a sequence of trials, each trial considered as resulting in success or failure. The x-axis is the "success axis," and the y-axis is the "failure axis." Starting from an origin in the lower left corner of the diagram, we go one unit to the right for each success, one unit up for each failure. After n trials we must reach one of the lattice points on the line $x + y = n$. The $n + 1$ points on this line thus constitute a sample space for the random experiment consisting of n trials of this kind.

The preceding results are readily generalized to the case of an urn containing balls with k different labels. As before, the second result may be obtained from the first by letting N become infinite, or it may be proved entirely independently.

THEOREM. *An urn contains N balls, of which Np_1 are labeled 1, Np_2 are labeled 2, $\cdots$, Np_k are labeled k, where $p_1 + \cdots + p_k = 1$. If n balls are withdrawn, the probability of obtaining x_1 balls labeled 1, x_2 balls labeled 2, $\cdots$, x_k balls labeled k, where $x_1 + \cdots + x_k = n$, is*

$$(7.12) \qquad f(x_1, \cdots, x_k) = \frac{\binom{Np_1}{x_1}\binom{Np_2}{x_2}\cdots\binom{Np_k}{x_k}}{\binom{N}{n}},$$

if the drawings are without replacement (generalized hypergeometric frequency function), or

$$(7.13) \qquad f(x_1, \cdots, x_k) = \frac{n!}{x_1!x_2!\cdots x_k!}\, p_1{}^{x_1}p_2{}^{x_2}\cdots p_k{}^{x_k},$$

if the drawings are with replacement (multinomial frequency function).

The proofs of (7.12) and (7.13) are direct generalizations of the proofs of (7.10) and (7.11). They are suggested as exercises in the list below. Note carefully that here $x_1, \cdots, x_k$ are distinct random variables, each with its own range of possible values; whereas in earlier sections we have used $x_1, \cdots, x_k$ to represent the possible values assumed by a single random variable. From considerations similar to those introduced following (7.9), the random variables $x_1, \cdots, x_k$ in (7.12) must obey the inequalities $0 \leq x_i \leq Np_i$, $i = 1, \cdots, k$.

Example 7.10. An urn contains 5 red, 2 white, 3 blue balls. If 5 balls are withdrawn, what is the probability of obtaining 3 red, 1 white, 1 blue ball?
Solution. Without replacement the probability is

$$P = \frac{\binom{5}{3}\binom{2}{1}\binom{3}{1}}{\binom{10}{5}} = \frac{5}{21}.$$

With replacement the probability is

$$P = \frac{5!}{3!}(.5)^3(.2)(.3) = \frac{3}{20}.$$

Example 7.11. An urn contains 5 red balls, 3 white balls, and 2 blue balls. Find the probability that 5 balls withdrawn at random include x red, y white, and z blue balls: (*a*) if the drawings are without replacement, (*b*) if the drawings are with replacement.
Solution. (*a*) For drawings without replacement the possible color distributions in a sample of 5 are as tabulated below:

x	0	1	1	2	2	2	3	3	3	4	4	5
y	3	2	3	1	2	3	0	1	2	0	1	0
z	2	2	1	2	1	0	2	1	0	1	0	0

Using these values, we may exhibit the probabilities, as determined from (7.12), in tabular form:

y \\ x	0	1	2	3	4	5
0	0	0	0	10/252	10/252	1/252
1	0	0	30/252	60/252	15/252	0
2	0	15/252	60/252	30/252	0	0
3	1/252	10/252	10/252	0	0	0

(*b*) For drawings with replacement the possible color distributions are:

x	0	0	0	0	0	0	1	1	1	1	1	2	2	2	2	3	3	3	4	4	5
y	0	1	2	3	4	5	0	1	2	3	4	0	1	2	3	0	1	2	0	1	0
z	5	4	3	2	1	0	4	3	2	1	0	3	2	1	0	2	1	0	1	0	0

By use of (7.13), we obtain the probabilities shown below:

y \ x	0	1	2	3	4	5
0	.00032	.00400	.02000	.05000	.06250	.03125
1	.00240	.02400	.09000	.15000	.09375	0
2	.00720	.05400	.13500	.11250	0	0
3	.01080	.05400	.06750	0	0	0
4	.00810	.02025	0	0	0	0
5	.00243	0	0	0	0	0

Example 7.12. Find the probability of obtaining a total of 9 when 4 dice are thrown.

Solution. Very much as in Example 7.11 we list the possible values on the dice that will yield the required sum. The table below gives the multinomial coefficient $\dfrac{n!}{x_1! x_2! \cdots x_k!}$ for each of these combinations of values. Since, for this example, $p_1 = p_2 = \cdots = p_6 = 1/6$, we may add the multinomial coefficients and multiply the total by $(1/6)^4 = 1/1296$. This gives $56/1296$ for the answer. An alternative approach to problems of this type is the method of generating functions, explained in Section 21.

Combination	Multinomial Coefficient
1 1 1 6	4
1 1 2 5	12
1 1 3 4	12
1 2 2 4	12
1 2 3 3	12
2 2 2 3	4
Total	56

Example 7.11 is an illustration of a *multivariate* distribution, that is, one in which the probabilities are dependent on more than one variable. Although 3 variables x, y, and z are involved, only 2 of them are essential to the analysis of the problem.

EXERCISE 7

7.1. In how many ways may 14 books be arranged on a shelf if the collection includes 3 identical volumes of history, 5 of mathematics, 4 of literature and 2 of sociology?

7.2. Mrs. Brown has acquired 12 different books for Christmas gifts for her grandchildren. Five must be sent to Los Angeles, 4 to Cleveland, and 3 to

New Orleans. Assuming that each book would be acceptable to each grand-child, in how many ways may the packages be made up?

7.3. A club consisting of 10 couples has an executive of 5 members. If the officers are randomly chosen as to sex, what is the probability that: (*a*) all are men; (*b*) 3 are men and 2 are women; (*c*) all are of the same sex; (*d*) exactly one couple is on the executive.

7.4. Assume jurors are drawn at random in a certain city which is 60% Republican, 40% Democrat. What is the probability that a jury of 12 will include 9 Republicans and 3 Democrats? Write a formula for the frequency function for the number of Republicans on a jury of 12.

7.5. What is the probability that a hand of 13 cards will contain 2 clubs, 4 diamonds, 5 hearts, and 2 spades? If x_1, x_2, x_3, x_4 are the numbers of clubs, diamonds, hearts, and spades, respectively, write a formula for the joint frequency function of x_1, x_2, x_3, x_4.

7.6. Six dice are rolled. What is the probability that 2 of them will show a "4," 3 will show a "5," and 1 will show a "6"? If x_1, x_2, x_3, x_4, x_5, x_6 are the numbers of 1's, 2's, 3's, 4's, 5's, and 6's when 6 dice are rolled, find the joint frequency function.

7.7. An urn contains 7 black and 3 white balls. If 5 balls are withdrawn, find the frequency function for the number of black balls obtained: (*a*) if drawings are made with replacement; (*b*) if drawings are made without replacement. Make line graphs for both distributions.

7.8. Find the probability of obtaining a total of 11 when 3 dice are thrown.

7.9. Use the argument of Example 7.5 to prove (7.12).

7.10. Prove that, as $N \to \infty$, the probability (7.12) approaches the probability (7.13) as a limit.

7.11. A man has a three-figure house number. What is the probability that the first 3 figures of his auto license will be identical with his house number? (Assume digits of auto license are all random.)

7.12. Assume the digits in license numbers are random. What is the probability that the last 2 digits: (*a*) total 9, (*b*) have a product of 12, (*c*) form a multiple of 3?

7.13. Assume that auto license numbers are assigned at random and that the individual digits are random numbers. What is the probability that 2 neighbors will have numbers with the same 2 final digits?

7.14. Assume girl babies and boy babies equally probable. Of 10 babies born, what is the probability that: (*a*) 5 are boys, (*b*) the first 3 are boys, (*c*) the first boy is preceded by 6 girls?

7.15. A bin of industrial parts contains 920 good pieces and 80 defectives. If all pieces are equally likely to be drawn, what is the probability that 50 pieces drawn at random will include exactly 3 defectives?

7.16. (*a*) A die is rolled until a "6" appears. Find the probability that the first "6" appears on the xth roll of the die. (*b*) A die is rolled until 10 6's have appeared. Find the probability that x trials are required.

7.17. A dichotomous random experiment has probability p for success and q for failure. The experiment is repeated until m successes have been achieved.

Show that the probability that x trials will be required is

$$P(X = x) = \binom{x - 1}{m - 1} p^m q^{x-m}.$$

7.18. Prove that, for the hypergeometric distribution, the probabilities total to 1, i.e.,

$$\sum_{x=0}^{n} \binom{Np}{x}\binom{Nq}{n - x} \Big/ \binom{N}{n} = 1,$$

or

$$\sum_{x=0}^{n} \binom{Np}{x}\binom{Nq}{n - x} = \binom{N}{n}.$$

To do this, prove that the sum on the left is the coefficient of u^n in the product $(1 + u)^{Np}(1 + u)^{Nq}$, while $\binom{N}{n}$ is the coefficient of u^n in $(1 + u)^N$.

7.19. Five species of fish in a lake are present in the ratio $7:4:2:1:1$. A drag net brings in 10 fish. Assuming all individual fish in the lake equally likely to be caught, what is the probability that the net will contain 2 of each species?

7.20. A party is attended by 10 couples. For a certain game the names of 3 women and of 3 men are drawn at random. What is the probability that the 6 players will include: (*a*) no couples, (*b*) 1 couple, (*c*) 2 couples, (*d*) 3 couples?

7.21. An experimental plot 5 feet by 20 feet has been randomly "seeded" with 100 earthworms. It is divided into 100 areas each 1 foot square. Assuming that the worms distribute themselves randomly and independently through the plot and that no reproduction or deaths take place, what is the probability that one of the areas chosen at random will contain: (*a*) no worms, (*b*) 1 worm, (*c*) 2 worms, (*d*) 3 worms?

7.22. A carnival game consists of rolling 3 balls into 9 slots labeled $1, 2, \cdots, 9$. A prize is given if the total is less than 7 or more than 21. Assuming that the placing of a ball in a particular slot is actually random, what is the probability of winning?

7.23. A factory has 3 sections, each having the same number of workers, each the same distance from the common cafeteria. If all employees stop work at the same time, what is the probability that of 10 employees taken at random from the lunch line, 3 will be from section A, 3 from section B, and 4 from section C? Assume population is so large it may be regarded as infinite without serious inaccuracy.

7.24. A bus takes on 12 passengers downtown and has 10 stops on its way to the outskirts of town. Assuming passengers equally likely to get off at any stop, what is the probability that at least one passenger will get off at each stop?

7.25. The Senate has 2 senators from each state (use 50 states). What is the probability that a committee of 20, randomly drawn without regard to state, has no more than 1 senator from any state?

7.26. Immigrants from country A have a probability $p = .03$ of carrying native malaria; immigrants from country B have a similar probability $p = .05$.

What is the probability that a group consisting of 25 immigrants from A and 75 from B have among them 6 active cases of malaria?

7.27. A test for extrasensory perception consists of naming 3 cards randomly drawn from a deck of 13 different cards. Find the probability that, by chance alone, the subject will correctly name: (*a*) no cards, (*b*) 1 card, (*c*) 2 cards, (*d*) 3 cards. (The subject is not required to name the cards in the order in which they were drawn.)

7.28. (*a*) An urn contains n_1 black balls and n_2 white balls. A ball is drawn and discarded without being examined. Find the probability that the next ball drawn is black.

(*b*) For the urn described above, 2 balls are withdrawn and discarded without being examined. Find the probability that the next ball drawn is black.

7.29. Urn A contains 3 black and 2 white balls; urn B contains 1 black and 2 white balls. A ball is transferred from urn A to urn B, and, after mixing, a ball is drawn from urn B. What is the probability of obtaining a white ball?

7.30. Derive the formula (7.13) for the multinomial distribution in a manner analogous to the derivation of the binomial distribution following Example 7.8. [Use (7.6).]

7.31 By an argument paralleling that used in the derivation of (7.9), prove (7.12). Show that the frequency function (7.12) approaches the frequency functon (7.13) as $N \to \infty$.

8. MEAN, VARIANCE, STANDARD DEVIATION

A frequency distribution, we have seen, is a convenient way of summarizing or condensing the information contained in a set of data. The techniques of thus reducing a large bulk of data to a relatively few values are known, collectively, as *descriptive statistics*. In this book descriptive statistics will be regarded as *tools*, useful in the more basic matter of statistical inference. For this latter purpose it is desirable to have an even more condensed summary of the information in a sample or in a population than that provided by a frequency distribution. The measures to be described in this section and the next are those which are most useful, both as descriptive tools and for purposes of inference.

Consider the set of five values given in Table 8.1:

TABLE 8.1

Background radiation: 7, 8, 14, 9, 4

Each value was obtained from a 15-second count of background radiation by means of a radiation counter. In Figure 8.1 the 5 values are

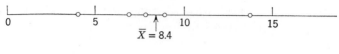

$\overline{X} = 8.4$

FIGURE 8.1

represented as points on a line. The *arithmetic mean,* or simply the *mean,* of these values is denoted by $\overline{X}$ and defined by

$$(8.1) \qquad \overline{X} = \frac{1}{n}\Sigma X.$$

Thus, for the data of Table 8.1, $\overline{X} = 42/5 = 8.4$. In Figure 8.1 this value is located by an arrowhead beneath the line. The figure also suggests a useful parallel from elementary mechanics: it can be shown that, if n equal weights are placed on a line, at distances $X_1, \cdots, X_n$ from an arbitrary origin, their *center of gravity* will be $\overline{X} = (1/n)\Sigma X$ units from the origin. Thus the arrowhead in Figure 8.1 can be regarded as a fulcrum which is so placed that the system of 5 equal weights will balance. This is our second illustration of a fruitful parallelism between mechanical and statistical concepts, which we shall emphasize from time to time throughout this book (see Figure 5.3).

The mean $\overline{X}$ serves to specify the *center* of a set of values. We need also to have a means of specifying the *spread* of the group; that is, how far, on the average, the members of the group are from their center. Given a set of n values $(X_1, \cdots, X_n)$, we consider the set of *deviations* $X_i - \overline{X}, i = 1, \cdots, n$; they are the distances of the individual values from the mean of the set. For the 5 values in Table 8.1 the set of deviations is $(-1.4, -.4, 5.6, .6, -4.4)$. We require some sort of average of this set of values. The arithmetic mean is useless for this purpose since it is readily shown that the sum of the deviations is always zero (see Exercise 8). One type of average that might be employed is the average of the absolute values of the deviations. This is rarely used because absolute values do not lend themselves readily to algebraic manipulation. A better type of average to use here is the *root mean square* (rms). This is obtained, for any set of values, by squaring each value in the set, averaging the squares, and taking the square root of the result. Symbolically the rms of the set $(X_1, \cdots, X_n)$ is given by

$$(8.2) \qquad \mathrm{rms}\,(X) = \sqrt{\frac{1}{n}\Sigma X^2}.$$

We may note that the rms gives more weight to extreme values in the set, large or small, than does the arithmetic mean. For example, the arithmetic mean of the set (1, 1, 1, 1, 10) is 2.8, while the rms is 4.56; the rms has been much more affected by the extreme value of 10 than has the mean.

The rms of the deviations from the mean is known as the *standard deviation*. Thus the standard deviation of the set $(X_1, \cdots, X_n)$ will be denoted by $D(X)$, and defined by

$$(8.3) \qquad D(X) = \text{rms} \, (X - \overline{X}) = \sqrt{\frac{1}{n} \Sigma (X - \overline{X})^2}.$$

We define the *variance* of the set to be the square of the standard deviation and denote it by var (X).

$$(8.4) \qquad \text{var} \, (X) = (D(X))^2 = \frac{1}{n} \Sigma (X - \overline{X})^2.$$

For computational purposes we want to avoid subtracting the mean from each value in the set. It can readily be shown that

$$\Sigma (X - \overline{X})^2 = \Sigma X^2 - n\overline{X}^2 = \frac{1}{n} (n \, \Sigma X^2 - (\Sigma X)^2).$$

Hence we obtain the basic computational formulas for the variance and the standard deviation:

$$(8.5) \quad \text{var} \, (X) = \frac{1}{n^2} (n \, \Sigma X^2 - (\Sigma X)^2), \quad D(X) = \frac{1}{n} \sqrt{n \, \Sigma X^2 - (\Sigma X)^2}.$$

These formulas are well suited to machine calculation.

Example 8.1. For the data of Table 8.1 we find

$$\Sigma X = 42, \quad \Sigma X^2 = 406, \quad \Sigma (X - \overline{X})^2 = 30.64$$
$$\text{var} \, (X) = 10.64, \quad D(X) = 3.262.$$

Quantities such as the mean, variance, and standard deviation, when calculated for a sample, are known as *statistics* (singular, *statistic*); the corresponding quantities calculated for a population are known as *parameters*. It is customary, as far as convenient, to use Roman letters for statistics and the corresponding Greek letters for parameters. Thus σ and s will represent, respectively, the population standard deviation (a parameter) and the sample standard deviation (a statistic). We are here considering only finite populations. We denote the set of values in the population by $\{x_1, \cdots, x_N\}$ and the population mean by μ. Thus we have

$$\text{Population mean} = \mu = \frac{1}{N}\Sigma x.$$

(8.6) $\text{Population variance} = \text{var}(x) = \sigma^2 = \frac{1}{N}\Sigma(x - \mu)^2.$

$$\text{Population standard deviation} = D(x) = \sigma = \sqrt{\frac{1}{N}\Sigma(x - \mu)^2}.$$

The mean of a sample $\overline{X}$ enjoys the property of being an *unbiased estimate* of the population mean μ in the following sense. Conceive of the population as a bowl containing N numbered balls, and consider that all possible samples of size n have been drawn, using drawings with replacement. There will be N^n such (ordered) samples (see Exercise 8.8). If the mean of each sample is computed, the grand mean of all the sample means will turn out to be precisely the population mean; this fact will be proved in Section 27. If, however, we compute the variance of each sample using (8.4) and average all these values, the result will be not σ^2 (the population variance but $[(n-1)/n]$ σ^2, as will be shown in Section 27. Thus, if (8.4) is used for the sample variance, we obtain a *biased estimate* of the population variance. This bias is corrected if we define the *sample standard deviation* by

(8.7) $s_x = \sqrt{\dfrac{1}{n-1}\Sigma(X = \overline{X})^2} = \sqrt{\dfrac{n\,\Sigma X^2 - (\Sigma X)^2}{n(n-1)}},$

and the *sample variance* by

(8.8) $s_x^2 = \dfrac{1}{n-1}\Sigma(X - \overline{X})^2 = \dfrac{n\,\Sigma X^2 - (\Sigma X)^2}{n(n-1)} = \dfrac{n}{n-1}\text{var}(X).$

We are asserting, then, that (8.8) gives an unbiased estimate of the population variance. One would be tempted to conclude that (8.7) provided an unbiased estimate of the population standard deviation, but this is *not* the case. For the data of Table 8.1 we readily find that $s_x^2 = 13.30$ and $s_x = 3.647$.

Statistical calculations are sometimes simplified by the use of a *linear transformation* of the form $Y = aX + b$. Thus, if we know the mean and standard deviation of X, we may obtain those of Y from the following

(8.9)   THEOREM. *Let the set of values* $\{X_1, \cdots, X_n\}$ *possess mean* $\overline{X}$ *and standard deviation* s_x. *Then, if the set of values* $\{Y_1, \cdots, Y_n\}$ *is related to the set* $\{X_1, \cdots, X_n\}$ *by the equation* $Y_i = aX_i + b$, $i = 1$, $\cdots$, n, *the mean and standard deviation of the set* $\{Y_1, \cdots, Y_n\}$ *are given by*

$$\overline{Y} = a\overline{X} + b, \qquad s_y = |a| s_x.$$

Proof. Since $Y = aX + b$, $\Sigma Y = a\Sigma X + nb$, so that $\overline{Y} = a\overline{X} + b$. Then $Y - \overline{Y} = a(X - \overline{X})$, and

$$s_y^2 = \frac{1}{n-1}\Sigma(Y - \overline{Y})^2 = \frac{1}{n-1}a^2\Sigma(X - \overline{X})^2 = a^2 s_x^2,$$

so that $s_y = |a| s_x$.

The use of (8.9) is illustrated in the following example:

Example 8.2.   The following determinations of the acceleration due to gravity (g) were made at 5 stations in Ottawa, Canada:

980.62200, 980.62295, 980.62265, 980.62929, 980.62194.

Find the mean and standard deviation of the 5 values.

Solution. We simplify the numbers by subtracting 980.62 from each, and we eliminate decimals by multiplying the residuals by 10^5. The resulting values, denoted by X, are as follows:

200, 295, 265, 929, 194.

They are related to the original values Y by the equation $Y = 10^{-5}X + 980.62$. We now readily find $\overline{X} = 376.6$ and $s_x = 311.8$, and hence, using (8.9), $\overline{Y} = 980.62377$ and $s_y = 0.003118$.

A frequently useful transformation is

(8.10) $$Z = (X - \overline{X})/s_x,$$

which yields a variable Z with zero mean and unit standard deviation. Such a variable is said to be in *standard units* or to be a *standardized variable.* Its origin is at the mean of the given set of values, and the unit of the new scale is the standard deviation of the given set. Thus the new scale may be said to measure how far each of the given values is, in multiples of the standard deviation, from the mean of the set.

Example 8.3.   The 5 values of Table 8.1 were found to have a mean of $\overline{X} = 8.4$ and a standard deviation of $s_x = 3.647$. Thus the corresponding standardized variable Z is defined by $Z = (X - 8.4)/3.647$; the 5 standardized values corresponding to the original observations are:

$-.384$, $-.110$, 1.536, 0.165, -1.207.

The mean of these values is readily found to be zero, and the standard deviation is 1.000.

When a set of data is available in the form of a frequency distribution, the calculation of mean, variance, and standard deviation can be considerably shortened. As a simple example, consider the frequency distribution of Table 4.1, which is reproduced in Table 8.2, together with columns of fX and fX^2.

TABLE 8.2

X	f	fX	fX^2
2	5	10	20
3	1	3	9
4	6	24	96
5	2	10	50
6	1	6	36
7	4	28	196
8	1	8	64
	20	89	471

The first item in the fX column, namely 10, gives the sum of all X-values for which $X = 2$; and similarly with the other entries. Thus the sum of the fX column, namely $\Sigma fX = 89$, is nothing other than the quantity previously denoted by ΣX. A similar argument shows that ΣfX^2 is the same as ΣX^2, summed over the whole group. The formulas for the mean, variance, and standard deviation can now be written in a form suitable for data that have been arranged in a frequency distribution, as follows:

$$(8.11) \quad \begin{cases} \bar{X} = \dfrac{1}{n}\Sigma fX \\[2mm] s_x{}^2 = \dfrac{n\,\Sigma fX^2 - (\Sigma fX)^2}{n(n-1)} \\[2mm] s_x = \sqrt{\dfrac{n\,\Sigma fX^2 - (\Sigma fX)^2}{n(n-1)}} \end{cases}$$

Example 8.4. Using formulas (8.11) with the distribution of Table 8.2, we find

$$\bar{X} = 89/20 = 4.45, \quad s_x{}^2 = \frac{20 \times 471 - 89^2}{20 \times 19} = 3.946, \quad s_x = 1.986.$$

For large samples for which a frequency distribution is available, a method known as *coding* is frequently employed in order to simplify the computations. It amounts to employing the linear transformation $u = X - X_0$, where X_0 is a value near the center of the distribution. Since $X = X_0 + u$, we deduce from (8.9) that the mean and standard deviation of X are related to the corresponding quantities for u according to the following equations:

$$(8.12) \qquad \bar{X} = X_0 + \bar{u}, \quad s_x = s_u.$$

Example 8.5. For the data of Table 8.2, let us choose $X_0 = 5$; any other choice of X_0 would yield the same values of X and s_x but might involve working

TABLE 8.3

X	f	u	fu	fu^2
2	5	-3	-15	45
3	1	-2	-2	4
4	6	-1	-6	6
5	2	0	0	0
6	1	1	1	1
7	4	2	8	16
8	1	3	3	9
	20		-11	81

with larger numbers. The code u is shown in Table 8.3; note that the column of u may be obtained by subtracting $X_0 = 5$ from each value of X. We thus obtain

$$\bar{u} = -11/20 = -.55, \quad s_u^2 = \frac{20 \times 81 - (-11)^2}{20 \times 19} = 3.946,$$

$$s_u = \sqrt{3.946} = 1.986.$$

Hence, from (8.12)

$$\bar{X} = -.55 + 5 = 4.45, \quad s_x = 1.986.$$

These are the values obtained in Example 8.4

In Table 4.3 the haemacytometer data of Table 4.2 were organized in the form of a grouped frequency distribution. A simple adaptation of coding serves to simplify the computation of mean and standard deviation for a grouped frequency distribution. We select an interval near the center of the distribution and assign to it the code value $u = 0$, and we let X_0 denote the midvalue of this interval. The code values for the remaining intervals form a sequence of consecutive integers, positive and negative. Then, if ΔX is the size of the X-interval, and if X is the midvalue of the interval whose code is u, we have the relation $X = X_0 + u \, \Delta X$ and from (8.9)

$$(8.13) \qquad \bar{X} = X_0 + \bar{u} \, \Delta X, \quad s_x = s_u \, \Delta X.$$

Example 8.6. In order to apply the general method of coding to the distribution of Table 4.3, we set up the code u and the columns of fu and fu^2 shown below:

Interval	f	u	fu	fu^2	
1–2	63	−2	−126	252	$\bar{u} = -.420$
3–4	139	−1	−139	139	$s_u{}^2 = 1.182$
5–6	124	0			$s_u = 1.087$
7–8	55	1	55	55	$\bar{x} = 5.5 + (-.420)(2)$
9–10	15	2	30	60	$= 4.66$
11–12	4	3	12	36	$s_x = 1.087 \times 2$
	400		−168	542	$= 2.174$

Here X_0 will be 5.5, and from (8.13) the results shown on the right of the table are readily obtained.

EXERCISE 8

8.1. Given the set of values $\{2, 7, 8, 11, 15, 17\}$, find $\bar{X}$, rms (X), var (X), $D(x)$, $s_x{}^2$ and s_x.

8.2. Prove $\Sigma(X - \bar{X}) = 0$.

8.3. Prove $\Sigma(X - \bar{X})^2 = \Sigma X^2 - \bar{X} \Sigma X = \Sigma X^2 - \dfrac{1}{n}(\Sigma X)^2$.

8.4. Use the identity $X - a = (X - \bar{X}) + (\bar{X} - a)$ to prove that

$$\Sigma(X - a)^2 = \Sigma(X - \bar{X})^2 + n(\bar{X} - a)^2,$$

where a is any real number.

8.5. Show that for a given set of values $[X_1, \cdots, X_n]$ the expression $\Sigma(X - a)^2$ is a quadratic function of a which is a minimum when $a = \bar{X}$.

8.6. By expanding $(X - a)^3$ and summing, show that

$$\Sigma(X - a)^3 = \Sigma X^3 - 3a \, \Sigma X^2 + 3na^2 \bar{X} - na^3.$$

8.7. Derive the identity $\dfrac{1}{n} \Sigma X^2 = \bar{X}^2 + \dfrac{1}{n} \Sigma(X - \bar{X})^2$ from Exercise 8.3, and use it to show that the rms of any set of numbers is greater than or equal to their arithmetic mean. Under what circumstances is the rms equal to the arithmetic mean? Why?

8.8. A population consists of 3 numbered balls: $\{1, 3, 4.\}$ If drawings are made with replacement, then there are $3^3 = 27$ ordered samples of size 3 that can be drawn from the population:

$(1,1,1)$, $(1,1,3)$, $(1,1,4)$, $(1,3,1)$, $(1,3,3)$, $(1,3,4)$, $(1,4,1)$, $(1,4,3)$, $(1,4,4)$, $(3,1,1)$, $(3,1,3)$, $(3,1,4)$, $(3,3,1)$, $(3,3,3)$, $(3,3,4)$, $(3,4,1)$, $(3,4,3)$, $(3,4,4)$, $(4,1,1)$, $(4,1,3)$, $(4,1,4)$, $(4,3,1)$, $(4,3,3)$, $(4,3,4)$, $(4,4,1)$, $(4,4,3)$, $(4,4,4)$.

Calculate the sample mean $\overline{X}$ and the sample variance s_x^2 [using (8.8)] for each of the 27 samples. Record the results in tabular form:

Sample	ΣX	ΣX^2	$3\Sigma X^2 - (\Sigma X)^2$	$\overline{X}$	s_x^2
$(1,1,1)$	3	3	0	1	0
$(1,1,3)$	5	11	8	5/3	4/3
.	.	.	.	.	.
.	.	.	.	.	.
.	.	.	.	.	.

Now compute μ and σ^2 for the original population $\{1,3,4\}$, and verify that the average of all 27 values of $\overline{X}$ is μ, and that the average of all 27 values of s_x^2 is σ^2.

8.9. For what value of t is the variance of the set (X_1, X_2, X_3, t) a minimum? For what value of t is the variance of the set $(X_1, \cdots, X_n, t)$ a minimum?

8.10. One set of 10 values has a mean of $\overline{X} = 25.6$ and a variance of $s_x^2 = 56.4$; a second set of 10 possesses a mean of $\overline{Y} = 25.6$ and a variance of $s_y^2 = 43.2$. Find the mean and variance of all 20 values. Generalize to the case in which the first set of n_x values has mean $\overline{X}$ and variance s_x^2 and the second set of n_y values has a mean $\overline{Y}$ and a variance s_y^2.

8.11. A set of n values has mean $\overline{X}$ and variance s_x^2. If the value $X = a$ is added to the set, making $n + 1$ values in all, find the new mean and variance.

8.12. From the identity $X - a = (X - b) + (b - a)$, by squaring both sides and summing, prove that $\Sigma(X - a)^2 = \Sigma(X - b)^2 + n(b - a)(2\overline{X} - a - b)$.

8.13. In Exercise 4.1 the following frequency distribution was obtained for the number of heads obtained in 100 tosses of 20 coins:

X	3	4	5	6	7	8	9	10	11	12	13	14	15
f	1	1	0	3	5	11	15	23	11	12	11	5	2

Use the coding method illustrated in Example 8.5 in order to find the mean, variance, and standard deviation of this distribution.

8.14. In Exercise 4.2 the following frequency distribution of radiation counts was obtained:

X	2	3	4	5	6	7	8	9	10	11	12	13	14	15	16	17	18
f	1	1	4	3	11	9	16	11	11	9	8	6	4	2	2	1	1

Use the coding method illustrated in Example 8.5 to find the mean, variance, and standard deviation of this distribution.

8.15. In Exercise 4.3 the frequency distribution of the haemacytometer data of Table 4.2 was obtained:

X	1	2	3	4	5	6	7	8	9	10	11	12
f	20	43	53	86	70	54	37	18	10	5	2	2

Find the mean, variance, and standard deviation of this distribution, using the coding method of Example 8.5.

8.16. Show that, if one wished to make the quantity Σu^2 as small as possible, when u is the code value employed in the coding method of Example 8.5, one should select for X_0 a value as near as possible to the mean.

8.17. Four determinations of g, the acceleration due to gravity, were made at stations in Washington, D. C., as follows: 980.09959, 980.10120, 980.10088, 980.12056. Find the mean and standard deviation, making use of a linear transformation.

8.18. Suppose that the set of values $\{X_1, \cdots, X_n\}$ has mean zero and that Y is a variable defined by $Y = X^2$. Show that $\overline{Y} = \text{var}(X)$.

8.19. According to he 1957 edition of the *Statistical Abstract of the United States*, the distribution of family sizes in the United States is as follows:

Size of Family	Number of Families, in millions
2	13.921
3	9.770
4	8.955
5	5.251
6	2.520
7 or more	2.426
	42.843

Find the mean and standard deviation of family sizes, on the assumption that families of size ≥ 7 may be neglected.

9. TCHEBYCHEFF'S INEQUALITY

The standard deviation is a measure of how closely the values in a set are concentrated about their mean. We shall find that it is possible to predict, at least roughly, the proportion of the set that will lie within a range of k standard deviations on either side of the mean. Tchebycheff's inequality asserts that *at least* $100 \left(1 - \dfrac{1}{k^2} \right) \%$ of the values in the set will lie within an interval $2k$ standard deviations wide, centered on the mean. Thus, for $k = 2$, it implies that at least 75% of the values are within two standard deviations of the mean. This is a very conservative statement, as may be seen from Figure 9.1, which shows line graphs of six distributions of various shapes. Below each diagram a pair of vertical lines is shown, 1 standard deviation on either side of the mean, and a second pair 2 standard deviations on either side of the mean. For these six distributions, from 47 to 80% of the cases lie within a range of 1 standard deviation on either side of the mean, and from 90 to 100% of the cases lie within a range of 2 standard deviations on either side of the mean. If we put $k = 1$ in Tcheby-

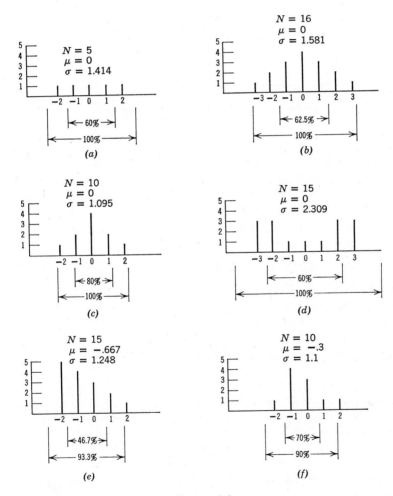

FIGURE 9.1

cheff's result, we find that *at least* 0% of the cases lie within 1 standard deviation of the mean—certainly a conservative statement!

While Tchebycheff's result is valid for any set of values, it is more usually applied to the set of values representing a *population,* in which case proportions become *probabilities.* The inequality then takes the form

$$(9.1) \qquad P(|X - \mu| < k\sigma) \geqq 1 - \frac{1}{k^2}.$$

For purposes of proof we shall restrict ourselves to the case of a population (random experiment). We regard the values in the set as equiprobable points of the sample space, which may be represented on a number scale as in Figure 9.2. The interval B of the line includes

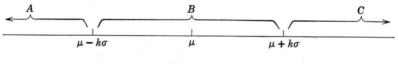

Figure 9.2

all points within k standard deviations from the mean, that is, all points of the line for which $|x - \mu| < k\sigma$. The remaining portions of the line are labeled A and C. Let the number of points in the sets A, B, and C be, respectively, N_A, N_B, and N_C, where $N_A + N_B + N_C = N$, the total number of values in the set. From the definition of the standard deviation

$$(9.2) \quad N\sigma^2 = \Sigma(x - u)^2 = \Sigma_A(x - \mu)^2 + \Sigma_B(x - \mu)^2 + \Sigma_C(x - \mu)^2.$$

In the final expression of (9.2) the summation has been separated into three parts, corresponding to the intervals A, B, and C. In $\Sigma_A(x - \mu)^2$ and $\Sigma_C(x - \mu)^2$, each squared term $(x - \mu)^2$ is greater than or equal to $k^2\sigma^2$. Hence $\Sigma_A(x - \mu)^2 \geqq N_A k^2 \sigma^2$, and $\Sigma_C(x - \mu)^2 \geqq N_C k^2 \sigma^2$. Furthermore $\Sigma_B(x - \mu)^2 \geqq 0$. Thus

$$(9.3) \qquad N\sigma^2 \geqq N_A k^2 \sigma^2 + N_C k^2 \sigma^2.$$

We next note that $\sigma^2 \geqq 0$, except in the trivial case when all values in the set are concentrated at a point. Excluding this case, we may divide (9.3) through by σ^2 to obtain

$$N \geqq k^2(N_A + N_C) = k^2(N - N_B),$$

so that, finally, $N_B/N \geqq 1 - 1/k^2$, which asserts that the proportion of values lying between $\mu - k\sigma$ and $\mu + k\sigma$ is at least $1 - 1/k^2$.

Many distributions with which we must work have a shape that approximates that of the normal distribution (Section 15). We shall find that, for a normal distribution, 68.2% of the cases lie within 1 standard deviation of the mean and 95.5% within 2 standard deviations of the mean. These proportions should be compared with those in Figure 9.1. Facts such as these provide a useful means of checking the calculation of the standard deviation. For example, suppose we had obtained a standard deviation of 2.1 for Figure 9.1c. Then 100% of the cases would lie within a range of 1 standard deviation on either side of the mean. This is evidence that we should recalculate the standard deviation.

EXERCISE 9

*9.1. The sample space of a random experiment consists of $2n + 1$ equally spaced points on the interval from $-1/2$ to $1/2$, one sample point having the value $x = -1/2$, and one the value $x = 1/2$. Let these $2n + 1$ points be equiprobable. The mean is thus $\mu = 0$. Find the variance of the random experiment, and show that as n approaches infinity the variance approaches $1/12$.

*9.2. Show that for the distribution of the preceding exercise, if n is large, the proportion of sample points within a range of 1 standard deviation is approximately $1/\sqrt{3}$, while all the sample points will lie within a range of 2 standard deviations.

*9.3. (a) We have seen that it follows from the Tchebycheff inequality that at least 75% of the values are within 2 standard deviations of the mean. We can, however, readily construct an urn model for which as close as we please to 25% of the values are more than 2 standard deviations from the mean. Let the urn contain 1000 balls with the following distribution:

x	$-a$	-1	0	1	a
f	124	200	352	200	124

Show that the number a can be chosen so that $a > 2\sigma$, where σ is the standard deviation, with the result that 24.8% of the values in the set are more than 2 standard deviations from the mean. (b) Show that an urn can be similarly set up for which 24.9% of the values are more than 2 standard deviations from the mean.

10. DISTRIBUTION FUNCTION—MEDIAN

Let X be a random variable, and let $F(x)$ denote the probability of obtaining *a value less than or equal to x on a single trial*. That is,

$$(10.1) \qquad\qquad F(x) = P(X \leqq x).$$

The function $F(x)$ is called the *distribution function* of the random variable. It provides a useful and compact description of a random experiment.

Example 10.1. For a single die, $P(X \leq 2) = 1/3$. Also, $P(X \leq 2.5) = 1/3$, $P(X \leq 2.9) = 1/3$. In fact, for every value of x in the interval $2 \leq x < 3$, $P(X \leq x) = 1/3$, while for the interval $1 \leq x < 2$, $P(X \leq x) = 1/6$. Thus, using the notation $[a, b)$ for the half-open interval $a \leq x < b$, the distribution function for a single die may be expressed:

Interval of x	$x < 1$	$[1, 2)$	$[2, 3)$	$[3, 4)$	$[4, 5)$	$[5, 6)$	$x \geq 6$
$F(x)$	0	1/6	1/3	1/2	2/3	5/6	1

The graph of $F(x)$ appears as shown in Figure 10.1; a function with a graph of this type is called a step function. Note that each horizontal segment of the

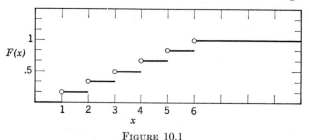

FIGURE 10.1

graph has a dot on the left end, to indicate that the segment is closed on the left, open on the right. It is readily seen that the distribution function of any discrete random variable is a step function.

The distribution function of a random experiment is closely related to the *cumulative probability distribution*, obtained by cumulating the probabilities (see Section 4). If we denote cumulative probability by cp, we obtain the values given below for a single die:

x	1	2	3	4	5	6
p	1/6	1/6	1/6	1/6	1/6	1/6
cp	1/6	1/3	1/2	2/3	5/6	1

Note that the dots in Figure 10.1 provide a graph of cp versus x. This suggests a method of constructing the graph of the distribution function: first determine the values of cp, graph these values against x, and construct the step function by inserting horizontal segments, as in Figure 10.1. Thus for 2 dice we have:

x	2	3	4	5	6	7
p	1/36	2/36	3/36	4/36	5/36	6/36
cp	1/36	3/36	6/36	10/36	15/36	21/36

x	8	9	10	11	12
p	5/36	4/36	3/36	2/36	1/36
cp	26/36	30/36	33/36	35/36	36/36

and the graph of the distribution function appears as in Figure 10.2.

One of the virtues of Definition (10.1) of the distribution function is that it applies, without modification, to continuous random variables as well as to discrete random variables. Although the systematic discussion of such matters is reserved for Chapter 2, a simple illustration may be based on Example 5.9, in which a spinner model was constructed to correspond to the random experiment of Example 1.5.

Example 10.2. Let X be the random variable specified by the spinner scale of Figure 5.4. In Example 5.9 a functional relationship was noted between the x-scale on the outside of the circle of Figure 5.4 and the u-scale on the inside; this relationship was denoted by $u = F(x)$. From (5.9) it follows that, if x is any value in the range of the random variable X,

$$P(X \leqq x) = F(x).$$

Thus the function $F(x)$ of Example 5.9 is actually the distribution function. In Figure 10.3 its graph is shown. Actually this curve is a portion of the graph of the cubic function $F(x) = (1/3375)(45x^2 - 2x^3)$, which was chosen as one of the simplest algebraic functions possessing the essential characteristics of a distribution function. These characteristics will be systematically explored in Chapter 2.

The *median* is a measure of the center of a population or of a sample. For a sample we shall denote it by $\tilde{X}$ and define it as follows:

(10.2) DEFINITION. *If n is odd, the median is the middle value when the values in the sample are arranged in order of size. If n is even, the median is the average of the two middle values.*

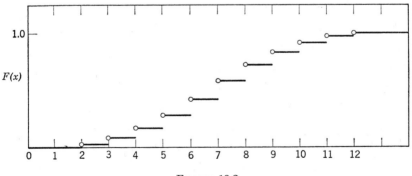

FIGURE 10.2

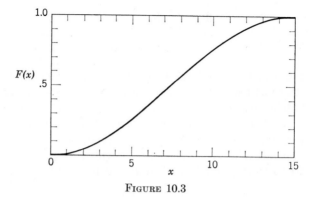

FIGURE 10.3

Example 10.3. For the sample of Table 8.1 the median is 8; for that given at the beginning of Section 4 the median is 4.

The median is particularly valuable as a descriptive measure when we are dealing with a non-symmetrical frequency distribution, such as that which would be obtained if one were to form a distribution of annual income in a community. The median is totally insensitive to a shift in one or several of the extreme values of a group, provided the middle values are left unaltered. Suppose, for example, that a certain city has 10 industries employing the following numbers of persons:

$$100, \ 150, \ 160, \ 200, \ 550, \ 1200, \ 1700, \ 2500, \ 2800, \ 5200.$$

The median is seen to be $\tilde{X} = 875$, while the mean is $\overline{X} = 1456$. Suppose that the largest factory increases its payroll to 8300 workers. The mean will increase to $\overline{X} = 1766$, while the median remains at $\tilde{X} = 875$. There are occasions when this insensitivity to fluctuations of all but the midmost values in a group is a useful characteristic.

Example 10.4 involves a considerable amount of careful enumeration of the possible outcomes of the experiment of throwing 4 dice. This enumerative technique is usually a last resort, to which one turns when more elegant methods are not available. There are, however, many problems for which the enumerative approach is the only one open to us.

Example 10.4. *Distribution of the median of 4 dice.* When 4 dice are thrown there are $6^4 = 1296$ equiprobable sample points. We wish to determine how many of these points are associated with each of the following possible values for the median: 1.0, 1.5, 2.0, 2.5, 3.0, 3.5, 4.0, 4.5, 5.0, 5.5, 6.0. In order to obtain the median of the 4 values appearing on the dice, we must arrange these values in order and then find the average of the 2 middle values. The smallest value the median can assume is 1. This can occur when the dice show the sequence 1111; it can also occur with the sequences 1112, 1113, 1114, 1115, and 1116 or with any of the possible permutations of these sequences. Since there are 4 possible permutations for each of the sets 1112, $\cdots$, 1116 and only 1 arrangement of the set 1111, we conclude that a total of 21 sample points have a median of 1. We next note that a median of 6 will likewise be associated with 21 sample points since this value of the median can arise with the sequences 6666, 1666, 2666, $\cdots$, 5666 and that each of the sequences 1666, $\cdots$, 5666 possesses 4 permutations. In fact it is readily concluded that the distribution we are forming is *symmetrical*, in the sense that values of $\tilde{X}$ equally distant from the mean $\mu = 3.5$ will have the same number of sample points associated with them. As a result of this observation our computational work is greatly reduced since we need to work with only one half of the distribution. The table below gives a suitable arrangement of the details of the enumeration. The letters a and b are used for variables.

Median $\tilde{X}$	Possible Ordered Sets	Number of Arrangements	Frequency
1.0	1 1 1 a	a: 1 2 3 4 5 6 f: 1 4 4 4 4 4	21
1.5	1 1 2 a	a: 2 3 4 5 6 f: 6 12 12 12 12	54
2.0	1 1 3 a	a: 3 4 5 6 f: 6 12 12 12	111
	a 2 2 b	a,b: 1,2 1,3 1,4 1,5 1,6 2,2 2,3 2,4 2,5 2,6 f: 4 12 12 12 12 1 4 4 4 4	
2.5	1 1 4 a	a: 4 5 6 f: 6 12 12	156
	a 2 3 b	a,b: 1,3 1,4 1,5 1,6 2,3 2,4 2,5 2,6 f: 12 24 24 24 6 12 12 12	
3.0	1 1 5 a	a: 5 6 f: 6 12	201
	a 2 4 b	a,b: 1,4 1,5 1,6 2,4 2,5 2,6 f: 12 24 24 6 12 12	
	a 3 3 b	a,b: 1,3 1,4 1,5 1,6 2,3 2,4 2,5 2,6 3,3 3,4 3,5 3,6 f: 4 12 12 12 4 12 12 12 1 4 4 4	
3.5	1 1 6 a	a: 6 f: 6	210
	a 2 5 b	a,b: 1,5 1,6 2,5 2,6 f: 12 24 6 12	
	a 3 4 b	a,b: 1,4 1,5 1,6 2,4 2,5 2,6 3,4 3,5 3,6 f: 12 24 24 12 24 24 6 12 12	
4.0	the same as $\tilde{X} = 3.0$		201
4.5	the same as $\tilde{X} = 2.5$		156
5.0	the same as $\tilde{X} = 2.0$		111
5.5	the same as $\tilde{X} = 1.5$		54
6.0	the same as $\tilde{X} = 1.0$		21
			1296

Figure 10.4 shows a line graph for the distribution obtained in Example 10.4.

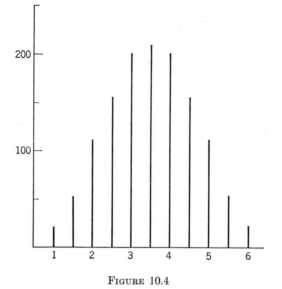

FIGURE 10.4

EXERCISE 10

10.1 According to an article in the Saturday Evening Post, the backwoods farmer of Brazil "has devised a simple method of estimating the weight and value of a drove of hogs. The man who owns the hogs and the prospective purchaser forgather in the presence of the hogs, and for the space of several minutes observe them reflectively. Finally the buyer, pointing to the biggest, fattest hog, will say, 'I wish to buy that hog.' The seller in his turn points to the smallest, scrawniest hog. 'I will be pleased to sell that hog,' he says. The chosen hogs are then separated from their fellows and the process continues— the buyer picking the best, the seller the poorest hog—until only two are left. These then are caught and weighed, and their average weight is judged to be the weight of each hog in the herd." (Saturday Evening Post, Aug. 6, 1960.) Describe this process of estimation mathematically, showing how the concepts of the mean and the median enter in.

10.2. In Example 7.7 we obtained the frequency function for the number of hearts obtained when 5 cards are drawn from a pack of 52. From this frequency function form the corresponding distribution function. Present $F(x)$ in both tabular and graphical form, as in Example 10.1.

10.3. For the random experiment of rolling 2 dice construct a figure like that of Figure 2.3, showing for each of the 36 sample points the median of the 2 values showing on the dice. In this way, obtain the distribution of the median. Compare this distribution with that of the mean of the 2 throws.

10.4. In Exercise 8.8 the 27 samples that could be drawn, with replacements, from the population {1, 3, 4} are listed. For each sample, find the median and hence the sampling distribution of the median.

*10.5. Using the enumerative approach of Example 10.4, find the distribution of the median of throws of 3 dice.

11. POPULATION PARAMETERS

In Section 8 a distinction was made between the descriptive characteristics of a sample, called *statistics*, and those of a population, called *parameters*. The systematic consideration of parameters is based upon the notion of *mathematical expectation*, to which we now turn. The term "expectation" seems historically to be derived from games of chance; but the concept has become so broad as now to be an essential part of the foundations of probability theory.

In order to illustrate the concept of mathematical expectation, consider the following simple example. An individual enters a game of chance involving throws of a single die. The die is to be rolled once, and he is to receive in dollars the amount showing on top of the die. How much is it worth to him to enter the game for a single throw of the die? He will say, "Since I may receive \$1, \$2, \$3, \$4, \$5, or \$6 and since these amounts are equally likely, I should pay the average of these values, that is, \$3.50." This amount is called the mathematical expectation associated with the game.

Now consider the more general situation represented by the urn U_x.

$$U_x: \begin{cases} \text{Value,} & x \quad x_1 \cdots x_k \\ \text{Frequency,} & \phi \quad \phi_1 \cdots \phi_k \\ \text{Probability,} & p \quad p_1 \cdots p_k \end{cases}$$

If an individual is to receive x_i dollars if he draws a ball labeled x_i, he will conclude, on the same basis as that of the previous illustration, that he should pay the average value of all the balls in the urn in order to enter a game of chance of this type. That is, he should pay

$$(11.1) \qquad \mu = \Sigma\phi_i x_i/N = \Sigma p_i x_i.$$

For the urn U_x specified above we define the *mathematical expectation of X*, or *expectation of X*, or *expected value of X*, by the equation

$$(11.2) \qquad E(X) = \Sigma p_i x_i.$$

This is, of course, identical with the population mean μ. But, whereas we have, up to this point, considered the mean as being derived from a frequency distribution, the above formulas define the mean for a population whose probabilities may be irrational numbers and therefore not representable by means of an urn. Similarly we define the variance of a non-urnlike population by means of the formula $\sigma^2 = E(X^2) - \mu^2$, which reduces to the formula previously given if the population is urnlike. We have used a capital X in $E(X)$ because this is thought of as the expectation of a random value X (a "sample" consisting of a single value) which has not yet been drawn. (See the discussion regarding the use of capital letters following Example 1.5.)

A reasonable extension of Definition (11.2) leads us to define the expectation of X^n, denoted by $E(X^n)$, by the equation

$$(11.3) \qquad\qquad E(X^n) = \Sigma p_i x_i{}^n.$$

This quantity is also known as the *nth moment about the origin,* for which the symbol is μ_n'. The mean and variance of the population are readily expressible in terms of the first two moments:

$$(11.4) \qquad \begin{aligned} \mu &= E(X) = \mu_1' \\ \sigma^2 &= E(X^2) - (E(X))^2 = \mu_2' - (\mu_1')^2. \end{aligned}$$

It is useful to conceive of these more general expected values in terms of the urn model. Just as $E(X)$ may be regarded as the average of the balls in the urn, so $E(X^n)$ may be thought of as the average of a second number x^n written (say in red) on each ball of the urn. If $g(x)$ is any function of x and if we imagine its value written on each ball, then $E(g(X))$ is the average of all these values:

$$E(g(X)) = \frac{1}{N} \Sigma \phi_i\, g(x_i),$$

or

$$(11.5) \qquad\qquad E(g(X)) = \Sigma p_i\, g(x_i),$$

the latter definition holding for distributions not representable as urns.

The *central moments,* or *moments about the mean,* are defined by

$$(11.6) \qquad\qquad \mu_n = E(X - \mu)^n = \Sigma p_i (x_i - \mu)^n.$$

It is readily verified that

$$\mu_1 = 0, \qquad \mu_2 = \sigma^2.$$

A distribution is said to be *symmetrical* if its frequency function $f(x)$ is such that, for all real x, $f(\mu + x) = f(\mu - x)$. It can be shown (see Exercise 11.13) that for a symmetrical distribution the odd central moments vanish. This suggests that the odd central moments of a distribution will measure its departure from symmetry, that is, its *asymmetry.* It is convenient to use, instead of the central moments themselves, expressions which are unaffected by a linear transformation $Y = aX + b$. It can be shown (see Exercise 11.6) that the ratio $(\mu_r)^p/(\mu_p)^r$ is unaffected by a linear transformation. The simplest such ratio is $(\mu_3)^2/(\mu_2)^3$. We call the positive square root of this ratio the *skewness*, denoted by γ_1:

$$(11.7) \qquad \gamma_1 = \frac{\mu_3}{(\mu_2)^{3/2}} = \frac{\mu_3}{\sigma^3}.$$

For a sample, the moments about the origin and the central moments are defined by formulas analogous to (11.3) and (11.6):

$$m_r' = \frac{1}{n}\Sigma f X^r, \qquad m_r = \frac{1}{n}\Sigma f(X - \bar{X})^r.$$

These two are sample estimates of the corresponding parameters. The skewness of a sample distribution is

$$(11.8) \qquad g_1 = \frac{m_3}{(m_2)^{3/2}}.$$

It must be noted that, although g_1 and γ_1 are zero for symmetrical distributions, the converse is not true; it is possible for these quantities to vanish for non-symmetrical distributions. For this reason their use as measures of lack of symmetry is limited. Similar considerations affect the use of higher moments. Thus the quantity

$$(11.9) \qquad g_2 = \frac{m_4}{(m_2)^2} - 3 \quad \text{or} \quad \gamma_2 = \frac{\mu_4}{\sigma^4} - 3$$

is sometimes used to measure the "peakedness" of a distribution, but its interpretation presents even more difficulties than those involved in the interpretation of g_1 or γ_1.

EXERCISE 11

11.1. Find, for a single die, the values of $E(X)$, $E(X^2)$, σ^2, $E(X^3)$, $E(\log_{10} X)$, $E(1/X)$.

11.2. For the distribution of Example 7.8, find $E(X - 2)^2$, $E(\sin \pi x)$, $E(\sqrt{X})$.

11.3. Find m_1', m_2', m_3', m_2, m_3, and g_1 for the set $\{-5, -1, 0, 1, 5\}$.

11.4. Find m_1', m_2', m_3', m_2, m_3, and g_1 for the distribution

x	1	2	3	4	5
$f(x)$	.1	.2	.4	.2	.1

11.5. Use the binomial theorem to prove the identities

(a) $m_3 = m_3' - 3m_1'm_2' + 2m_1'^3$.

(b) $m_4 = m_4' - 4m_1'm_3' + 6m_1'^2m_2' - 3m_1'^4$.

11.6. Show that, if X and Y are related by the linear transformation $Y = aX + b$, then $Y - \bar{Y} = a(X - \bar{X})$ and $(Y - \bar{Y})^r = a^r(X - \bar{X})^r$. Hence show that under the transformation $Y = aX + b$ the rth central moment m_r is multiplied by a^r. Show, however, that the ratio $(m_r)^p/(m_p)^r$ is unaffected by the transformation $Y = aX + b$, where r and p are positive integers, and $p > 1$.

11.7. (a) If $Y = aX^2 + b$, find $E(Y)$ and $D^2(Y)$ in terms of the moments of X.

(b) Do likewise for the transformation $Z = aX^2 + bX + c$.

11.8. Find a formula expressing m_r in terms of m_1', m_2', $\cdots$, m_r', a generalization of the formulas in Exercise 11.5.

11.9. Prove the Charlier identity

$$\frac{1}{n}\Sigma(X+1)^r = m_r' + rm_{r'-1}' + \binom{r}{2}m_{r'-2}' + \binom{r}{3}m_{r'-3}' + \cdots + rm_1' + 1.$$

This identity may be used as a means of checking the computation of moments. State the corresponding identity for population parameters.

*11.10. Prove that the mean of the hypergeometric distribution (7.10) is $\mu = np$ by filling in the details of the following argument:

$$\mu = \sum_{x=0}^{n} x \binom{Np}{x}\binom{Nq}{n-x} \Big/ \binom{N}{n}.$$

Note, first, that the summation might just as well run from $x = 1$ to $x = n$. Next, show that

$$\binom{Np}{x} = Np\binom{Np-1}{x-1}.$$

Hence

$$\mu = \sum_{x=1}^{n} Np\binom{Np-1}{x-1}\binom{Nq}{n-x} \Big/ \binom{N}{n}.$$

From Exercise 7.18,

$$\sum_{x=1}^{n}\binom{Np-1}{x-1}\binom{Nq}{n-x} = \binom{N-1}{n-1},$$

so that finally $\mu = np$.

*11.11. By a method analogous to that used in Exercise 11.10 show that for the hypergeometric distribution (7.10)

$$E[X(X-1)] = E(X^2) - E(X) = \frac{np(n-1)(Np-1)}{N-1}.$$

Hence, using the result of Exercise 11.10, show that $\sigma^2 = \dfrac{n(N-n)pq}{N-1}.$

*11.12. In Section 7 it was found that the limiting form of the hypergeometric distribution as $N \to \infty$ is the binomial distribution. Use this fact to deduce, from Exercises 11.10 and 11.11, the mean and variance of the binomial distribution with frequency function (7.11).

*11.13. If the frequency function $f(x)$ of a distribution satisfies the criterion $f(\mu + x) = f(\mu - x)$ for all x, the distribution is said to be *symmetrical*. If the mean is taken as origin this criterion becomes $f(x) = f(-x)$. Using this origin for x, show that the odd central moments vanish for a symmetrical distribution.

11.14. The 10 hearts, from ace to 10, are withdrawn from a pack. Numbers 1 to 4 are placed in pile A, numbers 5 to 10 in pile B. A penny is tossed. If it falls heads up, a card is drawn from pile A; if tails up, a card is drawn from pile B. If X is the value of the card finally drawn, find the frequency function of X and its mean and variance.

*12. GENERATING FUNCTIONS

Let us consider more closely the effect of forming the mathematical expectation of X^n, as was done in the last section. X^n is a function of the two variables X and n. When we form the expectation of X^n, we obtain a quantity μ_n' which depends only on n. The process of forming the expectation has the effect of suppressing the variable X. Let us experiment with some other functions of two variables, one of which is X.

The expectations of tX and of $tX + s$ turn out to be

$$E(tX) = \Sigma p_i t x_i = t \Sigma p_i x_i = t\, E(X),$$

$$E(tX + s) = \Sigma p_i(t x_i + s) = t\, E(X) + s.$$

These functions yield nothing that is essentially new. Much more interesting are the expectations of t^X and e^{tX}, known, respectively, as the *generating function* and the *moment generating function* of X. The generating function of X will be denoted by G_x, or $G_x(t)$, and defined by

(12.1) $$G_x = G_x(t) = E(t^x) = \Sigma p_i t^{x_i}, \quad t > 0.$$

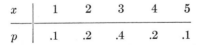

No numerical significance will be attached to the variable t; its analytical usefulness will be brought out in Chapter 3. The generating function is simply a polynomial in t whose coefficients are the probabilities and whose exponents are the corresponding values of x.

Example 12.1. If X has the distribution

x	1	2	3	4	5
p	.1	.2	.4	.2	.1

then $G(t) = .1t + .2t^2 + .4t^3 + .2t^4 + .1t^5$. Note that the generating function specifies the distribution compactly and conveniently.

The moment generating function of X will be denoted by M_x or $M_x(t)$, and defined by

$$(12.2) \qquad M_x = M_x(t) = E(e^{tx}) = \Sigma p_i e^{tx_i}.$$

Note that this function is obtained from the generating function simply by replacing t by e^t. In fact

$$(12.3) \qquad M_x(t) = G_x(e^t), \qquad G_x(t) = M_x(\log_e t).$$

For the random variable X of Example 12.1 the moment generating function is $.1e^t + .2e^{2t} + .4e^{3t} + .2e^{4t} + .1e^{5t}$.

An interesting result becomes evident when we expand as power series the exponential functions entering into (12.3). We obtain

$$M(t) = p_1 \left(1 + tx_1 + \frac{(tx_1)^2}{2!} + \frac{(tx_1)^3}{3!} + \cdots \right)$$

$$+ p_2 \left(1 + tx_2 + \frac{(tx_2)^2}{2!} + \frac{(tx_2)^3}{3!} + \cdots \right)$$

$$\cdots \cdots \cdots \cdots \cdots$$

$$+ p_k \left(1 + tx_k + \frac{(tx_k)^2}{2!} + \frac{(tx_k)^3}{3!} + \cdots \right).$$

When we collect the coefficients of powers of t in the above expression, adding by columns, we find

$$M(t) = (p_1 + \cdots + p_k) + t(p_1 x_1 + \cdots + p_k x_k)$$

$$+ \frac{t^2}{2!}(p_1 x_1{}^2 + \cdots + p_k x_k{}^2) + \frac{t^3}{3!}(p_1 x_1{}^3 + \cdots + p_k x_k{}^3) + \cdots$$

$$= 1 + \mu_1' t + \frac{1}{2!}\mu_2' t^2 + \frac{1}{3!}\mu_3' t^3 + \cdots$$

Thus the moments serve as coefficients in the Maclaurin expansion of the moment generating function. This suggests that the moments are actually derivatives of the moment generating function. In fact we may verify directly from the original definition (12.2) that

$$(12.4) \qquad \left. \frac{d^r}{dt^r} M(t) \right|_{t=0} = \Sigma p_i x_i{}^r = \mu_r'.$$

The moment generating function thus "generates" the moments of the distribution in the sense that they can be obtained from the moment generating function by differentiation. The most important applications of both generating function and moment generating function occur in connection with the derivation of sampling distributions, as will appear in Chapters 3 and 5.

Example 12.2. The first and second derivatives of the moment generating function of the random variable of Example 12.1 are

$$\frac{dM}{dt} = .1e^t + .4e^{2t} + 1.2e^{3t} + .8e^{4t} + .5e^{5t}$$

$$\frac{d^2M}{dt^2} = .1e^t + .8e^{2t} + 3.6e^{3t} + 3.2e^{4t} + 2.5e^{5t}.$$

Evaluating these derivatives for $t = 0$ we find the following moments:

$$\mu_1' = \mu = 3.0, \quad \mu_2' = 10.2, \quad \sigma^2 = \mu_2' - \mu^2 = 1.2.$$

Of great importance in the advanced theory of statistics is the *characteristic function* $E(e^{itx})$, where $i = \sqrt{-1}$. Whereas the generating function and the moment generating function will not exist unless all moments of X are finite, the characteristic function will always exist. Thus much more general distributions can be investigated using characteristic functions. This portion of statistical theory is beyond the level of this book.

EXERCISE 12

12.1. Form the generating function and the moment generating function for:
(a) A single die.
(b) Random numbers 0 to 9.
(c) The variable x whose distribution is

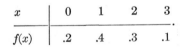

x	0	1	2	3
$f(x)$	.2	.4	.3	.1

12.2. Obtain μ_1', μ_2', μ_3' for each of the distributions in Exercise 12.1 by differentiating the moment generating function and evaluating for $t = 0$. Hence obtain μ and σ^2 for each distribution.

12.3. By the use of the binomial theorem, show that the generating function for the binomial distribution (7.11) is $G(t) = (pt + q)^n$ and that the moment generating function is $M(t) = (pe^t + q)^n$.

12.4. Obtain the first and second derivative of the moment generating function of the binomial distribution, as found in Exercise 12.3. Hence find $\mu_1' = \mu$, μ_2', and σ^2 for the binomial distribution.

12.5. If $G(t)$ is the generating function of a random variable and if its first and second derivatives are denoted by $G'(t)$ and $G''(t)$, show that

(a) $G(t) = 1$.

(b) $\mu = G'(1)$.

(c) $\sigma^2 = G''(1) + G'(1) - (G'(1))^2$.

By this means and using the results of Exercise 12.3, find the mean and variance of the binomial distribution (7.11).

12.6. The rth factorial moment of a random variable x is simply the expectation $E(X(X - 1) \cdots (X - r + 1))$. Show that, if $G^{(r)}(t)$ is the rth derivative of the generating function $G(t)$, the rth factorial moment is $G^{(r)}(1)$.

12.7. According to (5.7), the Poisson frequency function is $f(x) = k^x e^{-k}/x!$, extending over the infinite sample space $\{0, 1, 2, 3, \cdots\}$. The functions $G(t)$ and $M(t)$ are still defined by (12.1) and (12.2) for such distributions, provided that the series involved are convergent. Find $G(t)$ and $M(t)$ for the Poisson distribution and hence its mean and variance.

12.8. Using the result of Example 5.6, find the generating function and the moment generating function for the sum of 2 dice. Verify that the generating function for the sum of 2 dice is simply the square of the generating function for a single die and that a similar relation holds for the moment generating functions.

HOW TO MAKE A SIMPLE SPINNER

The spindle on which the spinner rotates may be made of brass or even from a common nail, sharpened to a conical point and driven through the piece of wood which will serve as base.

The bearing for the needle should be so constructed that the center of gravity of the needle is below the point of suspension, as shown in Figure A. The bearing may be constructed of brass, on a lathe, and the needle attached to it by burring over the portion of the bearing

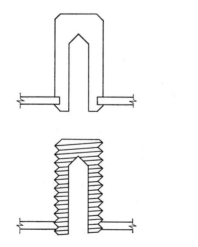

FIGURE A

FIGURE B

that extends through the needle (Figure A). A simpler bearing may be constructed from a piece of $\frac{1}{4}$-inch bolt, $\frac{1}{2}$ inch long. A hole $\frac{3}{8}$ inch deep and $\frac{1}{8}$ inch in diameter is drilled into the bolt. The needle is made of aluminum, 5 to 7 inches in length, and $\frac{1}{2}$ inch wide at the center. A hole is drilled at the center of the needle of such a diameter that the piece of bolt can be force-threaded into it, giving a tight fit (Figure B).

In using the spinner, it is inadvisable to let the needle come to rest of its own accord, partly because it takes too long and partly because it will tend to stop in certain preferred positions. Better results are secured by using one's finger as a brake, placing it on top of the bearing. If this is done without looking at the needle, the results represent a satisfactory approximation to "randomness." This requires, of course, that the top of the bearing be quite flat and at right angles to the hole drilled into it.

CHAPTER 2

Continuous Distributions

13. SAMPLING FROM A CONTINUOUS POPULATION— CLASSIFICATION

Most of the data with which science deals are continuous rather than discrete. Whenever a measurement is made of length, time, velocity— in fact, of any quantity which can be measured by means of a scale or dial—we are dealing with a continuous variate. Such quantities are continuous in the sense that each particular value within a certain range might conceivably be the true result of the process of measurement, although we shall always be obliged to approximate the true result. For example, an ear of corn, in its growth, passes through all values within a certain range of weight. In such a situation there can be no excluded values within the range in question. Thus, if we take sample ears from a field of corn, any value within a range of perhaps a pound or so might be encountered. Such considerations will clearly apply to a wide variety of phenomena, not only to those involving growth but also to those in which any physical quantity may be conceived to vary continuously.

Practically, however, we measure only to a limited degree of accuracy. In weighing ears of corn, we may decide to measure to the nearest tenth of a gram, and in so doing we agree to ignore smaller differences in weight. For example, suppose we have 4 ears of corn whose weights, to the nearest thousandth of a gram, are 195.379, 195.421, 195.394 and 195.449 grams. Measured to the nearest tenth of a gram, all four of these weights would be called 195.4 grams. Thus our system of recording the weights has the effect of assigning a single number, namely 195.4, to all weights within an interval, namely, the interval from 195.35 to 195.45 grams.

The ordinary process of measurement thus assigns each ear of corn (or other measured object) to a particular interval of a system of intervals. In the example of the previous paragraph a few of these

82

intervals would be 195.35 to 195.45, 195.45 to 195.55, 195.55 to 195.65, etc. All values falling within a particular interval are designated by a single value, namely, the midvalue of the interval. For the intervals named above the midvalues are 195.4, 195.5, and 195.6. Thus we find that, as soon as we have chosen our scale and the degree of accuracy to which the data will be recorded, the data are virtually transformed into discrete data, for we can obtain only certain prespecified values and no values in between. The continuous nature of the quantity being measured will become evident, not in the data themselves, but in the freedom we have to choose the scale and the degree of accuracy to which we shall make our measurements. We are, in fact, free to choose any set of intervals we please and to assign the objects under observation to these intervals; but we cannot escape the necessity of making the choice because the process of measurement depends upon it.

Consider Table 13.1, which gives to the nearest tenth of a millimeter the lengths of 157 lima beans, listed in the order in which they happened to be picked up. This system of weighing has the effect of assigning the lima beans to 94 possible intervals, the first from 15.75

TABLE 13.1

20.6	21.7	23.3	19.4	18.1	22.2	22.5	18.9	20.1	19.8
20.6	22.0	22.0	22.5	20.9	18.6	21.7	21.1	17.1	19.3
22.5	20.6	19.0	20.5	20.1	20.8	23.1	22.0	21.3	21.6
20.1	22.8	21.1	22.1	18.9	20.5	21.4	20.3	17.0	21.6
19.5	21.5	20.1	20.1	23.7	23.2	22.2	20.1	20.5	20.6
18.7	22.3	18.2	19.3	19.0	20.7	20.7	21.9	17.5	18.1
20.7	20.3	21.4	20.0	22.7	20.9	22.0	20.5	22.0	20.8
16.7	21.2	19.4	18.4	18.7	19.8	21.6	18.2	20.6	16.4
19.0	18.5	20.7	17.8	20.7	19.4	20.4	18.1	19.7	19.1
22.1	21.1	19.1	18.6	21.8	20.6	17.5	21.0	19.9	16.8
19.4	21.3	20.6	20.8	23.1	18.7	20.7	18.7	18.3	20.0
21.5	19.6	22.0	20.6	20.7	22.3	19.8	20.2	20.4	18.0
21.2	21.5	16.6	20.0	20.5	21.6	21.1	19.7	20.5	16.7
17.0	18.7	20.8	22.5	23.1	20.5	25.1	21.0	21.5	21.6
22.3	19.8	15.8	19.7	20.7	19.0	21.2	22.1	22.6	23.7
21.8	21.8	20.7	22.4	19.4	21.1	19.2			

to 15.85, the last from 25.05 to 25.15. It would be inconvenient to use a frequency distribution employing so many intervals. Since the system of intervals employed is in any case arbitrary, we exercise our freedom to select a system that will be more convenient. This selection of a suitable system of intervals is basically similar to what was done in Table 4.3, where for convenience of computation the values entering into a frequency distribution were grouped.

The most convenient number of intervals to use will generally lie between 10 and 20. With more than 20 intervals we are introducing more refinement, and more labor, into our calculations than is generally justified by the ultimate use of the results. With fewer than 10 intervals we are sacrificing too much of the information in the data. We select a suitable size of interval, denoted by Δx, in the following way: The maximum of the set is 25.1, the minimum is 15.8, and the range is thus $25.1 - 15.8 = 9.3$. With 10 intervals, each would be approximately $9.3/10 = .93$ mm.; with 20 intervals, each would be approximately $9.3/20 = .465$ mm. We choose a convenient size of interval somewhere between .465 mm. and .93 mm., or just beyond this range. Let us choose $\Delta x = .9$. Actually, the value $\Delta x = 1.0$ would lead to simpler computations. In the exercises the student is asked to make the computation using $\Delta x = 1.0$ for comparison.

The *upper and lower limits* of the intervals are simply the largest and smallest values in each interval. It is convenient to begin by selecting the lower limits of all intervals. The lower limit of the lowest interval must be less than or equal to the minimum of the set, 15.8; the other lower limits will then be obtained by repeated addition of $\Delta x = .9$. The choice of 15.0 for the first lower limit gives us the sequence of lower limits shown on the left side of Table 13.2. The upper limit of each interval is obtained by starting from the lower limit of the next higher interval and stepping down one unit in the last significant decimal position.

The midvalue for each interval is simply the average of the upper and lower limits. This rule yields the midvalues shown in Table 13.2.

The *boundaries* of the intervals give the actual points of division, on a continuous scale, between the intervals. Consider, for example, lima beans whose lengths, correct to .001 mm., are 16.749 and 16.751. Rounded to the nearest .1 mm., the first would be called 16.7 and would be assigned to the interval 15.9 to 16.7; the second would be called 16.8 and would be assigned to the interval 16.8 to 17.6. Thus 16.75 is the actual dividing line between these 2 intervals, and it is reasonably called the boundary between them. The boundaries for each interval may be obtained by adding one-half the interval size to the midvalue

TABLE 13.2

Interval		Mid-value X	Tally	Frequency f
Limits	Boundaries			
15.0–15.8	14.95–15.85	15.4	/	1
15.9–16.7	15.85–16.75	16.3	⦀	4
16.8–17.6	16.75–17.65	17.2	⦀ /	6
17.7–18.5	17.65–18.55	18.1	⦀ ⦀	10
18.6–19.4	18.55–19.45	19.0	⦀ ⦀ ⦀ ⦀ ///	23
19.5–20.3	19.45–20.35	19.9	⦀ ⦀ ⦀ ⦀ //	22
20.4–21.2	20.35–21.25	20.8	⦀ ⦀ ⦀ ⦀ ⦀ ⦀ ⦀ ⦀ //	42
21.3–22.1	21.25–22.15	21.7	⦀ ⦀ ⦀ ⦀ ⦀ ///	28
22.2–23.0	22.15–23.05	22.6	⦀ ⦀ ///	13
23.1–23.9	23.05–23.95	23.5	⦀ //	7
24.0–24.8	23.95–24.85	24.4		0
24.9–25.7	24.85–25.75	25.3	/	1
				157

and by subtracting the same quantity from the midvalue. When the boundaries for one interval are obtained, the remaining ones are readily obtained by repeated addition of the interval size.

The use of the class limits is primarily in assigning the observed values to the intervals, a job more easily performed with the class limits than with the class boundaries. The class boundaries, on the other hand, will turn out to be important in the calculation of order statistics (Section 14).

We have noted that the process of measurement has the effect of assigning a single value to all measurements falling within a certain interval. After having assigned all the values of the sample to the set of intervals, we shall proceed to use them as if all the values in each interval were concentrated at the midvalue of the interval. In this process we are arbitrarily reducing some values and arbitrarily increasing others, but it may be expected that on the average these effects will nearly counteract each other. There is, in fact, no systematic effect on the mean, but the variance tends to be slightly increased. Sometimes a slight adjustment for this effect, known as Sheppard's correction, is applied to the variance. For purposes of statistical inference we may ignore such corrections.

TABLE 13.3

Mid-   Fre-
value quency Code

X	f	u	fu	fu^2
15.4	1	-6	-6	36
16.3	4	-5	-20	100
17.2	6	-4	-24	96
18.1	10	-3	-30	90
19.0	23	-2	-46	92
19.9	22	-1	-22	22
20.8	42	0	0	0
21.7	28	1	28	28
22.6	13	2	26	52
23.5	7	3	21	63
24.4	0	4	0	0
25.3	1	5	5	25
	157		-68	604

$N = 157,\ \Sigma fu = -68,\ \Sigma fu^2 = 604$

$\bar{u} = -68/157 = -.4331$

$$s_u{}^2 = \frac{157 \cdot 604 - (-68)^2}{157 \cdot 156} = 3.683$$

$s_u = \sqrt{3.683} = 1.919$

$\bar{X} = \bar{u}\,\Delta x + X_0 = -.390 + 20.8 = 20.410$

$s_x = (\Delta x)(s_u) = 1.727$

In Table 13.2 we show the limits, boundaries, midvalues, and a tally of our 157 values, summarized in a frequency distribution. The result is called a *grouped* or *classified* frequency distribution.

The *mode* of a grouped frequency distribution is defined as the midvalue of the interval with greatest frequency. The mode is a very unstable measure, fluctuating not only from sample to sample but also with changes of the interval system.

The coding method of (8.13) is especially convenient when the set of data have been put in the form of a grouped frequency distribution. In Table 13.3 a code has been set up; it is usually convenient to put the code value $u = 0$ at or near the mode. Note that the code values increase by unit steps, the increase in u being in the same direction as the increase in X. Columns of fu and fu^2 are computed and totaled as in Section 8. Equations (8.13) are finally used to obtain $\bar{X}$ and s_x.

EXERCISE 13

13.1. For the lima bean data, set up a system of intervals with an interval size of $\Delta x = 1.0$, using 15.0 as the lower limit of the first interval. Make a frequency distribution of the values in Table 13.1 with this system of intervals. Calculate $\bar{X}$ and s_x, using a code.

13.2. The thickness of 100 washers was measured to the nearest .0001 inch, with the results tabulated below. Set up a suitable system of intervals, classify the data, draw a histogram, and calculate $\overline{X}$ and s_X, using a code.

THICKNESS OF 100 WASHERS, IN 0001 INCH

685	662	589	629	664	629	602	639	622	689
640	656	677	622	662	606	635	621	602	640
632	604	572	621	583	621	619	593	618	589
639	617	668	610	693	633	618	646	620	580
650	686	636	660	558	564	617	707	671	630
630	646	589	661	589	610	569	607	609	702
617	604	684	670	591	616	681	629	662	633
617	610	640	607	641	628	660	629	650	686
605	680	629	647	646	661	654	672	615	689
611	643	604	622	611	592	629	607	613	623

13.3. Bessel made the following observations of the diameter of Saturn's ring in the years 1829 to 1831. Proceed as in Exercise 13.2.

38.91	39.35	39.41	39.02	39.32	39.25	39.40	39.01
38.93	39.14	39.36	38.86	39.31	39.47	39.20	39.51
39.17	39.29	39.42	39.21	39.04	39.32	39.30	39.17
39.57	39.40	39.41	39.60	39.46	39.33	39.43	39.54
39.30	39.28	39.43	39.45	39.03	39.62	39.36	39.72

13.4. The following determinations were made of lipase in blood serum of 91 normal adults. Proceed as in Exercise 13.2.

.36	.71	.22	.45	.43	.13	.22	.85	.37	.22	.41	.91	.10
.14	.76	.45	.91	.61	.31	.21	.38	.15	.65	.62	.73	.42
.33	.41	.42	.18	.26	.36	.75	.52	.16	.63	.85	1.09	.15
.27	.32	.91	.32	.33	.42	.65	.56	.71	.63	.23	.32	.44
.63	.18	.24	.98	.83	.37	.31	.46	.59	.62	.75	.17	.31
.62	.51	.92	1.13	.08	.29	.36	.57	.62	.75	.42	.45	.62
.43	.53	.51	.62	.26	.27	.39	.65	.72	.39	.53	.78	.74

14. ORDER STATISTICS

In Table 14.1 we have reproduced the column of upper boundaries and the column of f from Table 13.2, and we have added columns of cumulative frequency(cf) and cumulative relative frequency (crf), the latter obtained by dividing each cf value by the total frequency, $n = 157$.

TABLE 14.1

Upper Boundaries	f	cf	crf
15.85	1	1	.006
16.75	4	5	.032
17.65	6	11	.070
18.55	10	21	.134
19.45	23	44	.280
20.35	22	66	.420
21.25	42	108	.688
22.15	28	136	.866
23.05	13	149	.949
23.95	7	156	.994
24.85	0	156	.994
25.75	1	157	1.000
	157		

It is readily verified that the following properties of the *cf* and *crf* will hold:

(14.1)   *The cumulative frequency for any interval gives the number of values in the set which are less than the upper boundary of the interval.*

(14.2)   *The cumulative relative frequency for any interval gives the proportion of values in the set which are less than the upper boundary of the interval.*

For example, there are 11 values in the set which are less than 17.65, and the proportion which are less than 17.65 is .070.

If we graph the values of the cumulative frequency as ordinate against the upper boundaries as abscissa, we obtain Figure 14.1, in which the points have been joined to form the *cumulative frequency polygon*. On the right side of the graph is an additional scale, running from 0 to 1, which permits us to regard the graph as a *cumulative relative frequency polygon*.

The median has been defined, in Section 10, for a set of discrete values. By applying the definition given there to the data of Table 13.1, the median would be the 79th value when the values in the sample are arranged in order of size. With a little labor, this is found to be $\tilde{X} = 20.6$. We shall now develop a suitable method of obtaining the median when the data have been classified in the form of a frequency

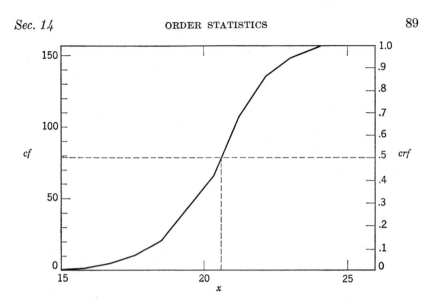

FIGURE 14.1. Cumulative (relative) frequency polygon, data of Table 14.1.

distribution and are regarded as a random sample from a continuous population.

In Section 15 it will be shown that, as the sample size is increased and the intervals are simultaneously decreased in size, the *crf* polygon approaches a smooth curve, the *distribution curve*, which characterizes the population. Let us regard the *crf* polygon as an approximation to the distribution curve and ask how we may estimate the population median. If the *crf* were computed for the whole population, the median would, from (14.2), correspond to the value *crf* = .5. Hence, as an estimate of the population median we shall use the abscissa of the *crf* polygon corresponding to an ordinate of .5. The graphical construction is shown in Figure 14.1. The ordinate *crf* = .5 is, of course, measured on the right-hand scale and corresponds, on the left-hand scale, to a value of $n/2 = 157/2 = 78.5$. Since we are dealing with a polygon, the graphical procedure suggests linear interpolation. We set up the following interpolation table (note that the values labeled x are upper boundaries):

x	cf	
20.35	66	
$\tilde{X}$	78.5	$\tilde{X} = 20.35 + \dfrac{22.5}{42} \times .9 = 20.83.$
21.25	108	

By the usual method of linear interpolation, we find $\tilde{X} = 20.83$, which agrees satisfactorily with the value $\tilde{X} = 20.6$ obtained from the original data. Both of these values may be regarded as estimates of the population median.

The graphical method suggested above and the interpolation which is its analytical counterpart can be extended to find values of x which divide the group of values in any given ratio. It is to be emphasized that the interpolation procedure provides *estimates* of the values which divide the population in given ratios. Such values are known as *order statistics* since to compute them we must either arrange the group in order of size or organize the data in a frequency distribution. Such statistics are assuming an increasingly important role in modern statistical work since in their use fewer assumptions need to be made about the population from which the samples are drawn than in the use of statistics based on the mean, variance, and other moments.

The values which divide the group into 4 equal parts are called the *quartiles*, denoted by Q_1, Q_2 (identical with the median), and Q_3. The values which divide the group into 10 equal parts are the *deciles*, denoted by $D_1, \cdots, D_9$, and the values which divide the group into 100 equal parts are the *centiles* or *percentiles*, denoted by $P_1, \cdots, P_{99}$. Each of them may be obtained from the (relative) cumulative frequency polygon or by interpolation. To obtain Q_1, for example, we first find $.25n = .25 \times 157 = 39.25$. Using this value as ordinate, we may approximate Q_1 from the graph. To interpolate, we note that 39.25 lies between the values 21 and 44 of the *cf* column, and we set up an interpolation table as follows:

x	*cf*	
18.55	21	
Q_1	39.25	$Q_1 = 18.55 + \dfrac{18.25}{23} \times .9 = 19.26.$
19.45	44	

Thus approximately a quarter of the values in the sample are less than 19.26; further, approximately a quarter of the values in the population of which this is a random sample will likewise be less than 19.26.

EXERCISE 14

14.1. For the distribution of Table 14.1, compute the following order statistics: Q_3, P_{20}, P_{65}, P_{95}.

14.2. Find the cumulative frequency for the distribution of Exercise 13.2. Compute the median, the quartiles Q_1 and Q_3, and P_{35}, P_{62}, and P_{87}.

14.3. Suppose we have the discrete distribution

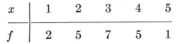

x	1	2	3	4	5
f	2	5	7	5	1

If we wished to find the median of this distribution by a method similar to that of this section, we might associate the given frequencies with intervals as follows:

Interval	.5–1.5	1.5–2.5	2.5–3.5	3.5–4.5	4.5–5.5
f	2	5	7	5	1

Investigate whether the interpolation procedure of this section, applied to the above distribution, yields the same value of the median as that defined by (10.2).

15. DENSITY AND DISTRIBUTION FUNCTIONS— THE NORMAL DISTRIBUTION

We now turn to the problem of selecting a suitable mathematical model for a continuous random experiment. In Section 5 this question was treated informally, using the properties of the spinner as a guide in our considerations. There we saw that the concept of the distribution function $F(x)$ could be reasonably extended to the case of a continuous random variable. We shall presently return to the distribution function; first, we must see what our analysis of the lima bean data implies concerning the underlying mathematical model for the random experiment of selecting a bean and measuring its length.

It has been pointed out, in Section 13, that, when a system of intervals has been selected, a continuous random variable is virtually converted into a discrete random variable. For with each of the intervals we may associate a probability, which is the limit of the relative frequency for that interval as the sample size is increased without limit. Given a sample, the sample relative frequencies may be computed, and they will provide estimates of the corresponding probabilities. In Table 15.1 these values are computed for the lima bean data, using the interval system selected in Section 13. In addition to the columns of f and rf, a column labeled $rf/\Delta x$ has been provided, obtained by dividing each value in the rf column by the interval size Δx. This quantity, which we may call the *relative frequency per unit of* x, has the virtue that, when the histogram is drawn with this vertical scale, as in Figure 15.1, its total area is unity and the area of each bar gives the sample

TABLE 15.1

Boundaries	f	rf	$rf/\Delta x$
14.95–15.85	1	.006	.007
15.85–16.75	4	.025	.028
16.75–17.65	6	.038	.042
17.65–18.55	10	.064	.071
18.55–19.45	23	.146	.162
19.45–20.35	22	.140	.155
20.35–21.25	42	.268	.297
21.25–22.15	28	.178	.198
22.15–23.05	13	.083	.092
23.05–23.95	7	.045	.049
23.95–24.85	0	0	0
24.85–25.75	1	.006	.007
	157	.999	1.108

relative frequency for the corresponding interval. This fact becomes evident when we note that each bar of the histogram has a width of Δx and a height of $rf/\Delta x$, and thus an area of rf.

The flat tops of the bars of the histogram suggest that the values are evenly distributed through each interval, which is unlikely to be the case. The nature of the population distribution is better suggested by a smooth curve known as the *frequency curve*, or *probability density curve*, or simply *density curve*, to which the histogram is an approximation. A sketch of such a curve, drawn so as to approximate the histogram of Figure 15.1, is shown in Figure 15.2. We should expect the approximation to improve if the sample were greatly increased in

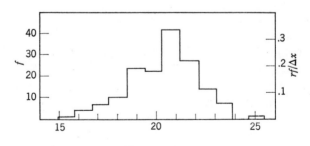

FIGURE 15.1

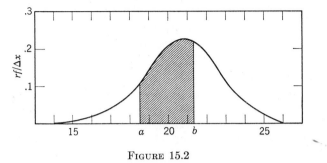

FIGURE 15.2

size, and the interval size decreased. Consider a sequence of histograms, based on samples of progressively larger size, with progressively smaller interval sizes. We shall *assume* that the histograms will tend to approach a smooth curve whose area will be unity since each histogram in the sequence has unit area (we here assume that the vertical scale for each histogram is $rf/\Delta x$).

We now conclude that, in the model of the continuous random experiment provided by the frequency curve, the probability that a random value x shall fall in a particular interval $a < x < b$ is given by the area under the curve and above the interval, as shown by the shaded portion of Figure 15.2. For suppose that the sequence of interval systems referred to in the previous paragraph is so set up that the points $x = a$ and $x = b$ are always end points of intervals. Consider any histogram of the sequence. The total area of all the blocks of the histogram above the interval (a, b) will be the relative frequency of sample values falling in the interval. Thus in the limit, as the histograms approach the curve, the limiting relative frequency for the interval (a, b) will equal the shaded area in Figure 15.2, which must thus give the probability $P(a < X < b)$.

The use of the word "density" in the term "probability density curve" is quite similar to its use in population statistics when we speak of the density of population in a given area, meaning thereby the number of people per unit area. If we think of the observations in a sample as represented by dots on the horizontal axis (compare Figure 8.1), the quantity $f/\Delta x$ will give the frequency density of the dots per unit of x. Thus $rf/\Delta x$ might be called the relative frequency density of the points on the line. If we now consider a sequence of unit histograms tending to approach the frequency curve, the relative frequency density, given by the ordinate of the unit histogram, will approach the probability density, given by the ordinate of the frequency curve.

Note the analogy between the density of a material body and probability density. The sample distribution is analogous to a weightless rod carrying equal weights at points corresponding to the values of x. The distribution of the population, which arises from that of the sample as the sample size is made indefinitely large, is analogous to a rod of non-uniform density. The probability density is then analogous to the density of the rod *at a point.*

The frequency curve is, of course, merely a graphical representation of a function $f(x)$ which we shall call the *frequency function* of the random experiment, or the *probability density function*, or simply the *density function*. We note two properties of the function $f(x)$ which may be immediately deduced from its relation to the sequence of histograms:

(a) $f(x)$ cannot be negative.

(15.1)   (b) $\int_a^b f(x)\, dx = 1$, where the interval (a, b) constitutes the sample space of the experiment.

For convenience, we regard every density function as extending along the complete x-axis, from $-\infty$ to ∞. If the density is originally given over an interval $a \leqq x \leqq b$, we shall extend it to the remainder of the x-axis by defining $f(x) = 0$ for all $x < a$ and for all $x > b$. With this understanding we make the following definition of probability:

(15.2)   DEFINITION. *If $f(x)$ is the density function of a continuous random variable X and if $x_1 < x \leqq x_2$ is an interval of the x-axis, we define*

$$P(x_1 < X \leqq x_2) = \int_{x_1}^{x_2} f(x)\, dx.$$

In geometrical terms, the probability associated with any interval has been defined to be the area under the frequency curve and lying between ordinates erected at $x = x_1$ and $x = x_2$.

If the points x_1 and x_2 coincide, (15.2) implies that the probability is zero; that is, the probability associated with a single point is zero. Thus there is no difference between the probabilities associated with closed, open, or half-open intervals, so that

$$P(x_1 < X \leqq x_2) = P(x_1 \leqq X < x_2) = P(x_1 \leqq X \leqq x_2)$$
$$= P(x_1 < X < x_2).$$

We shall arbitrarily choose the first of these forms $P(x_1 < X \leqq x_2)$ as the standard way of writing the probability associated with an interval. Note that, as soon as we specify the degree of accuracy to which we shall record our measurements in some experiment, any particular value of x is actually associated with an interval and thus, in general, has a non-zero probability associated with it.

The *distribution function* for a continuous random variable is defined as follows:

(15.3)   DEFINITION.   *Let X be a continuous random variable with density* $f(x)$. *The distribution function of X is given by*

$$F(x) = P(X \leqq x) = \int_{-\infty}^{x} f(t) \, dt.$$

The probability associated with an interval may be conveniently expressed in terms of the distribution function. From the elementary properties of integrals we have

$$\int_{x_1}^{x_2} f(x) \, dx = \int_{-\infty}^{x_2} f(x) \, dx - \int_{-\infty}^{x_1} f(x) \, dx,$$

so that

(15.4) $P(x_1 < X \leqq x_2) = F(x_2) - F(x_1).$

The density of a continuous random variable may be obtained from its distribution function by differentiation, as follows immediately from (15.3):

(15.5) $f(x) = \dfrac{dF(x)}{dx}.$

We call the graph of the distribution function the *distribution curve* associated with the random variable. In Figure 15.3 we show the distribution curve corresponding to the frequency curve sketched in Figure 15.2. When, as in this case, the frequency curve has a single mode at which $f(x)$ is a maximum, the distribution curve will tend to rise slowly at first, then more rapidly, and finally more slowly. Such a curve is sometimes called an *ogive,* from the term employed in architecture for S-shaped curves.

We now show that the fact, established earlier, that the density curve may be regarded as the limit of a sequence of histograms implies that the distribution curve is the limit of the corresponding sequence

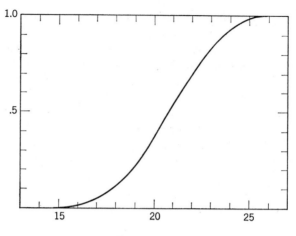

of cumulative relative frequency (*crf*) polygons. For a particular sample of size n, with a particular interval system, let x be the abscissa of an arbitrary point on the x-axis, and let x' denote the upper boundary of the interval containing x. Then, denoting by *crf* (x') the cumulative relative frequency corresponding to x', by (14.2), we have

$$crf(x') = \text{proportion of the sample which is less than } x'$$

$$\doteq \text{proportion of the sample which is less than } x.$$

The sign $\doteq$ means "is approximately equal to." This approximation will tend to improve as $\Delta x \to 0$. On the other hand, by 10.1 we have

$$\text{Proportion of the sample which is less than } x \doteq P(X \leq x) = F(x),$$

and this approximation will tend to improve as n is increased. We thus conclude that $crf(x') \doteq F(x)$ and that as $n \to \infty$ and $\Delta x \to 0$ this approximate equality will tend toward an equality. Since $crf(x')$ is the ordinate of a vertex of the *crf* polygon while $F(x)$ is the ordinate of a point on the distribution curve, we conclude that the distribution curve is the limiting form of the *crf* polygon as $n \to \infty$ and $\Delta x \to 0$.

In Sections 10 and 14 we have considered the median of a sample. The median $\mu_{.5}$ of a population may be defined as the value for which $P(X \geq \mu_{.5}) = .5$, that is, for which $F(\mu_{.5}) = .5$. It is here convenient to use the *inverse function* $F^{-1}(u)$ of the distribution function; by using this function, the median may be simply defined by $\mu_{.5} = F^{-1}(.5)$.

Other values of x may be similarly defined, playing the same role for the population that the percentiles and similar measures play for the sample. If u is any real number in the interval (0, 1), the value $\mu_u = F^{-1}(u)$ is called the 100u *percentage point* (or the 100u *percentile*) of the distribution. It is common practice to provide tables of the basic distribution functions which give a selected series of percentage points of the distribution, as is done in Tables 3, 4, and 5 at the end of this book.

As a first illustration of the preceding general ideas, consider the following example, which we shall show to be closely related to the spinner discussed in Sections 2 and 5.

Example 15.1. *Uniform random variable.* Consider a random variable U with density:

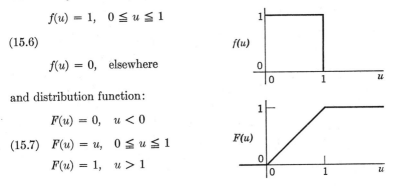

$$f(u) = 1, \quad 0 \leqq u \leqq 1$$

(15.6)

$$f(u) = 0, \quad \text{elsewhere}$$

and distribution function:

$$F(u) = 0, \quad u < 0$$

(15.7) $$F(u) = u, \quad 0 \leqq u \leqq 1$$

$$F(u) = 1, \quad u > 1$$

The graphs of these functions are shown to the right, above. The variable U, thus defined, is said to be a *uniform random variable* and to possess a *uniform distribution*.

By referring to Examples 2.8 and 5.8, it will be seen that a spinner equipped with the uniform scale of Example 2.8 yields a uniform random variable. A second realization, to any desired degree of approximation, is afforded by random numbers prefixed by a decimal point. To see this, let the circumference of a spinner scale be divided into 10,000 equal segments, labeled .0001, .0002, $\cdots$, .9999. The use of a spinner with such a scale is evidently equivalent to the use of four-figure random numbers, prefixed by a decimal point. Since the spinner scale described above approximates, to four-figure accuracy, a uniform scale, we conclude that four-figure random numbers prefixed by a decimal point yield, approximately, a uniform random variable.

Example 15.2. The uniform random variable of Example 15.1 is a special case of the more general random variable specified by the *rectangular distribution:*

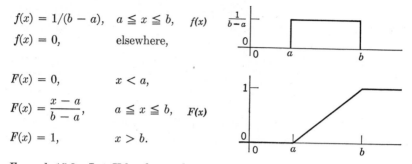

$$f(x) = 1/(b - a), \quad a \leqq x \leqq b,$$
$$f(x) = 0, \qquad\qquad \text{elsewhere,}$$

$$F(x) = 0, \qquad\qquad x < a,$$
$$F(x) = \frac{x - a}{b - a}, \qquad a \leqq x \leqq b,$$
$$F(x) = 1, \qquad\qquad x > b.$$

Example 15.3. Let X be the random variable whose density is

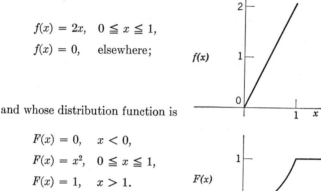

$$f(x) = 2x, \quad 0 \leqq x \leqq 1,$$
$$f(x) = 0, \quad \text{elsewhere;}$$

and whose distribution function is

$$F(x) = 0, \quad x < 0,$$
$$F(x) = x^2, \quad 0 \leqq x \leqq 1,$$
$$F(x) = 1, \quad x > 1.$$

It is readily verified that these functions satisfy the conditions (15.1) and (15.3) for a density and a distribution function. Their graphs are shown to the right.

Of the many possible theoretical densities that are available to us, each satisfying the requirements (15.1), by far the most useful is the *normal density*, whose simplest form is

(15.8)
$$f_N(x) = \frac{1}{\sqrt{2\pi}} e^{-x^2/2}.$$

We shall refer to the distribution whose density is (15.8) as the *unit normal distribution*. In Section 19 it will be proved that this distribution has mean $\mu = 0$ and variance $\sigma^2 = 1$. The general normal distribution has the density

(15.9)
$$f_N(x \mid \mu, \sigma^2) = \frac{1}{\sigma\sqrt{2\pi}} e^{-(x-\mu)^2/2\sigma^2}.$$

This distribution will be shown, in Section 19, to possess mean μ and variance σ^2. It will be denoted by $N(\mu, \sigma^2)$, so that the unit normal distribution, with density (15.8), may be denoted by $N(0, 1)$. The relationship between these distributions is given in the following theorem:

(15.10)   THEOREM. *If Z has the distribution $N(0, 1)$ and X is defined by $X = \sigma Z + \mu$, then X has the distribution $N(\mu, \sigma^2)$. Conversely, if X has the distribution $N(\mu, \sigma^2)$ and Z is defined by $Z = (X - \mu)/\sigma$, then Z has the distribution $N(0, 1)$.*

The proof will be deferred to the next section. (See Example 16.4.)

The principal reasons for the extensive use of the normal distribution in statistical theory are the following:

(*a*) Many random variables encountered in practice appear to possess distributions which are satisfactorily approximated by the normal distribution. It should be noted, however, that for most measured characteristics there is a contradiction involved in asserting that the quantity is normally distributed. The contradiction arises from the fact that the normal density extends from $-\infty$ to ∞. Thus to say that the heights of men are normally distributed implies that there is a finite probability that a man drawn at random will have a negative height * or a height greater than a mile. Fortunately this is a purely logical issue since such extreme probabilities are negligible for all practical purposes.

(*b*) There is a theorem, one of the most remarkable in all mathematics, known as the central limit theorem, which states that, even though a distribution may not itself be normal, the sum (or the mean) of a sample of n values from the distribution will be very nearly normally distributed, provided that n is not too small (say $n > 10$ for most distributions) and that the distribution has a finite variance. If the sample is large enough, other sample statistics (variance, median, etc.) will tend to be nearly normally distributed. In Chapters 3 and 5 we shall be considering various cases of the central limit theorem.

(*c*) The sampling theory associated with the normal distribution is considerably simpler than that associated with any other distribution. As a result the theory of statistical inference in general is greatly simplified when we can assume that the underlying population is normal.

The graph of the function $f_N(x)$, defined by (15.8) is shown in Figure 15.4, which also shows the percentages of the total area cut off by

---

*Note that a man with negative height would not be observable since he would walk on the underneath side of the ground.

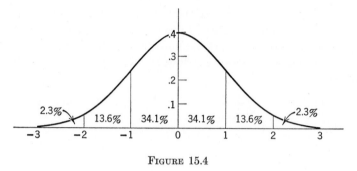

FIGURE 15.4

ordinates at -2, -1, 0, 1, and 2. In Section 24 it will be shown that the total area under this curve is unity. Since $f_N(x)$ is positive over its complete range, it fulfills the requirements for a density function.

The corresponding distribution function is defined by

$$(15.11) \qquad\qquad F_N(x) = \int_{-\infty}^{x} f_N(t)\, dt.$$

This integral is not expressible in terms of the elementary functions. Values of $F_N(x)$ may be obtained from Table 2, in the Appendix. This table gives, not $F_N(x)$ directly, but the integral $\int_0^x f_N(t)\, dt$. Since the density $f_N(x)$ is symmetrical with respect to the origin, it follows that $\int_{-\infty}^{0} f_N(t)\, dt = .5$. Hence, if $x > 0$,

$$F_N(x) = .5 + \int_0^x f_N(t)\, dt,$$

and, if $x < 0$,

$$F_N(x) = .5 - \int_0^{|x|} f_N(t)\, dt.$$

The use of Table 2 in evaluating probabilities associated with an arbitrary normal distribution is illustrated in the following example.

Example 15.4. Find the probability that a random value from $N(5, 9)$ shall: (a) be greater than 8.5; (b) be less than 6.2; (c) lie between 7.1 and 8.5; (d) lie between 2.2 and 6.2.

Solution. The essential steps are shown in the table. The various values of x are first transformed into z-values, using the linear transformation $z = (x - 5)/3$, according to (15.10). Values from Table 2 corresponding to $|z|$ are listed in the final column. In using the values from Table 2 (which give the

$$x \qquad z = \frac{(x - 5)}{3} \qquad \text{Table 2}$$

x	$z = \frac{(x-5)}{3}$	
2.2	$-.933$	.325
6.2	.4	.155
7.1	.7	.258
8.5	1.167	.366

areas from the center to the given value of z) to obtain the required probabilities, a sketch of the normal curve may be helpful, as suggested below:

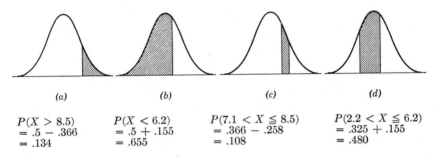

(a)	(b)	(c)	(d)
$P(X > 8.5)$	$P(X < 6.2)$	$P(7.1 < X \leqq 8.5)$	$P(2.2 < X \leqq 6.2)$
$= .5 - .366$	$= .5 + .155$	$= .366 - .258$	$= .325 + .155$
$= .134$	$= .655$	$= .108$	$= .480$

EXERCISE 15

15.1. Let a random variable X possess the density $f(x) = 1$, $1 \leqq x \leqq 2$, $f(x) = 0$ elsewhere.
   (a) Find $F(x)$.
   (b) Find $P(1.5 \leqq X \leqq 1.7)$.
   (c) Use three-figure random numbers in order to obtain 5 random values from this distribution.

15.2. Let a random variable X possess the density $f(x) = 3x^2$, for $0 \leqq x \leqq 1$, $f(x) = 0$ elsewhere.
   (a) Find $F(x)$.
   (b) Find $P(.2 \leqq X \leqq .9)$.
   (c) Use three-figure random numbers in order to obtain 5 random values from this distribution.

15.3. Let a random variable X possess the density $f(x) = e^{-x}$, $0 \leqq x < \infty$, $f(x) = 0$ elsewhere.
   (a) Find $F(x)$.
   (b) Find $P(X > 5)$.
   (c) Use three-figure random numbers in order to obtain 5 random numbers from this distribution.

15.4. Show that the general normal density (15.9) may be written as

$$\frac{1}{\sigma} f_N \left(\frac{x - \mu}{\sigma} \right), \text{ where } f_N \text{ is given by (15.8).}$$

15.5 Prove the following geometrical facts about the graph of the unit normal curve $y = f_N(x)$, where $f_N(x)$ is defined by (15.9):

(a) The curve is symmetrical with respect to the y-axis.

(b) The curve approaches the x-axis as an asymptote in both directions.

(c) The curve has a maximum at $x = 0$.

(d) The curve has inflection points at $A(1, (2\pi e)^{-1/2})$, $B(-1, (2\pi e)^{-1/2})$.

(e) The inflectional tangent at A crosses the x-axis at $(2, 0)$.

15.6. X is a random variable with the distribution $N(-5, 9)$. Find the following probabilities: (a) $P(X > 2)$, (b) $P(-1 < X < 0)$, (c) $P(-7 < X < -2)$, (d) $P(-9 < X < -6)$.

15.7. Use three-figure random numbers in order to obtain 5 random values from the distribution $N(200, 100)$.

15.8 Find the following percentage points (or percentiles) of the distribution $N(15, 10)$: 5th, 17th, 85th.

15.9. Show that the equation $\log_{10} y = a - bx^2$, where b is positive, is the equation of a normal curve. Sketch a normal curve by finding the value of $y = \text{antilog}(-x^2)$ for $x = 0, \pm.2, \pm.4, \cdots, \pm1.2, \pm1.4$.

15.10. Normal probability paper is formed with an "equal interval" scale (arithmetic scale) as the horizontal scale. The vertical scale is so constructed that the distance from the point labeled u on the scale to the origin is $F_N^{-1}(u)$ units. Thus if $F_N[(x - \mu)/\sigma]$ is plotted against x, a straight line is obtained. If an observed distribution is plotted on normal probability paper in such a way that each value of *crf* is plotted on the vertical scale against the corresponding value of x on the horizontal scale, and if the points lie nearly in a straight line, the observed distribution is nearly normal. Use a sheet of normal probability paper and the distribution given in Table 14.1 in order to test the lima bean distribution for normality.

16. DISTRIBUTION OF A FUNCTION OF A RANDOM VARIABLE

Let X be a random variable whose distribution is known, and let $g(X)$ be an arbitrary function. What can be said about the distribution of the random variable $Y = g(X)$? The essential ideas are best clarified by considering a simple example involving a discrete random variable.

Example 16.1. Let X be a discrete random variable whose distribution is

x	2	3	4	5
$f(x)$	.1	.1	.6	.2

We wish to find the distribution of a new variable Y defined by $Y = 2X - 1$. In Figure 16.1 the distribution of Y is depicted on the horizontal axis by means of dots whose sizes are proportional to the probabilities. The function $Y = 2X - 1$ defines a correspondence, or a transformation, or a mapping, between the points of the X-axis and the points of the Y-axis. Let L be the line whose equation is $Y = 2X - 1$. Then, if A is any point on the X-axis, its *image* under the mapping may be found in the following way: a vertical line through A cuts the line L in the point B; a horizontal line through B cuts the Y-axis in C. Then C is the image of A under the mapping, and conversely, A is the image of C under the inverse mapping $X = \frac{1}{2}(Y + 1)$.

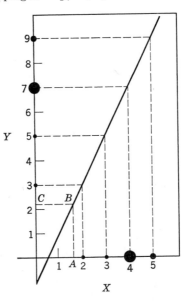

FIGURE 16.1

The images of $(2, 0)$, $(3, 0)$, $(4, 0)$, $(5, 0)$ on the X-axis are $(0, 3)$, $(0, 5)$, $(0, 7)$, $(0, 9)$ on the Y-axis. With these points we associate the probabilities of their *pre-images* (i.e., their images under the inverse mapping), so that the new distribution is as follows, where $f'(y)$ is the frequency function of the random variable Y:

y	3	5	7	9
$f'(y)$	.1	.1	.6	.2

It is helpful to regard the dots on the X-axis as representing weights. Under the mapping these weights are carried into 4 corresponding positions on the Y-axis, as indicated in Figure 16.1 by dotted lines.

The preceding discussion should be compared with Theorem (8.9), where we considered a linear transformation operating on the values in a sample. Here, a linear transformation is applied to the values in a population.

Let us generalize the ideas illustrated in Example 16.1. Let the random variable X possess the sample space $\{x_1, \cdots, x_k\}$ and the frequency function $f(x)$. Let a new random variable Y be defined by the function $Y = g(X)$. We shall assume that $g(X)$ possesses an inverse

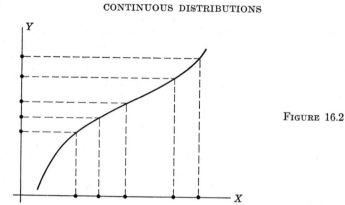

FIGURE 16.2

function $X = h(Y)$. This assumption requires that the function $Y = g(X)$ be *monotone* (more accurately, *strictly monotone*); that is, either always increasing or always decreasing. Graphically, the slope of the curve $Y = g(X)$ must be everywhere positive or everywhere negative except at isolated points. In Figure 16.2 a monotone increasing function is shown. Each weight of a distribution of weights (probabilities) on the X-axis has been carried vertically up to the curve, then horizontally to the Y-axis, thus giving rise to a distribution of weights on the Y-axis. If the sample space of the random variable Y is $\{y_1, \cdots, y_k\}$, where $y_i = g(x_i)$, $i = 1, \cdots, k$, then the new frequency function is $f'(y) = f(h(y))$.

Example 16.2. Suppose that X is the random variable of Example 16.1 and that a mapping is defined by $Y = 1/X$, which is monotone for $X > 0$. Then the sample space of the random variable Y is $\{1/2, 1/3, 1/4, 1/5\}$, and the frequency function is $f'(y) = f(1/y)$, where $f(x)$ is given by the first table of Example 16.1. The distribution of Y is thus

y	1/2	1/3	1/4	1/5
$f'(y)$	.1	.1	.6	.2

We now extend the preceding ideas to the case of a continuous random variable. Let X be a continuous random variable with density $f(x)$. Consider the interval $(x, x + dx)$ of length dx. The probability associated with this interval is $f(x)\, dx$ if we neglect differentials of higher order than the first. The expression $f(x)\, dx$ is called the *probability element*. Now suppose we have a monotone function $Y = g(X)$, whose inverse is $X = h(Y)$. Under the mapping $Y = g(X)$ the interval $(x, x + dx)$ is carried into the interval $(g(x), g(x + dx))$ whose length, neglecting differentials of higher order than the first, is $|g'(x)|\, dx$.

If we assume that the probability associated with the original interval $(x, x + dx)$ is carried into the new interval, then the density, or probability per unit of y, will be

$$\frac{f(x)\,dx}{|g'(x)|\,dx} = \frac{f(x)}{|g'(x)|}.$$

It is convenient to express this entirely in terms of the variable y. We have $f(x) = f(h(y))$, and

$$g'(x) = \frac{dy}{dx} = \frac{1}{dx/dy} = \frac{1}{h'(y)}.$$

Thus the density of Y is

$$\frac{f(x)}{|g'(x)|} = f(h(y))\,|h'(y)|.$$

Differentials were used in the preceding discussion because they bring out the close relationship of the continuous case to the discrete case discussed earlier. A more satisfactory proof of our basic result can be provided with the use of the distribution function, as is done in the following theorem:

(16.1) THEOREM. *Let X possess the density function $f(x)$ over the interval (a, b). Let $y = g(x)$ be a strictly monotone function over (a, b), and let $x = h(y)$ be its inverse. Then the density of the random variable $Y = g(X)$ is $f(h(y))\,|dh/dy|$.*

Proof. If $g(x)$ is monotone increasing, the condition $Y \le y$ implies $h(Y) \le h(y)$, that is, $X \le h(y)$. Hence, denoting the distribution function of Y by $G(y)$,

$$G(y) = P(Y \le y) = P(X \le h(y)) = F(h(y)).$$

The density of Y is obtained by differentiating $G(y)$ as a composite function:

$$\frac{d}{dy} G(y) = f(h(y)) \frac{dh}{dy}.$$

On the other hand, if $g(x)$ is monotone decreasing, then $Y \le y$ implies $X \ge h(y)$, and

$$G(y) = P(Y \le y) = P(X \ge h(y)) = 1 - F(g(y)).$$

Thus

$$\frac{d}{dy} G(y) = -f(h(y)) \frac{dh}{dy}.$$

But in this case dh/dy is negative so that in either case we have

$$\frac{d}{dy} G(y) = f(h(y)) \left| \frac{dh}{dy} \right|.$$

The relationship between the two densities of (16.1) may be pictured graphically as a sequence of two projections in the following way: Let the function $y = g(x)$ be represented as a curve in the x, y plane. The given density $f(x)$ is to be thought of as a non-uniform distribution of mass along the x-axis. We shall first project the mass vertically from the x-axis to the curve $y = g(x)$, then horizontally from the curve to the y-axis. In other words, let each element of mass be carried vertically until it reaches the curve $y = g(x)$; then let it be carried horizontally to the y-axis. We thus obtain on the y-axis a non-uniform distribution of mass, which represents the density of Y as given in (16.1).

Example 16.3. Let X be the random variable of Example 15.3. Suppose we wish to obtain the density of the quantity Y which is related to X by the equation $Y = 3X - 5$. We require the inverse function $X = h(Y) = \frac{1}{3}(Y + 5)$. By (16.1) the density of Y is

$$f(h(y)) \, |dh/dy| = 2(\tfrac{1}{3}(y + 5)\tfrac{1}{3} = \tfrac{2}{9}(y + 5).$$

Since x extends over the interval $(0, 1)$, y will extend over the interval $(-5, -2)$. A check on the work is afforded by integrating the density over this interval:

$$\int_{-5}^{-2} \tfrac{2}{9}(y + 5) \, dy = 1.$$

Example 16.4. Let Z be a random variable possessing the unit normal distribution, with density given by (16.1). Let X be a second random variable related to Z by the equation $X = \sigma Z + \mu$, where σ is positive. We note that the function $X = \sigma X + \mu$ and its inverse $Z = (X - \mu)/\sigma$ are monotone. Applying Theorem (16.1), we obtain the conclusions already stated in (15.10).

There are useful applications of (16.1) in which the given function $y = g(x)$ is not strictly monotone over the whole range of the density $f(x)$. Then we must break the range into portions over which $y = g(x)$ is monotone and add the resulting densities, as illustrated in the following example.

Example 16.5. Let X possess the rectangular distribution of Example 15.2, with $a = -1$, $b = 1$, $f(x) = 1/2$ for $-1 \leqq x \leqq 1$, zero elsewhere. Suppose we wish to obtain the distribution of $Y = g(X) = X^2$. It is strictly decreasing for $-1 \leqq x \leqq 0$ and increasing for $0 \leqq x \leqq 1$. We apply (16.1) separately to these 2 portions. For $-1 \leqq x \leqq 0$ we find $x = h(y) = -\sqrt{y}$, and the density of Y is

$$f(h(y)) \left| \frac{dh}{dy} \right| = \frac{1}{2} \frac{1}{2\sqrt{y}} = \frac{1}{4\sqrt{y}}.$$

Similarly, for $0 \leq x \leq 1$, $x = h(y) = \sqrt{y}$, and the density is again $1/4\sqrt{y}$. Adding these 2 expressions, we obtain $1/2\sqrt{y}$ for the density of Y over the interval $0 \leq y \leq 1$.

Example 16.6. If X has the distribution $N(0, 1)$, find the distribution of X^2.

Solution. We are here dealing with the transformation $Y = X^2$, as in Example 16.5. We must apply (16.1) separately for the intervals $x \leq 0$ and $x \geq 0$. In both cases $|dh/dy| = 1/2\sqrt{y}$, and so the density of Y is

$$2 \cdot \frac{1}{2\sqrt{y}} \frac{1}{\sqrt{2\pi}} e^{-y/2} = \frac{1}{\sqrt{2\pi}} y^{-1/2} e^{-y/2}.$$

In Section 18 we shall find that this is the density of a distribution known as the chi-square distribution with 1 d.f.

For all the continuous distributions considered in this book, the distribution function $u = F(x)$, and its inverse $x = F^{-1}(u)$, are monotone increasing functions, so that the following theorem is a direct consequence of (16.1):

(16.2) THEOREM. *Let $F(x)$ be a distribution function and $x = F^{-1}(u)$ its inverse. Then if U is a uniform random variable, $X = F^{-1}(U)$ is a continuous random variable with distribution function $F(x)$. Conversely, if X is a continuous random variable with distribution function $F(x)$, then $U = F(X)$ is a uniform random variable.*

Earlier in this section we remarked that random numbers, prefixed by a decimal point, yield random values possessing, approximately, a uniform distribution. This fact, together with (16.2), leads to

(16.3) *Method of obtaining a series of random values with a given distribution function. Let $F(x)$ be a distribution function and $F^{-1}(u)$ its inverse. Let .RN designate a sequence of random numbers, each with the same number of digits, prefixed by a decimal point. Then the sequence of values $F^{-1}(.RN)$ constitutes a random series with (approximately) the distribution function $F(x)$. Note that this procedure amounts to finding the 100(.RN) percentage point for each value of .RN.*

Example 16.7. Let us use (16.3) in order to obtain 5 random values with the distribution given in Example 15.3. From a table of random numbers we obtain the following sequence of four-figure numbers, each prefixed by a decimal point: .7837, .5220, .2049, .0939, .8424. The inverse of the given distribution function $u = F(x) = x^2$ is $x = \sqrt{u}$; we can ignore the negative root, since the given density restricts x to positive values. Hence, by (16.3), we obtain a series of random numbers with the given distribution by taking the square root of each of the 5 numbers previously given: .8853, .7225, .4527, .3064, .9178.

Example 16.8.   Given the 10 three-figure random numbers: .966, .316, .540, .871, .236, .402, .635, .477, .891, .777, find 10 random values from $N(0, 1)$, using the method of (16.3).

Solution.   According to (16.3), we require to evaluate $F_N{}^{-1}(.RN)$, where $F_N{}^{-1}(u)$ is the inverse of the normal distribution function, and $.RN$ represents any one of the given random values.   To find, for example, $F_N{}^{-1}(.966)$, we look up $.966 - .500 = .466$ in the body of Table 2, and find that it corresponds to a marginal value of 1.82, so that $F_N{}^{-1}(.966) = 1.82$.   To find $F_N{}^{-1}(.316)$ we look up $.500 - .316 = .184$ in the body of Table 2, obtaining the marginal value .48.   Thus $F_N{}^{-1}(.316) = -.48$.   Proceeding in this way, we obtain the following sequence of 10 random values from $N(0, 1)$:

$$1.82, \ -.48, \ .10, \ 1.13, \ -.72, \ -.25, \ .35, \ -.06, \ 1.23, \ .76.$$

Example 16.9   Obtain 10 random values from $N(-2, 9)$.

Solution.   Denoting by Z the random values from $N(0, 1)$ obtained in Example 16.1, we may, according to (15.10), convert them to values from $N(-2, 9)$ by means of the equation $X = 3Z - 2$.   We thus obtain the values 3.46, -3.44, -1.70, 1.39, -4.16, -2.75, $-.95$, -2.18, 1.69, .28.

A second type of realization of a random variable with arbitrary distribution function is based on (16.2) together with the fact that the spinner with a uniform scale provides a realization of a uniform random variable.   These facts imply that, if $F(x)$ is the distribution function of a random variable X and if $F^{-1}(u)$ is the inverse function, a random value U obtained by twirling the spinner may be converted into a random variable with the required distribution by evaluating $F^{-1}(U)$. But this can be more easily accomplished by constructing a new scale for the spinner in the following way: Let a uniform scale (u) be constructed on the *inside* of the circle.   On the outside of the circle let a scale of x be constructed such that each x-value is placed opposite the value $u = F(x)$ of the inner scale.   Then a twirl of the spinner will yield directly values of X with distribution function $F(x)$.   Figure 16.3 shows such a scale for the unit normal distribution.   A single twirl of the spinner with this *normal scale* yields a random value from $N(0, 1)$.

EXERCISE 16

16.1. Let X be a discrete random variable with distribution

x	1	2	3	4
p	.1	.3	.2	.4

Find the distribution of (*a*) X^2, (*b*) $1/X$.

16.2. If X is the random variable whose density is given in Exercise 15.1, find the density of $Y = 1/X$.

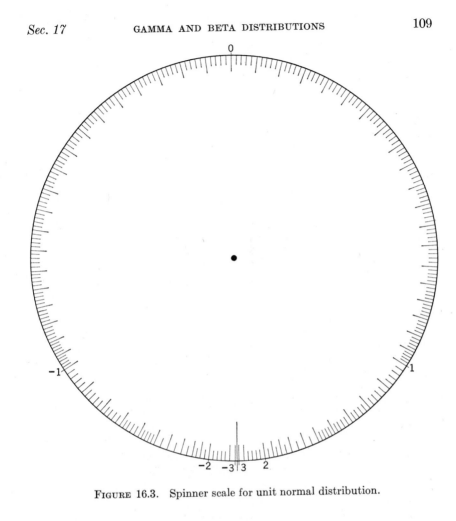

FIGURE 16.3.   Spinner scale for unit normal distribution.

16.3. If X is the random variable whose density is given in Exercise 15.2, find the density of $Y = X^2$.

16.4. If X is the random variable whose density is given in Exercise 15.3, find the density of $Y = 3X + 5$.

16.5. Let the random variable X possess the density $f(x) = \frac{1}{2}(x + 1)$ over the interval $-1 \leqq x \leqq 1$. Find the density of $Y = X^2$. (See Example 16.5.)

17. THE GAMMA AND BETA DISTRIBUTIONS— STIRLING'S APPROXIMATION

This section introduces the two distributions which, except for the normal distribution, have widest utility in mathematical statistics.

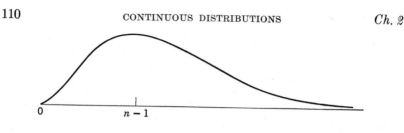

FIGURE 17.1

Under simple transformations they yield the chi-square and the F distribution which are of great importance in statistical inference. We shall incidentally be investigating certain integrals that are not ordinarily encountered in a first calculus course but that are essential for our purposes. These integrals have an interesting relation to the factorial function $n!$ and the binomial coefficient $\binom{n}{x}$, which were defined in Section 7 for integral values of n. They enable us to define new functions, continuous except at isolated points, which coincide with $n!$ and with $\binom{n}{x}$ when n and x are positive integers.

The *gamma distribution* is defined by the density

$$f(x) = kx^{n-1}e^{-x} \quad \text{for } x \geqq 0, n > 0$$

$$f(x) = 0 \qquad\qquad \text{for } x < 0$$

To investigate the shape of the graph of $f(x)$, we first note that $f(0) = 0$. Now $f(x)$ may be written as a fraction kx^{n-1}/e^x, whose numerator and denominator both approach ∞ as $x \to \infty$. In order to find the limit of $f(x)$ as $x \to \infty$, we therefore differentiate numerator and denominator as many times as may be necessary until one or the other remains finite as $x \to \infty$. After $n - 1$ differentiations the numerator is constant while the denominator is e^x. Hence, as $x \to \infty$, $f(x) \to 0$. We readily find that, if $n > 1$, $f(x)$ has a maximum when $x = n - 1$ and that its value is $f(n - 1) = (n - 1)^{n-1}e^{-(n-1)}$. These features are incorporated in Figure 17.1.

We must now determine the constant k so that $\int_0^\infty f(x)\,dx = 1$. The *gamma function*, denoted by $\Gamma(n)$, is defined by

$$(17.1) \qquad\qquad \Gamma(n) = \int_0^\infty x^{n-1}e^{-x}\,dx.$$

Integrating by parts gives

$$(17.2) \quad \Gamma(n) = (n-1)\int_0^\infty x^{n-2}e^{-x}\,dx = (n-1)\,\Gamma(n-1).$$

If we make, in succession, the substitutions

$$\Gamma(n-1) = (n-2)\,\Gamma(n-2),$$
$$\Gamma(n-2) = (n-3)\,\Gamma(n-3),$$

$$\cdot \quad \cdot \quad \cdot \quad \cdot \quad \cdot \quad \cdot \quad \cdot$$

$$\Gamma(n-r+1) = (n-r)\,\Gamma(n-r)$$

in the right side of (17.2), we obtain

$$(17.3) \qquad \Gamma(n) = (n-1)(n-2)\,\cdots\,(n-r)\,\Gamma(n-r).$$

We next note that $\Gamma(1) = \int_0^\infty e^{-x}\,dx = 1$. Hence, if n is an integer,

(17.3) yields

$$(17.4) \qquad \Gamma(n) = (n-1)(n-2)\,\cdots\,2.1 = (n-1)!$$

As in Section 7 we define $\Gamma(1) = 0! = 1$. In Section 24 it will be shown that $\Gamma(\tfrac{1}{2}) = \sqrt{\pi}$ (see also Exercise 17.10).

Example 17.1. Given that $\Gamma(13.5) = .8912$, find $\Gamma(4.35)$.
Solution. From 17.3, $\Gamma(4.35) = 3.35 \times 2.35 \times 1.35\,\Gamma(1.35) = 9.471$.

As a consequence of (17.1), the constant k in the density of the gamma distribution should be taken to be $k = 1/\Gamma(n)$. Thus the density is

$$(17.5) \qquad f(x) = \frac{1}{\Gamma(n)}\,x^{n-1}e^{-x}, \quad x \geq 0, \quad n > 0.$$

For many purposes a very satisfactory approximation to the factorial function and the gamma function is provided by Stirling's formula:

$$(17.6) \qquad \Gamma(n+1) = \sqrt{2\pi n}\; n^n e^{-n}.$$

The percentage error in Stirling's formula decreases rapidly as n increases, as shown in Figure 17.2. Derivations of Stirling's formula may be found in Cramér (3), Feller (5), Fry (7) and Munroe (13).

It may be shown (see Exercise 17.9) that the integral

$$(17.7) \qquad B(\alpha, \beta) = \int_0^1 x^{\alpha-1}(1-x)^{\beta-1}\,dx, \quad \alpha > 0, \quad \beta > 0$$

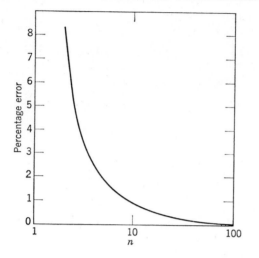

FIGURE 17.2

can be expressed in terms of the gamma function:

$$(17.8) \qquad\qquad B(\alpha, \beta) = \frac{\Gamma(\alpha)\,\Gamma(\beta)}{\Gamma(\alpha + \beta)}.$$

$B(\alpha, \beta)$ is called the *beta function* of α and β. The *beta distribution* has the density

$$(17.9) \quad f(x) = \frac{1}{B(\alpha, \beta)}\, x^{\alpha-1}(1-x)^{\beta-1}, \quad \alpha > 0, \quad \beta > 0, \quad 0 \leqq x \leqq 1.$$

It is readily seen that this function is $\geqq 0$ over the indicated range and that, from (17.7), $\displaystyle\int_0^1 f(x)\,dx = 1$. When $\alpha = \beta$ it is symmetrical

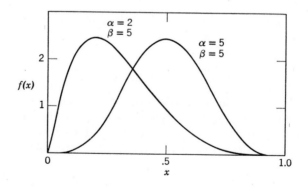

FIGURE 17.3

about the line $x = .5$. In Figure 17.3, $f(x)$ is graphed for $\alpha = 5, \beta = 5$ and for $\alpha = 2, \beta = 5$.

We have found that $\Gamma(n + 1)$ provides a continuous function coinciding with the factorial function for integral values of n. We shall now obtain a continuous function similarly related to the binomial coefficient

$$\binom{n}{x} = \frac{n!}{x!(n-x)!}.$$

We define

(17.10)
$$\begin{bmatrix} n \\ x \end{bmatrix} = \frac{\Gamma(n+1)}{\Gamma(x+1)\,\Gamma(n-x+1)}$$

$$= \frac{1}{(n+1)B(x+1, n-x+1)}$$

From (17.4) it is evident that $\binom{n}{x}$ and $\begin{bmatrix} n \\ x \end{bmatrix}$ will coincide whenever n and x are integers, and in addition $\begin{bmatrix} n \\ x \end{bmatrix}$ provides a continuous function for intervening values of n and x.

The graph of the binomial frequency function (7.11) consists of a series of discrete points. In order to obtain a continuous curve passing through these points, we replace $\binom{n}{x}$ by $\begin{bmatrix} n \\ x \end{bmatrix}$ in (7.11), obtaining

$\begin{bmatrix} n \\ x \end{bmatrix} p^x q^{n-x}$; then we graph the resulting continuous function. Thus, if 10 pennies are tossed, the resulting frequency function is $f(x) = 2^{-10} \binom{10}{x}$. The corresponding continuous function, say $\phi(x) =$

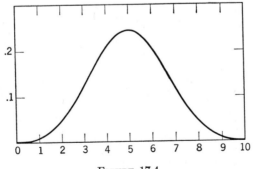

FIGURE 17.4

$2^{-10} \begin{bmatrix} 10 \\ x \end{bmatrix}$, is graphed in Figure 17.4. In Section 34 we shall show that the limiting form of the binomial distribution as $n \to \infty$ is normal. The continuous function $\phi(x) = \begin{bmatrix} n \\ x \end{bmatrix} p^x q^{n-x}$ will be helpful in the demonstration of this fact.

EXERCISE 17

17.1. Investigate whether the graph of the gamma density function, shown in Figure 17.1, is tangent to the x-axis at $x = 0$.

17.2. Given $\Gamma(.2) = 4.5908$, $\Gamma(.7) = 1.2981$, $\Gamma(.9) = 1.0686$, find $\Gamma(2.2)$, $\Gamma(3.7)$, $\Gamma(4.9)$.

17.3. From Table 6 it is found that $\log (100!) = 157.9700$. Compute an approximate value of $\log (100!)$ from Stirling's formula (17.6) and compare it with the value, correct to 4 decimals, given above.

17.4. By use of the substitution $z = ax$, show that

$$\int_0^\infty x^{n-1} e^{-ax} \, dx = a^{-n} \, \Gamma(n),$$

where $a > 0$.

17.5. Show that, if n is an even integer,

$$\int_{-\infty}^{\infty} x^n e^{-a^2 x^2} \, dx = 2 \int_0^\infty x^n e^{-a^2 x^2} \, dx,$$

while if n is an odd integer

$$\int_{-\infty}^{\infty} x^n e^{-a^2 x^2} \, dx = 0.$$

If n is an even integer, use the substitution $z = a^2 x^2$ to prove that

$$\int_{-\infty}^{\infty} x^n e^{-a^2 x^2} \, dx = a^{-(n+1)} \, \Gamma \left(\frac{n+1}{2} \right).$$

Show that, if $n > 0$, the last expression can be reduced to $2^{-n/2} a^{-(n+1)} \cdot 1 \cdot 3 \cdot 5 \cdots (n-1) \sqrt{\pi}$.

17.6. Use the substitution $\sqrt{z} = \sqrt{p}(x + q/2p)$ and the fact that $\Gamma(\frac{1}{2}) = \sqrt{\pi}$ in order to show that, if $p > 0$,

$$\int_{-\infty}^{\infty} e^{-(px^2 + qx + r)} \, dx = (\pi/p)^{1/2} e^{(q^2 - 4pr)/4p}.$$

17.7. Use the substitution $x = \sin^2 \theta$ and the definition $B(\alpha, \beta)$ in (17.7) to show that

$$\int_0^{\pi/2} \sin^{p-1} x \, \cos^{q-1} x \, dx = \tfrac{1}{2} B(p/2, q/2).$$

*17.8. Use integration by parts and the definition (17.7) of $B(\alpha, \beta)$ to prove

$$B(\alpha, \beta) = \frac{\beta - 1}{\alpha} B(\alpha + 1, \beta - 1).$$

If β is a positive integer, make repeated use of the above relation to prove

$$B(\alpha, \beta) = \frac{(\beta - 1)(\beta - 2) \cdots 2 \cdot 1}{\alpha(\alpha + 1) \cdots (\alpha + \beta - 2)} B(\alpha + \beta - 1, 1).$$

*17.9. Show that $B(\alpha, 1) = 1/\alpha$ by integration. Use this fact together with the results of Exercises 17.8, 17.3, and 17.4 to show that, if β is a positive integer,

$$B(\alpha, \beta) = \frac{\Gamma(\alpha) \, \Gamma(\beta)}{\Gamma(\alpha + \beta)}.$$

*17.10. Show that

$$B(\tfrac{1}{2}, \tfrac{1}{2}) = \int_0^1 \frac{du}{\sqrt{u(1 - u)}} = \pi = \Gamma(\tfrac{1}{2})^2.$$

Hence $\Gamma(\tfrac{1}{2}) = \sqrt{\pi}$.

*17.11. Use the results of Exercises 17.5 and 17.6 to prove that

$$\int_{-\infty}^{\infty} xe^{-(px^2+qx+r)} \, dx = \frac{-q\sqrt{\pi}}{2p\sqrt{p}} e^{(q^2-4pr)/4p},$$

where $p > 0$.

*17.12. Use the results of Exercises 17.5 and 17.6 to prove that

$$\int_{-\infty}^{\infty} x^2 e^{-(px^2+qx+r)} \, dx = \frac{1}{p} \sqrt{\frac{\pi}{p}} e^{(q^2-4pr)/4p}(\tfrac{1}{2} + q^2/4p),$$

where $p > 0$.

18. DISTRIBUTIONS DEFINED BY ELEMENTARY FUNCTIONS

While it is true that many distributions encountered in practice have the characteristics of a normal distribution, it is also true that many times we know that a certain distribution cannot be normal, perhaps because of a conspicuous lack of symmetry or perhaps because the sample space is clearly restricted to a portion of the real number line. In order to deal with the wide variety of distributions encountered in practice, we need to have at our disposal many different types of density functions. The choice of a suitable mathematical model for a random experiment has been called, by R. A. Fisher, the problem of *specification*. The density function which is selected will ordinarily contain one or more constants, or *parameters*, whose value must be estimated from the data in the sample. This is the problem of *estimation*, which usually involves the selection of a particular *statistic* or *estimator* which will provide an optimum estimate of the population parameter.

When we have selected a suitable statistic for the estimation of a parameter (for example, $\overline{X}$ as an estimate of μ), for certain purposes we need to know the *sampling distribution* of the statistic, that is, the distribution that arises when the statistic is calculated for all possible samples from the population. Sampling distributions form the principal topic of Chapters 3 and 5 of this book. Some of the distributions we shall introduce in this section are those that will arise as sampling distributions in later chapters. The process of deriving sampling distributions has been called by Fisher the problem of *distribution*. These three problems—specification, estimation, and distribution—together constitute the main territory of statistical theory, insofar as it prepares the way for statistical inference.

　Example 18.1. *The rectangular distribution.* The density of the rectangular distribution has already been given in Example 15.2. Its distribution function is

$$F(x) = \frac{(x - a)}{(b - a)}, \quad a \leqq x \leqq b.$$

It may be extended beyond this range in the usual way.

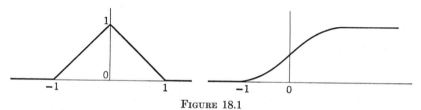

FIGURE 18.1

　Example 18.2. Consider the triangular distribution shown in Figure 18.1. Its density is

$$f(x) = 1 + x \quad \text{for } -1 \leqq x \leqq 0$$
$$f(x) = 1 - x \quad \text{for } \;\; 0 \leqq x \leqq 1$$
$$f(x) = 0 \qquad\qquad \text{elsewhere.}$$

Thus two algebraic functions are required to specify the density. Similarly, two functions are required to describe the distribution function:

$$F(x) = \int_{-1}^{x} (1 + t)\, dt = \tfrac{1}{2}(x + 1)^2 \qquad\qquad \text{for } -1 \leqq x \leqq 0$$

$$F(x) = \int_{-1}^{0} (1 + t)\, dt + \int_{0}^{x} (1 - t)\, dt = \tfrac{1}{2}(1 + 2x - x^2) \quad \text{for } 0 \leqq x \leqq 1.$$

The graph of $F(x)$ is also shown in Figure 18.1.

　Example 18.3. Consider the density function specified by a portion of a parabola:

$$f(x) = k(x - x^2), \quad \text{for } 0 \leqq x \leqq 1,$$
$$f(x) = 0, \qquad\qquad \text{elsewhere.}$$

To evaluate k, we have $\int_0^1 f(x)\,dx = k/6 = 1$. Hence k must be taken equal to 6, and

$$f(x) = 6(x - x^2), \quad 0 \le x \le 1, \qquad F(x) = 0, \qquad\qquad x \le 0,$$
$$f(x) = 0 \qquad\qquad \text{elsewhere}, \qquad F(x) = 3x^2 - 2x^3, \quad 0 \le x \le 1,$$
$$F(x) = 1, \qquad\qquad x \ge 1.$$

Thus the distribution curve is a portion of a cubic curve. The density and distribution functions are shown in Figure 18.2.

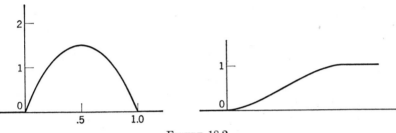

FIGURE 18.2

Example 18.4. The chi-square distribution. The chi-square distribution, which was discovered and named by Karl Pearson about 1900, ranks close to the normal distribution in general usefulness. Its density is

$$f(x) = kx^{m/2-1}e^{-x/2}, \quad x > 0.$$

The parameter m is called the "degrees of freedom." To evaluate k, we put $z = x/2$. We then have

$$\int_0^\infty x^{m/2-1}e^{-x/2}\,dx = 2^{m/2}\int_0^\infty z^{m/2-1}e^{-z}\,dz = 2^{m/2}\,\Gamma(m/2).$$

Hence k must be $1/(2^{m/2}\,\Gamma(m/2))$, and the density becomes

$$(18.1) \qquad f(x) = \frac{1}{2^{m/2}/\Gamma(m/2)}\,x^{m/2-1}e^{-x/2}, \quad x > 0.$$

Graphs of the chi-square distribution for $m = 1, 2, 3, 5,$ and 10 are shown in Figure 18.3. Note that as m increases the curve approaches the normal form. For $m = 30$, or larger, the chi-square distribution is, for many purposes, satisfactorily approximated by the normal distribution.

Example 18.5. The Cauchy distribution. Consider the function $f(x) = k/(1 + x^2)$. Note that the curve has a maximum at $x = 0$, that it is symmetrical with respect to a vertical axis at $x = 0$, and that it approaches the x-axis asymptotically in both directions. Thus it has a form similar to that of the normal curve. Its graph is shown in Figure 18.4.

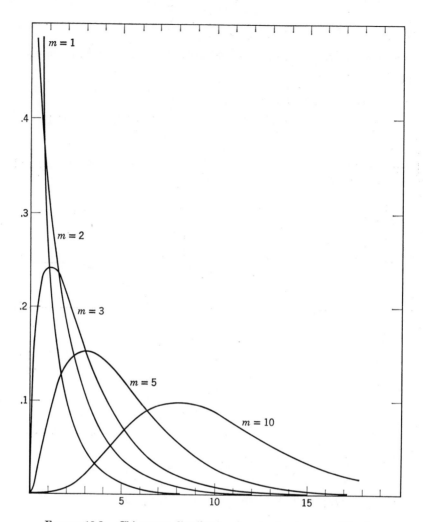

FIGURE 18.3.   Chi-square distribution for varying degrees of freedom.

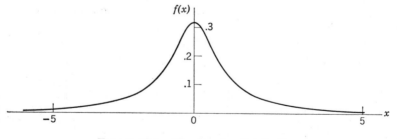

FIGURE 18.4.   The Cauchy distribution.

118

In order to find the value of k, we integrate

$$\int_{-\infty}^{\infty} f(x)\, dx = 2k \int_0^{\infty} \frac{dx}{1 + x^2} = k\pi.$$

Hence the density is

(18.2) $$f(x) = \frac{1}{\pi(1 + x^2)}, \quad -\infty < x < \infty.$$

The distribution function is given by

$$F(x) = \int_{-\infty}^{x} f(t)\, dt = \frac{1}{\pi} \text{arc tan } x + \tfrac{1}{2}, \quad -\infty < x < \infty.$$

A spinner equipped with the scale described in Example 2.9 yields a random variable X with the Cauchy distribution. To see this, let the point of contact of the circle and the line in Figure 2.7 be 0, let $OC = 1$, let $OP = x$, and let $\angle OCP = \theta$. Let us consider only those values of θ lying between $-\pi/2$ and $\pi/2$. Then θ will have the rectangular distribution whose density is

$$f(\theta) = \frac{1}{\pi}, \quad -\pi/2 < \theta < \pi/2.$$

We wish to find the distribution of $X = \tan \theta$. Since this is a strictly increasing function of θ, we use (16.1) and conclude that the density of X is

$$\frac{1}{\pi} \frac{d}{dx} (\text{arc tan } x) = \frac{1}{\pi(1+x^2)},$$

which is the Cauchy density.

The Cauchy distribution, named for the nineteenth-century French mathematician, A. L. Cauchy, is peculiar in possessing neither mean nor variance. Further, the central limit theorem, referred to in Section 15, fails to apply to the Cauchy distribution. It is famous as a counter-example which helped to define the necessary conditions which a distribution must fulfill in order that the central limit theorem may be valid for it.

Example 18.6. Obtain 5 random values from the Cauchy distribution.
Solution. We use the method of (16.3). Five four-figure random numbers, each prefixed by a decimal point, are: .2747, .4702, .4892, .6554, .0943. The inverse of the Cauchy distribution function is $x = \tan \pi(u - .5)$. Substituting the random numbers, we obtain: $-.854, -.094, -.031, .532, -3.271$. They are the desired values.

Example 18.7. Obtain 5 random values from the chi-square distribution with 10 degrees of freedom.
Solution. Table 3 gives selected percentage points for the chi-square distribution, for the degrees of freedom indicated in the left margin. We may equivalently say that Table 3 gives the inverse of the distribution function for the chi-square distribution. That is, if $F_{10}(x)$ is the chi-square distribution for 10 d.f. and if $F_{10}^{-1}(u)$ is its inverse, then the 10th line of the table gives the

values of $F_{10}^{-1}(u)$ for the values of u in the top margin. Using the same series of 5 random values as in Example 18.6, but taking only the first 3 decimals, by interpolation we find the following values: 7.0, 9.0, 9.2, 11.3, 4.8. This process of interpolating is dependable only to one decimal.

The t distribution, to be discussed in the next example, was discovered about 1907 by W. S. Gosset, who wrote under the pseudonym "Student." Its discovery marked the opening of the modern era in the theory of statistics. Its most frequent use is in statistical inference based on one or two small samples.

Example 18.8. The t distribution. An obvious generalization of the Cauchy distribution (18.2) is the density

$$f(x) = \frac{k}{(1 + x^2)^{\alpha/2}}, \quad \alpha \text{ a positive integer}, \quad -\infty < x < \infty.$$

In order to evaluate k, we put $x = \tan \theta$ and integrate from $-\infty$ to ∞, obtaining

$$\int_{-\infty}^{\infty} \frac{k \, dx}{(1 + x^2)^{\alpha/2}} = 2k \int_0^{\pi} \cos^{\alpha-2}\theta \, d\theta.$$

The final integral may be shown to be equal to $\frac{1}{2} B(\frac{1}{2}, (\alpha - 1)/2)$. (See Exercise 17.7.) Hence we may use as a density function

$$f(x) = \frac{1}{B\left(\dfrac{1}{2}, \dfrac{(\alpha - 1)}{2}\right)} (1 + x^2)^{-\alpha/2}, \quad -\infty < x < \infty.$$

If in this density we make the change of variables $x = t/\sqrt{n}$, $\alpha = n + 1$, put $\Gamma(\frac{1}{2}) = \sqrt{\pi}$, and make use of (16.1) and (17.8), we obtain the *Student distribution*, or the *t distribution*,

$$(18.3) \qquad f(t) = \frac{1}{\sqrt{n} \, B\left(\dfrac{1}{2}, \dfrac{n}{2}\right)} \left(1 + \frac{t^2}{n}\right)^{-(n+1)/2}$$

$$= \frac{\Gamma\left(\dfrac{n+1}{2}\right)}{\sqrt{n\pi} \, \Gamma\left(\dfrac{n}{2}\right)} \left(1 + \frac{t^2}{n}\right)^{-(n+1)/2}, \quad -\infty < t < \infty.$$

It may be shown (see Exercise 18.13) that this density tends toward that of $N(0, 1)$ as $n \to \infty$. Note that the t distribution for $n = 1$ reduces to the Cauchy distribution.

Example 18.9. The F-type distribution. A distribution closely related to the beta distribution (Section 17) is that defined by the density

$$(18.4) \qquad f(x) = kx^{\alpha-1}(1 + x)^{-(\alpha+\beta)}, \quad x > 0, \alpha > 0, \beta > 0.$$

A distribution with this density we call an F-type distribution. The integral $\int_0^{\infty} x^{\alpha-1}(1 + x)^{-(\alpha+\beta)} \, dx$ can be evaluated by means of the change of variables $x = y/(1 - y)$, which transforms the integral into

$$\int_0^1 y^{\alpha-1}(1-y)^{\beta-1}\,dy = B(\alpha,\beta).$$

Hence for $f(x)$ to qualify as a density we must put $k = 1/B(\alpha,\beta)$.

If, in the density (18.4), we make the substitutions $\alpha = m/2$, $\beta = n/2$, $x = mF/n$, the new density will be found to be, using (16.1),

$$(18.5) \quad f(F) = \frac{1}{B\left(\dfrac{m}{2},\dfrac{n}{2}\right)}\left(\frac{m}{n}\right)^{m/2}F^{m/2-1}\left(1+\frac{mF}{n}\right)^{-(m+n)/2}, \quad F > 0.$$

This is the F distribution [hence the name given to the density (18.4)], which is the basic distribution employed in the powerful method of analysis of variance.

EXERCISE 18

In each of Exercises 1 through 11, find the value of k (if possible) which makes the given expression a density function. Find $F(x)$, and sketch the graphs of $f(x)$ and $F(x)$.

18.1. $f(x) = kx(k-1)^2$ $0 \le x \le 1$.

18.2. $f(x) = kx^2(x-1)$ $0 \le x \le 1$.

18.3. $f(x) = k(1-x^2)^2$ $0 \le x \le 1$.

18.4. $f(x) = kx(1+x^2)^{-2}$ $0 \le x \le 1$.

18.5. $f(x) = \dfrac{kx}{(1+x^2)}$ $0 \le x < \infty$.

18.6. $f(x) = k\sin x$ $0 \le x \le \pi$.

18.7. $f(x) = kx\sin x$ $0 \le x \le \pi$.

18.8. $f(x) = ke^{-x}\sin x$ $0 \le x \le \pi$.

18.9. $f(x) = k(2-x)\log_e x$ $1 \le x \le 2$.

18.10. $f(x) = kx(1+x^2)^{-3}$ $0 \le x < \infty$.

18.11. $f(x) = \dfrac{k}{(x-\alpha)^2+\beta^2}$ $-\infty < x < \infty$

*18.12. Karl Pearson noted that many common density functions $f(x)$ satisfy the differential equation

$$\frac{df(x)}{dx} = \frac{x+a}{bx^2+cx+d}f(x), \quad \text{or} \quad \frac{d}{dx}\log_e f(x) = \frac{x+a}{bx^2+cx+d}$$

for suitable values of a, b, c, and d. He systematically investigated the various types of densities arising from this differential equation for various combinations of the parameters a, b, c, and d. Find $\dfrac{d}{dx}\log_e f(x)$ for the normal distribution (15.9), for the gamma distribution (17.5), for the beta distribution (17.9), for the t distribution (18.3), and for the F-type distribution (18.4), and show that in each case we obtain an expression of the form

$$\frac{x+a}{bx^2+cx+d}.$$

*18.13. Use Stirling's formula $\Gamma(n+1) \doteq \sqrt{2\pi n}\, n^n\, e^{-n}$ and the fact that $\lim\limits_{n\to\infty} \left(1 + \dfrac{x}{n}\right)^n = e^x$ to show that the density (18.3) approaches the unit normal density (15.8) as $n \to \infty$.

*19. PARAMETERS OF CONTINUOUS DISTRIBUTIONS

The concept of mathematical expectation, or expected value, was introduced in Section 11 for discrete distributions, where we had the definitions

$$(19.1) \quad E(X) = \Sigma p_i x_i, \quad E(X^n) = \Sigma p_i x_i^n, \quad E(\phi(X)) = \Sigma p_i\, \phi(x_i).$$

We shall now show that, for a continuous random variable X with density $f(x)$ over the interval $a \leq x \leq b$, the analogous definitions will be

$$E(X) = \int_a^b x\, f(x)\, dx, \quad E(X^n) = \int_a^b x^n\, f(x)\, dx,$$

(19.2)

$$E(\phi(x)) = \int_a^b \phi(x)\, f(x)\, dx.$$

Note that each operation of summation in (19.1) is replaced by an operation of integration in (19.2). We shall find this type of parallelism throughout our study of discrete and continuous random variables. We shall show that the definitions in (19.2) follow logically from those in (19.1) for the case of a continuous random variable with *finite range*; considerations of continuity will make it necessary for the same definitions to apply to variables with infinite range. Let X be a continuous random variable possessing the density $f(x)$ and the distribution function $F(x)$ over the range $a \leq x \leq b$. Let the range of x be divided into n equal intervals, each of length Δx, by the points of division $a = x_0, x_1, \cdots, x_n = b$. The probability that the random variable X will fall in the ith interval is $F(x_i) - F(x_{i-1})$. By the mean value theorem there is a value x_i' in the ith interval such that

$$F(x_i) - F(x_{i-1}) = f(x_i')\, \Delta x.$$

Hence we can set up a discrete random variable X' whose frequency function is

$$f'(x_i') = P(X' = x_i') = f(x_i')\, \Delta x.$$

The expected value of X' is, from (19.1),

$$E(X') = \Sigma x_i'\, f(x_i')\, \Delta x.$$

If we now let n approach infinity, the sum on the right will approach an integral, while the random variable X' will become identical with X, so that we are justified in defining $E(X)$ by the first of the integrals in (19.2). The other two can obviously be derived from the corresponding expressions in (19.1) by the same kind of limiting process that we have just used.

By analogy with the case of discrete variables, we shall define the mean and variance of a continuous distribution by means of

$$(19.3) \qquad \mu = E(X), \quad \sigma^2 = E(X^2) - \mu^2.$$

The central moments μ_n and the moments about the origin μ_n' are defined by formulas (11.3) and (11.6), as in the discrete case.

The generating function and the moment generating function of a continuous random variable may now be defined in a manner which parallels the corresponding definitions in Section 12, for discrete random variables. We define the generating function (g.f.), $G_x(t)$, corresponding to the density $f(x)$ by the equation

$$(19.4) \quad G_x = G_x(t) = E(t^x) = \int_{-\infty}^{\infty} t^x f(x) \, dx, \quad \text{if the integral exists.}$$

Similarly we define the moment generating function (m.g.f.) by

$$(19.5) \quad M_x = M_x(t) = E(e^{tx}) = \int_{-\infty}^{\infty} e^{tx} f(x) \, dx, \quad \text{if the integral exists.}$$

Neither of these integrals exist, for example, in the case of the Cauchy distribution. They exist, fortunately, for the two distributions most useful in statistical theory: the normal distribution and the chi-square distribution. Generally the integral in (19.5) is more convenient to evaluate than that in (19.4), and for this reason the moment generating function is more frequently useful than the generating function. Note that the two functions are related by

$$(19.6) \qquad M_x(t) = G_x(e^t), \quad G_x(t) = M_x(\log_e t).$$

We found, in Section 12, that when the moment generating function is expanded in a power series, the coefficients are the non-central moments μ_r', each divided by a factorial. This result may be verified in the continuous case by expanding the factor e^{tx} in a power series and integrating term by term. As a result the moments of the distribution whose density is $f(x)$ may be obtained by differentiating the moment generating function repeatedly and evaluating the result at $t = 0$. We are thus led to the following formula, analogous to (12.4):

(19.7) $$\frac{d^r}{dt^r} M(t) \Big|_0 = \int_{-\infty}^{\infty} x^r f(x)\, dx = \mu_r'.$$

Example 19.1. The density of the uniform random variable of Example 15.1 is $f(x) = 1$, $0 \leq x \leq 1$, $f(x) = 0$ elsewhere. Its moment generating function is thus

$$M_x(t) = \int_0^1 e^{tx}\, dx = \frac{1}{t}(e^t - 1).$$

Example 19.2. The density corresponding to the distribution $N(\mu, \sigma^2)$ is given in (15.9). To find the moment generating function we must evaluate

$$M_x(t) = \frac{1}{\sigma\sqrt{2\pi}} \int_{-\infty}^{\infty} e^{tx} e^{-(x-\mu)^2/2\sigma^2}\, dx$$

The exponent of e in the integrand is the quadratic function $-\frac{1}{2\sigma^2}(x^2 - 2x(\mu + \sigma^2 t) + \mu^2)$. Making use of the result stated in Exercise 17.6, the m.g.f. is found to be $M_x(t) = e^{(\sigma^2 t^2 + 2\mu t)/2}$.

The following example illustrates the importance of the proviso "if the integral exists" in (19.4) and (19.5).

Example 19.3. Let us attempt to find the moment generating function of a random variable X whose density is $f(x) = e^{-x}$, $x > 0$, $f(x) = 0$, $x \leq 0$, using (19.5). We find,

$$M_x(t) = \int_0^{\infty} e^{tx} e^{-x}\, dx = \int_0^{\infty} e^{x(t-1)}\, dx.$$

This is an improper integral, which does not exist if $t \geq 1$. The moment generating function exists only if $t < 1$, and for this range of values of t, $M_x(t) = 1/(1 - t)$.

Example 19.4. The density of the chi-square distribution with m degrees of freedom is given by (18.1). Hence the m.g.f. is

$$M_x(t) = \frac{1}{2^{m/2}\, \Gamma\left(\dfrac{m}{2}\right)} \int_0^{\infty} e^{tx} x^{m/2} e^{-x/2}\, dx.$$

The existence of the integral on the right depends on the value of t. If $t < \frac{1}{2}$ we can evaluate the integral by the use of the substitution $z = x(\frac{1}{2} - t)$, which enables us to express the integral in terms of the gamma function. Using (17.1) we then find $M_x(t) = (1 - 2t)^{-m/2}$, $t < \frac{1}{2}$.

Example 19.5. We may now verify that the mean and variance of the general normal density (15.9) are indeed μ and σ^2. The first and second derivatives of the m.g.f. obtained in Example 19.2 are

$$M_x'(t) = (\sigma^2 t + \mu)e^{(\sigma^2 t^2 + 2\mu t)/2},$$

$$M_x''(t) = (\sigma^2 + (\sigma^2 t + \mu)^2)e^{(\sigma^2 t^2 + 2\mu t)/2}.$$

When these are evaluated at $t = 0$, from (19.7) we find $\mu_1' = \mu$, $\mu_2' = \sigma^2 + \mu^2$.

EXERCISE 19

19.1. The random variable X has the density $f(x) = e^{-x}$ for $x \geq 0$, $f(x) = 0$ for $x < 0$. Find the general expression for the nth moment $\mu_n' = E(X^n)$, and from this the mean and variance.

19.2. Find the moment generating function of a random variable with density $f(x) = ae^{-ax}$, $a > 0$, $x > 0$. Note that the m.g.f. is defined only for the range $t < a$. (Compare Example 19.3.) Use (19.7) to find μ_1' and μ_2'.

19.3. The random variable X has a rectangular distribution with density $f(x) = \frac{1}{2}$, $-1 \leq x \leq 1$, $f(x) = 0$ elsewhere. Find the nth moment μ_n'. Show that the moment generating function is $M_x(t) = (1/t) \sinh t$.

19.4. Find the general expression for the nth moment of a random variable X with the rectangular distribution of Example 15.2. Find the moment generating function.

19.5. A random variable X has the density $f(x) = 4x^3$, $0 \leq x \leq 1$, zero elsewhere. Find μ_1', μ_2', μ_3'. Find also the moment generating function.

19.6. Find μ_1', μ_2', μ_3' for a random variable X with the density of Example 18.3.

19.7. Find μ_1' and μ_2' for a random variable with the triangular distribution of Example 18.2.

19.8. Find the moment generating function of a random variable with the density $f(x) = (a/2) \sin ax$, $0 \leq x \leq \pi/a$.

19.9. Making use of the result stated in Exercise 17.5, find $\mu_n' = E(X^n)$ for a random variable with the distribution $N(0, 1)$.

19.10. By direct integration show that for the chi-square distribution with density (18.1)

$$\mu_n' = 2^n \frac{\Gamma(n + m/2)}{\Gamma(m/2)}.$$

19.11. Prove (19.7).

19.12. Verify, for the continuous case, the expansion

$$M_x(t) = 1 + \mu_1't + (\mu_2'/2!)t^2 + (\mu_3'/3!)t^3 + \cdots$$

derived in Section 12 for the case of a discrete random variable with finite sample space.

19.13. Prove Tchebycheff's inequality (9.1) for a continuous random variable X with density $f(x)$. Break the range from $-\infty$ to ∞ into three portions A, B, and C, as in the proof of (9.1).

19.14. Show that, if k is a real number, $M_{kx}(t) = E(e^{ktX}) = M_x(kt)$, $M_{x+k}(t) = E(e^{t(X+k)}) = e^{kt}M_x(t)$.

19.15. If $g(x)$ is an arbitrary function of x, then the moment generating function of $g(x)$ is defined to be

$$M_{g(x)}(t) = E(e^{tg(X)}) = \int_{-\infty}^{\infty} e^{tg(x)} f(x) \, dx,$$

if the integral exists. Show that $M_{\log x}(t) = E(X^t) = \mu_t'$.

19.16. Show that, if k is a real number, $M_{kg(x)}(t) = M_{g(x)}(kt)$, $M_{g(x)+k}(t) = e^{kt}M_{g(x)}(t)$.

19.17. In Exercise 19.1 it was found that for the density $f(x) = e^{-x}$, $x > 0$, $\mu_n' = n!$ Hence express the m.g.f. for this density as a power series in t, using the result of Exercise 19.12. Note that the power series converges only for $|t| < 1$, so that by this method the m.g.f. exists only for $|t| < 1$. Compare with Example 19.3.

19.18. Show that the moment generating function of the binomial distribution, with frequency function given by (7.11), is $M_x(t) = (q + pe^t)^n$.

19.19. Use (19.3) and the basic integrals of Exercise 17 in order to show that the mean and variance of the general normal distribution (15.9) are actually μ and σ_2.

CHAPTER 3

Sampling Distributions I

In Chapter 1 numerous examples of bivariate and multivariate distributions were presented in the illustrative examples, especially in Sections 6 and 7. Attention was called, in passing, to several sampling distributions (Examples 5.5 and 5.6). We must now consider systematically the properties of bivariate and multivariate distributions, both discrete and continuous. In so doing, we shall be laying the foundations for the discussion of sampling distributions in this chapter and in Chapter 5. It fortunately happens that many of the results we need can be obtained by considering only bivariate distributions. For this reason, our principal emphasis will be on the bivariate case. Only occasionally will the appropriate generalizations to multivariate distributions be mentioned.

20. BIVARIATE AND MULTIVARIATE DISTRIBUTIONS

A bivariate random experiment is one in which each repetition of the experiment yields an ordered pair of values (X_1, X_2). Similarly, a multivariate random experiment will yield ordered sets of, say, n values: $(X_1, \cdots, X_n)$. If an individual is selected at random from some population and his height X_1 and weight X_2 are recorded, we have a bivariate random experiment; if 2 or more such measurements are made, the experiment is multivariate.

An important class of multivariate experiments includes those in which the experiment consists of drawing a sample from some population, with or without replacement, and recording the same measurement on each member of the sample. Example 1.5, involving the measurement of the heights of corn plants, was of this type; it should be reviewed by the student at this point. (See also the discussion following Example 2.9.) As a second illustration, suppose that 10 students in a certain university are randomly selected and given a particular test. Then the set of scores $(X_1, \cdots, X_{10})$ may be regarded as the outcome of the experiment. The sample space will consist of all such ordered sets. If the test score is regarded as a continuous variable which may range, say, from 0 to 80, then the sample space is the *region*

$$(20.1) \qquad (0 \leqq x_1 \leqq 80, \quad 0 \leqq x_2 \leqq 80, \cdots, 0 \leqq x_{10} \leqq 80).$$

As was pointed out in connection with Example 1.5, the term "region" as used here can be given intuitive geometrical meaning if the sample contains 1, 2, or 3 values. It is not possible to visualize the region (20.1), and all properties of such a region which we may require to use must be derived algebraically.

The preceding example, as well as Example 1.5, illustrates the case in which the outcome of a multivariate random experiment is specified by means of continuous quantities. To illustrate the discrete type of multivariate experiment, consider a factory which each day selects, randomly, 10 out of several hundred lots of incoming material. A sample of, say, 300 pieces is drawn from each of the 10 lots and inspected, and the number of defectives, X, is determined for each sample. The basic sample point may be taken to be the set of values obtained on a given day, say $(X_1, \cdots, X_{10})$. If we regard the number of defectives in the ith sample as being capable of ranging from 0 to 300, there are 301^{10} different sample points in the sample space, namely, those obtained by letting each of the sample values $X_1, \cdots, X_{10}$ assume the 301 possible values.

Example 20.1. In Exercise 8.8 it is pointed out that, if samples of size 3 are drawn, with replacement, from a population consisting of the set of values $\{1, 2, 3\}$, there are $3^3 = 27$ possible samples, listed in Exercise 8.8. These 27 possible samples may be regarded as the 27 points of the sample space of the random experiment. Each of the quantities listed in the heading of the table in Exercise 8.8 is a random variable defined over the sample space. Other random variables that could be studied are the range, the median, and the rms of each sample.

Let us now consider a bivariate random experiment with outcomes (X, Y), where both X and Y are discrete random variables, X with the range $\{x_1, \cdots, x_n\}$ and Y with the range $\{y_1, \cdots, y_k\}$. The sample space of such an experiment may be represented either as a two-way table (Tables 20.1 and 20.2) or as a rectangular array of points (Figure 20.1).

If the random experiment is urnlike, then Table 20.1 may be viewed as specifying the frequency distribution of an urn containing N balls, of which ϕ_{ij} are labeled (x_i, y_j), $i = 1, \cdots, h$, $j = 1, \cdots, k$. The mar-

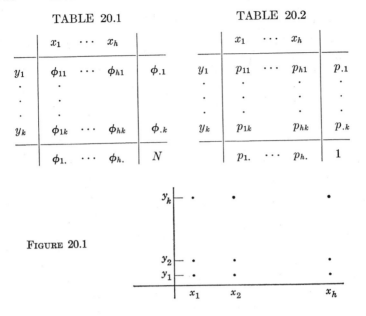

TABLE 20.1

	x_1	$\cdots$	x_h	
y_1	ϕ_{11}	$\cdots$	ϕ_{h1}	$\phi._1$
.	.			.
.	.			.
.	.			.
y_k	ϕ_{1k}	$\cdots$	ϕ_{hk}	$\phi._k$
	$\phi_{1.}$	$\cdots$	$\phi_{h.}$	N

TABLE 20.2

	x_1	$\cdots$	x_h	
y_1	p_{11}	$\cdots$	p_{h1}	$p._1$
.	.		.	.
.	.		.	.
.	.		.	.
y_k	p_{1k}		p_{hk}	$p._k$
	$p_{1.}$	$\cdots$	$p_{h.}$	1

FIGURE 20.1

ginal totals are denoted by replacing one of the subscripts by a dot, namely, the index over which summation has taken place. Thus

$$\phi_{i.} = \sum_{j=1}^{k} \phi_{ij}, \quad \phi_{.j} = \sum_{i=1}^{h} \phi_{ij}.$$

In general, whether or not the experiment is urnlike, we may attach probabilities to the sample points, as indicated in Table 20.2. The probabilities are real numbers, arbitrary except that each $p_{ij} \geqq 0$, and $\sum_{ij} p_{ij} = 1$. The marginal totals of Table 20.2 are known as *marginal probabilities* and are defined by

$$p_{i.} = \sum_{j=1}^{k} p_{ij}, \quad p_{.j} = \sum_{i=1}^{h} p_{ij}.$$

These quantities are sometimes called *unconditional probabilities*, in contrast to the conditional probabilities soon to be defined. The quantity $p_{i.}$, for example, denotes the probability of obtaining the number x_i, irrespective of the value of y which is obtained. Thus

$$P(X = x_i) = p_{i.}, \quad P(Y = y_j) = p_{.j}.$$

If the random experiment is urnlike, with frequencies given by Table 20.1, then

(20.2) $\qquad p_{ij} = \phi_{ij}/N, \quad p_{i.} = \phi_{i.}/N, \quad p_{.j} = \phi_{.j}/N.$

Probabilities are altered if we impose a restriction on the values that may be obtained. If, for example, we know that $Y = y_j$, what is the probability that $X = x_i$? This is called a *conditional probability*, denoted by $P(X = x_i | Y = y_j)$ (read this symbol as "the probability that $X = x_i$, given that $Y = y_j$"). If the experiment is urnlike, the frequency distribution of balls with the label $Y = y_j$ is given in the jth row of Table 20.1, with total frequency $\phi_{.j}$. Hence the conditional probability is

$$(20.3) \qquad P(X = x_i | Y = y_j) = \phi_{ij}/\phi_{.j}.$$

Similarly

$$(20.4) \qquad P(Y = y_j | x = x_i) = \phi_{ij}/\phi_{i.}.$$

We may use (20.2) to eliminate ϕ_{ij}, $\phi_{.j}$, and $\phi_{i.}$ from (20.3) and (20.4), obtaining

$$(20.5) \quad P(X = x_i | Y = y_j) = p_{ij}/p_{.j}, \quad P(Y = y_j | X = x_i) = p_{ij}/p_{i.}.$$

The expressions (20.5) will be taken as the *definitions* of the conditional probabilities when the random experiment is *not* urnlike.

Example 20.2. An urn possesses the distribution

x	1	2	3
ϕ	2	5	3

Find the marginal and conditional distributions for the random experiment consisting of two drawings *without replacement* from this urn.

Solution. Let the sample space be denoted by the set of pairs (x, y), where x and y are the results of the first and second drawings, respectively. Using the approach of Section 7, we recognize that there are $_{10}P_2 = 90$ equally likely outcomes, of which $_2P_2 = 2$ are associated with the sample point $(1, 1)$, $2 \times 5 = 10$ with the sample point $(1, 2)$, etc. We thus obtain the frequency, probability, and conditional probability tables shown below:

FREQUENCY

x / y	1	2	3	
1	2	10	6	18
2	10	20	15	45
3	6	15	6	27
	18	45	27	90

PROBABILITY

x / y	1	2	3	
1	1/45	1/9	1/15	1/5
2	1/9	2/9	1/6	1/2
3	1/15	1/6	1/15	3/10
	1/5	1/2	3/10	1

CONDITIONAL PROBABILITIES OF
x, GIVEN y

y \ x	1	2	3	
1	1/9	5/9	1/3	1
2	2/9	4/9	1/3	1
3	2/9	5/9	2/9	1

CONDITIONAL PROBABILITIES OF
y, GIVEN x

y \ x	1	2	3
1	1/9	2/9	2/9
2	5/9	4/9	5/9
3	1/3	1/3	2/9
	1	1	1

The conditional probability distributions of x for given values of y are given in the rows of the table on the lower left; the columns have no significance. A similar remark applies to the table in the lower right.

Example 20.3. For the random experiment of Example 20.2, what is the conditional probability distribution of x, given that $x + y = 4$?

Solution. From the frequency table of Example 20.1, the frequency distribution of x, given $x + y = 4$, is obtained from the 3 frequencies in the "north-east" diagonal of the table. Thus we obtain the frequency and probability distributions below:

x	1	2	3
ϕ	6	20	6
p	3/16	10/16	3/16

An especially simple type of bivariate experiment occurs when the experiment may be subjected to 2 dichotomous classifications $\{A, A'\}$ and $\{B, B'\}$, which form a cross-classification with the 4 outcomes $\{AB, AB', A'B, A'B'\}$; the outcomes form the sample space of the random experiment. Then Table 20.2 takes the form

	A	A'	
B	$P(AB)$	$P(A'B)$	$P(B)$
B'	$P(AB')$	$P(A'B')$	$P(B')$
	$P(A)$	$P(A')$	1

Equation (20.5) thus gives rise to 8 possible equations, of which 2 are:

$$(20.6) \qquad P(A|B) = \frac{P(AB)}{P(B)}, \quad P(B|A) = \frac{P(AB)}{P(A)}.$$

The second of them may be solved for $P(AB)$, yielding

$$(20.7) \qquad P(AB) = P(A) \cdot P(B|A).$$

Thus the probability of the compound event AB is the product of the unconditional probability of A and the conditional probability of B, given that A has occurred. This result is the so-called *multiplication theorem for dependent events*, a generalization of the more restricted multiplication theorem for independent urnlike events given in (6.2). It should be emphasized that this result is an immediate consequence of the *definition* of conditional probability in (20.5).

Consider the assertion that $P(A \mid B) = P(A)$, that is, the probability of A, given that B has occurred, is the same as the probability of A. This suggests that the occurrence of B has no effect on the probability of A, and we accordingly say that the event A is independent of the event B. We next show that this fact will also imply that the event B is independent of the event A, so that we may say that the events A and B are *mutually independent*, or simply *independent*. For, given

$P(A \mid B) = P(A)$ and using (20.6), we find

$$P(A) = P(AB)/P(B) \quad \text{or} \quad P(AB) = P(A)P(B).$$

Hence, using (20.7), $P(B \mid A) = P(B)$; that is, the event B is independent of the event A. We shall consequently make the following definition:

(20.8)   DEFINITION.   *The events A and B are stochastically independent if any one of the three equivalent conditions is satisfied*:

(a) $P(AB) = P(A) \cdot P(B).$

(b) $P(A \mid B) = P(A).$

(c) $P(B \mid A) = P(B).$

The adverb "stochastically" is equivalent to the phrase "in the probability sense" and is used to distinguish this kind of independence from other uses of the word in mathematics.

More generally, if a random experiment may be cross-classified under the dichotomies $\{A_1, A_1'\}$, $\{A_2, A_2'\}$, $\cdots$, $\{A_n, A_n'\}$, we define independence as follows:

(20.9)   *The events $A_1, A_2, \cdots, A_n$ are stochastically independent if the equation*

$$P(A_i A_j A_k \cdots) = P(A_i)P(A_j)P(A_k) \cdots$$

holds for every subset $\{i, j, k, \cdots\}$ of the subscripts $\{1, 2, \cdots, n\}$.

A table of the form of Table 20.2 suffices to specify completely a discrete bivariate experiment. Consider now a continuous bivariate experiment.   The data in a sample may be presented in the form of a two-way frequency distribution, similar to that of Table 20.1 (see Table 50.1).   We may represent the data visually by means of a *unit solid histogram*, obtained by erecting, over each cell of the table, a rectangular prism whose volume is equal to the relative frequency for that cell, so that the total volume is unity (see Figure 45.2).

In Section 15 it was assumed that, if a sequence of samples of increasing size is drawn from a stable continuous population and if unit histograms are constructed with decreasing interval size, the limiting form of the histogram will be a smooth curve, the frequency curve. Analogously we may consider a sequence of samples of increasing size from a continuous bivariate population.   We shall assume that, if a unit solid histogram is constructed for each sample using a decreasing sequence of interval sizes for the successive samples, the histograms will approach a smooth surface as a limit, called the *probability surface*, or the *frequency surface*.   Since each solid histogram has unit volume, the volume under the frequency surface is unity.   We shall assume that the probability surface extends over a certain region R of the x,y plane, as shown in Figure 20.2.

If we perform the measurements x and y on a random member of the population, we obtain a random pair of values which may be plotted as the point (X, Y).   Consider the probability that (X, Y) will fall within a region R' interior to R (Figure 20.2).   For any particular solid histogram of the sequence considered in the preceding paragraph, there will be a certain number of the prisms whose bases lie within R'.   The volume of these prisms gives an approximation to the relative frequency with which the values in the sample fall in R'.   In the limit the volume of these prisms whose bases lie in R' will converge to the volume under the surface and above the region R', so that we may regard the latter volume as giving the probability that a random point (X, Y) will fall within the region R'.

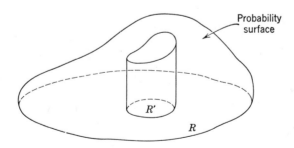

FIGURE 20.2

If the probability surface has the equation $z = f(x, y)$, the function $f(x, y)$ is called the bivariate *frequency function*, or *probability density function*, or simply the *density*. To justify the use of the latter term, we note that the unit solid histogram was so constructed that the volume of each prism was the relative frequency for the cell on which the prism was erected. Thus the height of the prism is the relative frequency per unit of area, or *relative frequency density*. In the limit, as the sequence of solid histograms approaches the frequency surface, the height of the prisms will approach $f(x, y)$, which may thus be regarded as measuring probability per unit area, or probability density.

The requirements which a function $f(x, y)$ must satisfy in order to qualify as a density are:

(20.10)

  (a) $f(x, y) \geq 0$ *over its range* R;

  (b) $\displaystyle\iint_R f(x, y)\, dx\, dy = 1.$

If R' is any region interior to R, we use the notation "$(X, Y) \in R'$" to mean "the random point (X, Y) is contained in R'," and we define

(20.11) $$P((X, Y) \in R') = \iint_{R'} f(x, y)\, dx\, dy.$$

The key concept in the relationship of random variables is that of independence. We shall define the concept of independence in the continuous case as follows:

(20.12) DEFINITION. *Two continuous random variables* X *and* Y *are called independent if the events* $a \leq X < b$ *and* $c \leq Y < d$ *are independent for all real numbers* a, b, c, d *for which* $a < b, c < d$.

This implies, according to (20.8), that

(20.13) $P(a \leq X < b,\ c \leq Y < d) = P(a \leq X < b)\, P(c \leq Y < d)$
for all a, b, c, d such that $a < b, c < d$.

Suppose that X and Y are independent and have densities $f(x)$ and $g(y)$, which are considered as extending over the whole real number line. Then

$$P(a \leq X < b) = \int_a^b f(x)\, dx, \quad P(c \leq Y < d) = \int_c^d g(y)\, dy,$$

and, using (20.13) and the properties of integrals, we conclude that

$$P(a \leq X < b,\ c \leq Y < d) = \int_a^b \int_c^d f(x)\, g(y)\, dy\, dx.$$

By comparison with (20.11) we see that the function $f(x)\, g(y)$ may be taken to be the joint density of X and Y. In fact

(20.14) THEOREM. *If X and Y are independent random variables with densities $f(x)$ and $g(y)$, then their joint density is $f(x)\, g(y)$. Conversely, if the joint density of a pair of random variables X and Y may be expressed in the form $f(x)\, g(y)$, then X and Y are independently distributed.*

Proof. We have already proved the first part. Now suppose that the joint density of X and Y is, in fact, $f(x)\, g(y)$. Let a, b, c, d be real numbers such that $a < b,\, c < d$. Then by (20.11)

$$P(a \leq X < b,\ \ c \leq Y < d) = \int_a^b \int_c^d f(x)\, g(y)\, dy\, dx$$

$$= \int_a^b f(x)\, dx \int_c^d g(y)\, dy$$

$$= P(a \leq X < b)P(c \leq Y < d).$$

Thus, from (20.8) and (20.12), X and Y are independent.

If X and Y possess the joint density $f(x, y)$, we define the *marginal densities* $f_1(x)$ and $f_2(y)$ as follows:

$$(20.15) \qquad f_1(x) = \int_{-\infty}^{\infty} f(x, y)\, dy, \quad f_2(y) = \int_{-\infty}^{\infty} f(x, y)\, dx.$$

The process of eliminating one of the variables from a density function, as is done in (20.15), is sometimes called "integrating out" the variable in question. Note that, if X and Y are independently distributed so that $f(x, y) = f(x)\, g(y)$, then

$$f_1(x) = \int_{-\infty}^{\infty} f(x)\, g(y)\, dy = f(x)$$

so that the marginal density of X is the same as the given density.

As a first illustration of the use of the marginal densities, consider the problem of evaluating $P(a \leq X < b)$, where a and b are real numbers such that $a < b$, with no restriction on Y. This means that Y may be any real value whatever. Hence

$$P(a \leq X < b) = P(a \leq X < b,\ -\infty < Y < \infty)$$

$$= \int_a^b \int_{-\infty}^{\infty} f(x, y)\, dy\, dx = \int_a^b f_1(x)\, dx,$$

using (20.15). Similarly we can show that, if c and d are real numbers such that $c < d$,

$$P(c \leq Y < d) = \int_c^d f_2(y)\, dy.$$

Consider now the conditional probability $P(a \leq X < b \,|\, Y = y)$. We shall define this as the limit, as $\Delta y \to 0$, of the conditional probability $P(a \leq X < b \,|\, y \leq Y < y + \Delta y)$. Using (20.6), we first express the latter conditional probability as a ratio of two integrals; we then apply the mean value theorem for integrals to simplify the resulting expression. In this way we find

$$P(a \leq X < b \,|\, y \leq Y < y + \Delta y) = \frac{P(a \leq X < b,\ y \leq Y < y + \Delta y)}{P(y \leq Y < y + \Delta y)}$$

$$= \frac{\displaystyle\int_a^b \int_y^{y+\Delta y} f(s,\, t)\, dt\, ds}{\displaystyle\int_{-\infty}^{\infty} \int_y^{y+\Delta y} f(s,\, t)\, dt\, ds}$$

$$= \frac{\displaystyle\int_a^b f(x,\, y')\, dx}{f_2(y'')}.$$

We have here used the mean value theorem for integrals in both numerator and denominator of the fraction. Thus y' and y'' are values in the interval $y \leq Y < y + \Delta y$. If we now let $\Delta y \to 0$, then y' and y'' will both approach y, and we have

$$P(a \leq X < b \,|\, Y = y) = \frac{\displaystyle\int_a^b f(x,\, y)\, dx}{f_2(y)}.$$

This leads us to define the *conditional density* of x, *given* $Y = y$, as

$$f_1(x \,|\, y) = \frac{f(x,\, y)}{f_2(y)},$$

and the *conditional density* of y, *given* $X = x$, as

$$f_2(y \,|\, x) = \frac{f(x,\, y)}{f_1(x)}.$$

It can readily be shown, as was done for the discrete case in connection with (20.8), that an alternative condition for independence in the case of continuous random variables is either $f_1(x\,|\,y) = f_1(x)$ or $f_2(y\,|\,x) = f_2(y)$; i.e., the conditional densities reduce to the marginal densities.

The preceding ideas may now be extended to the case of a continuous n-variate distribution. The sample space here consists of the totality of ordered sets $(X_1, \cdots, X_n)$ (sample points), where each X_i, $i = 1$, $\cdots$, n, will be regarded as ranging over the whole set of real numbers. The sample space so defined is usually known in mathematics as Euclidean n-dimensional space, denoted by E_n. We shall assume that the variables $X_1, \cdots, X_n$ possess a joint density $f(x_1, \cdots, x_n)$ with the properties:

(20.16)   (a) $f(x_1, \cdots, x_n) \geqq 0$ *for all points of the sample space.*

(b) $\displaystyle\int_{-\infty}^{\infty} \cdots \int_{-\infty}^{\infty} f(x_1, \cdots, x_n)\, dx_1 \cdots dx_n = 1.$

(c) *If R is any region of n-dimensional space, then*

$P((X_1, \cdots, X_n) \in R)$

$$= \int \cdots \int_R f(x_1, \cdots, x_n)\, dx_1 \cdots dx_n.$$

The *marginal densities* are obtained by integrating out all except one of the variables. Thus, for example, the marginal density $f_1(x_1)$ is defined by

$$f_1(x_1) = \int_{-\infty}^{\infty} \cdots \int_{-\infty}^{\infty} f(x_1, \cdots, x_n)\, dx_2 \cdots dx_n.$$

If $X_1, \cdots, X_n$ are independently distributed, it may be shown, by the same kind of reasoning employed in proving (20.14), that the joint density is the product of the individual (marginal) densities $f_1(x_1), \cdots,$ $f_n(x_n)$. Conversely, if the joint density is the product of the marginal densities, then $X_1, \cdots, X_n$ are independently distributed. We summarize:

(20.17)   THEOREM. *A necessary and sufficient condition that the continuous random variables $X_1, \cdots, X_n$ with respective (marginal) densities $f_1(x_1), \cdots, f_n(x_n)$ be independent is that their joint density be expressible as the product $f_1(x_1) \cdots f_n(x_n)$.*

Our treatment of probability up to this point is open to the rather serious criticism that we have given several distinct definitions of probability, separating the discrete case from the continuous and the univariate case from the bivariate. The reason for this multiplicity of definitions is that in the discrete case we have associated non-zero probability with isolated points whereas in the continuous case isolated points must have zero probability. We shall now include all these cases in one comprehensive definition by assigning probability to *events*. In the discrete case the events will consist of sets of isolated points, whereas in the continuous case they will be intervals or regions.

We begin with a sample space S whose points may be called *elementary events* and whose subsets, in general, are called *events*. Both S itself and the empty set are to be regarded as events. To each event E we assign a non-negative real number $P(E)$, known as the probability of E, obeying the following postulates:

1. $P(S) = 1$.
2. If E_1 and E_2 are mutually exclusive events (i.e., their intersection is empty), then $P(E_1 \cup E_2) = P(E_1) + P(E_2)$.

It can be shown that these postulates are satisfied if we assign a probability measure to the sample space precisely as we have done for the discrete and continuous cases. For the discrete case this amounts to assigning an arbitrary set of non-negative numbers to the sample points. For the continuous case we define probability by means of the integral of a density function.

EXERCISE 20

20.1. If in Example 20.2 the drawings are made with replacement, there will be 10^2 equally likely pairs of values (x, y). Make a two-way frequency table, as in Example 20.2, for these 100 equally likely sample points and a two-way probability table. Find the marginal and conditional distributions.

20.2. An urn contains 100 balls, each bearing 2 numbers (x, y) specified by the table shown. Find the marginal and conditional distributions.

y \ x	1	2	3
1	10	15	5
2	5	20	5
3	15	10	15

20.3. For the distribution of Table 6.2, find the conditional distribution of x, given $x + y = 5$.

20.4. A firm has 50 employees, classified according to sex and type of work as in the following table:

	Male	Female
Office	3	7
Factory	27	13

Let A, A', B, B' represent, respectively, male, female, office worker, factory worker. Express in words, and find a numerical value for, each of the following probabilities:

$$(a)\ P(A'|B)\quad (b)\ P(B'|A)\quad (c)\ P(A|B')\quad (d)\ P(B|A').$$

20.5. Let the bivariate density $f(x, y)$ be defined as follows:
$$f(x, y) = k,\quad \text{over the region } x^2 + y^2 < 1,$$
$$= 0,\quad \text{elsewhere.}$$
Find the value of k and the marginal and conditional distributions.

20.6. Let the bivariate density $f(x, y)$ be defined as follows:
$$f(x, y) = k(1 - \sqrt{x^2 + y^2}),\quad \text{over the region } x^2 + y^2 \leq 1,$$
$$= 0,\quad \text{elsewhere.}$$
Find the value of k. Find $P(X^2 + Y^2 < .5)$.

20.7. Let the bivariate density $f(x, y)$ be defined as follows:
$$f(x, y) = k(1 - x - y),\quad \text{over the region } x \geq 0, y \geq 0, x + y \leq 1,$$
$$= 0,\quad \text{elsewhere.}$$
Find the value of k. Find the marginal and conditional distributions of x and y. Find $P(X + Y \leq 1/2)$.

20.8. Let the bivariate density $f(x, y)$ be defined as follows:
$$f(x, y) = kxy,\quad \text{over the region } 0 \leq x \leq 1, 0 \leq y \leq 1,$$
$$= 0,\quad \text{elsewhere.}$$
Find the value of k, and the marginal and conditional distributions of x.

20.9. Let the bivariate density $f(x, y)$ be defined as follows:
$$f(x, y) = k(1 - x^2 - y^2),\quad \text{over the region } x^2 + y^2 \leq 1,$$
$$= 0,\quad \text{elsewhere.}$$
Find the value of k. Find the marginal and conditional densities of x and y. Find $P(X^2 + Y^2 < 1/2)$; use the fact that the probability surface is a surface of revolution.

20.10. Let the bivariate density $f(x, y)$ be defined as follows:
$$f(x, y) = 3(1 - x),\quad \text{over the region } x < 1, y > 0, x - y > 0;$$
$$= 3(1 - y),\quad \text{over the region } x > 0, y < 1, x - y < 0;$$
$$= 0,\quad \text{elsewhere.}$$
Find the marginal and conditional distributions.

20.11. Let the bivariate density $f(x, y)$ be defined as follows:
$$f(x, y) = 6y,\quad \text{over the region } x - y > 0, x + y < 1, y > 0;$$
$$= 6x,\quad \text{over the region } x - y < 0, x + y < 1, x > 0;$$
$$= 6(1 - x),\quad \text{over the region } x - y > 0, x + y > 1, x < 1;$$
$$= 6(1 - y),\quad \text{over the region } x - y < 0, x + y > 1, y < 1.$$
Find the marginal and conditional distributions.

* 20.12. The *distribution function* $F(x, y)$ of the pair of continuous random variables X and Y with joint density $f(x, y)$ is defined by

$$F(x, y) = P(X \leq x, Y \leq y) = \int_{-\infty}^{y} \int_{-\infty}^{x} f(u, v) \, du \, dv.$$

Show that:

(a) $F(x, y) = F(x)F(y)$ if and only if X and Y are independent.

(b) If a, b, c, d are real numbers such that $a < b, c < d$, then $P(a \leq X \leq b, c \leq Y \leq d) = F(a, c) - F(a, d) - F(b, c) + F(b, d)$.

(c) $f(x, y) = \dfrac{\partial^2}{\partial x \, \partial y} F(x, y)$.

(d) The average density of probability per unit area over the rectangle with vertices $(a, c), (b, c), (b, d), (a, d)$ is

$$\frac{F(a, c) - F(a, d) - F(b, c) + F(b, d)}{(b - a)(d - c)}.$$

Show that, if $b \to a$ and $d \to c$, this expression approaches

$$\frac{\partial^2}{\partial x \, \partial y} F(x, y) \Big|_{\substack{x=a \\ y=c}}.$$

(e) The marginal distribution functions of X and Y are obtained by substituting ∞ for x or y in $F(x, y)$:

$$F_1(x) = P(X \leq x) = \int_{-\infty}^{\infty} \int_{-\infty}^{x} f(s, t) \, ds \, dt = F(x, \infty),$$

$$F_2(y) = P(Y \leq y) = \int_{-\infty}^{\infty} \int_{-\infty}^{y} f(s, t) \, dt \, ds = F(\infty, y).$$

(f) The marginal densities $f_1(x) = \int_{-\infty}^{\infty} f(x, y) \, dy, f_2(y) = \int_{-\infty}^{\infty} f(x, y) \, dx$ may be obtained by differentiating the marginal distribution functions.

(g) If X and Y are independently distributed, then $F(x, y) = F_1(x) \, F_2(y)$.

20.13. A farmer offers to find water for \$25.00 and to find pure drinking water for \$50.00. His successes have been recorded in a long series of trials, with the following results: His probability of finding water is .21, of finding pure drinking water is .12. What is the probability that, given that water has been found, it will be impure?

20.14. A dealer experienced in buying used cars finds that he makes serious errors of judgment on the motor about 7% of the time, serious errors on the rear end 15% of the time, and serious errors on the clutch or fluid drive 5% of the time. He makes errors on all three 1% of the time, on motor and rear end 4% of the time, on motor and clutch 2% of the time, and on rear end and clutch 2% of the time.

(a) What per cent of the time is his judgment right in all 3 respects?

(b) What per cent of the time is he correct in his estimation of clutch and motor, but wrong in regard to the rear end?

(c) What per cent of the time will he correctly evaluate the motor on cars for which he correctly judges the condition of rear end and clutch?

20.15. A biology teacher finds that, on a field trip, the average student has the following probabilities for identification of birds:

(*a*) Probability of identifying species = .72
(*b*) Probability of identifying sex = .36
(*c*) Probability of identifying both species and sex = .16.
Find: (*a*) Probability of mis-identifying both species and sex.
(*b*) Probability of identifying species but mis-identifying sex.
(*c*) Probability of identifying sex, given that species is correctly identified.

21. SAMPLING DISTRIBUTIONS AND GENERATING FUNCTIONS

Suppose a discrete bivariate distribution is specified by means of a two-way table such as those used in Sections 6 and 20. The cells of the table correspond to the points of the sample space, and any function $g(X, Y)$ of the random variables X and Y is likewise a random variable over the sample space, that is, a statistic. The distribution of $g(X, Y)$ is the sampling distribution of the statistic. In this section we shall investigate the sampling distributions of some simple statistics by means of generating functions.

The generating function (g.f.) of a discrete random variable X was defined, in Section 12, by

(21.1) $$G_x(t) = E(t^x) = p_1 t^{x_1} + \cdots + p_n t^{x_n}.$$

We are here limiting ourselves to the case in which the sample space contains a finite number of points. Under these circumstances, the generating function is simply a polynomial in which the exponents are the values of the random variable, while the coefficients are the corresponding probabilities. Thus the g.f.'s of the 2 distributions involved in Example 6.1 are

$$G_x = .1s + .2s^2 + .4s^3 + .2s^4 + .1s^5$$
$$G_y = .2 + .1t + .4t^2 + .3t^3.$$

The variables s and t serve merely to link together the values of the random variable and the corresponding probabilities, and have no numerical significance.

The usefulness of the generating functions begins to become apparent when we multiply the 2 g.f.'s given above:

$$
\begin{aligned}
G_x \cdot G_y = \quad & .02s \;\; + .04s^2 \;\; + .08s^3 \;\; + .04s^4 \;\; + .02s^5 \\
& + .01st \;\; + .02s^2 t \;\; + .04s^3 t \;\; + .02s^4 t \;\; + .01s^5 t \\
& + .04st^2 + .08s^2 t^2 + .16s^3 t^2 + .08s^4 t^2 + .04s^5 t^2 \\
& + .03st^3 + .06s^2 t^3 + .12s^3 t^3 + .06s^4 t^3 + .03s^5 t^3.
\end{aligned}
$$

The terms have been arranged in such a way as to correspond to the cells of Table 6.2. It will be noted that each term in the product $G_x \cdot G_y$ corresponds to one of the cells in Table 6.2. The coefficient of the term corresponds to the probability in the cell, while the exponents of s and t correspond to the values of x and y in the cell. Thus $G_x \cdot G_y$ is the g.f. of the bivariate distribution of Table 6.2. This remark contains the key to the usefulness of g.f.'s.

When a single letter, say s, is used for both g.f.'s, the law of exponents comes into operation. By replacing the letter t by s in G_y, the product of the 2 polynomials becomes

$$G_x \cdot G_y = .02s + .04s^2 + .08s^3 + .04s^4 + .02s^5$$
$$+ .01s^2 + .02s^3 + .04s^4 + .02s^5 + .01s^6$$
$$+ .04s^3 + .08s^4 + .16s^5 + .08s^6 + .04s^7$$
$$+ .03s^4 + .06s^5 + .12s^6 + .06s^7 + .03s^8$$

$$.02s + .05s^2 + .14s^3 + .19s^4 + .26s^5 + .21s^6 + .10s^7 + .03s^8$$

The final product is the g.f. for the sum $X + Y$, whose distribution was obtained in Example 6.1a. In fact, each step in the arithmetic involved in forming Table 6.2 and in using it to obtain the distribution of $X + Y$ has also been performed in the multiplication of $G_x \cdot G_y$. This illustrates the important result contained in the following theorem:

(21.2) THEOREM. *If X and Y are random variables with g.f.'s $G_x = \sum_{i=1}^{h} p_i s^{xi}$ and $G_y = \sum_{j=1}^{k} p_j s^{yj}$, then the g.f. of the random variable $Z = X + Y$ is the product $G_x \cdot G_y$. Symbolically,*

$$G_{x+y} = G_x \cdot G_y.$$

Proof. The hk terms in the product $G_x \cdot G_y$ will correspond to the hk cells of Table 20.2, the coefficient of each term corresponding to the probability in the cell, and the exponent corresponding to the sum $x + y$. Thus, when the coefficients of like powers of s are added, we obtain the total probability associated with the corresponding value of $x + y$.

By mathematical induction Theorem (21.1) may be extended to the case of n random variables:

(21.3)   THEOREM.   *If $X_1, \cdots, X_n$ are independent random variables with g.f.'s $G_1, \cdots, G_n$, then $Z = X_1 + \cdots + X_n$ is a random variable whose g.f. is the product $G_1 \cdot G_2 \cdots G_n$.*

Proof.   From (21.1) it follows that the sum $X_1 + X_2$ has the g.f. $G_1 \cdot G_2$.   Again, the sum $X_1 + X_2 + X_3 = (X_1 + X_2) + X_3$ is the sum of 2 random variables, the first, $X_1 + X_2$, having the g.f. $G_1 \cdot G_2$, and the second, X_3, having the g.f. G_3.   Using (21.1) we conclude that $X_1 + X_2 + X_3$ has the g.f. $G_1 \cdot G_2 \cdot G_3$.   Making use of mathematical induction, the theorem is established.

An important corollary of (21.2) is the following:

(21.4)   THEOREM.   *If the random variable X has the g.f. G_x, then the sum of n independent values of X will have the g.f. $(G_x)^n$.*

In Section 19, the g.f. of a continuous random variable was defined, using an integral in place of a sum.   With this definition, Theorems (21.2), (21.3), and (21.4) can be extended to continuous random variables.

Example 21.1.   Find the sampling distributions of the sums of 2, 3, and 4 dice, using generating functions.   The g.f. for a single die is $G_1 = \frac{1}{6}(s + s^2 + s^3 + s^4 + s^5 + s^6)$.   Raising this polynomial to the second, third, and fourth powers, we obtain

$$G_2 = (G_1)^2 = \tfrac{1}{36}(s^2 + 2s^3 + 3s^4 + 4s^5 + 5s^6 + 6s^7 + 5s^8 + 4s^9 + 3s^{10} + 2s^{11} + s^{12})$$

$$G_3 = (G_1)^3 = \tfrac{1}{216}(s^3 + 3s^4 + 6s^5 + 10s^6 + 15s^7 + 21s^8 + 25s^9 + 27s^{10} + 27s^{11} + 25s^{12} + 21s^{13} + 15s^{14} + 10s^{15} + 6s^{16} + 3s^{17} + s^{18})$$

$$G_4 = (G_1)^4 = \tfrac{1}{1296}(s^4 + 4s^5 + 10s^6 + 20s^7 + 35s^8 + 56s^9 + 80s^{10} + 104s^{11} + 125s^{12} + 140s^{13} + 146s^{14} + 140s^{15} + 125s^{16} + 104s^{17} + 80s^{18} + 56s^{19} + 35s^{20} + 20s^{21} + 10s^{22} + 4s^{23} + s^{24})$$

Histograms corresponding to these distributions are shown in Figure 21.1.   Note especially the tendency for the figure to become more bell-shaped as the number of dice is increased.   It will be proved in Section 44 that the limiting form of the histogram, as the number of dice is increased without limit, is actually a normal distribution.

A convenient computational device for the multiplication of generating functions, especially when a calculating machine is available, is the *moving strip method*, illustrated in Figure 21.2 for the g.f.'s $G_x = .1s + .2s^2 + .4s^3 + .2s^4 + .1s^5$ and $G_y = .2 + .1s + .4s^2 + .3s^3$.   The coefficients of the polynomial G_x are written with even spacing.   In general, if powers are missing from the polynomial, spaces must be left.

The coefficients of the second polynomial, G_y, are written in reverse order on a strip of paper, with the same spacing as used for G_x. The strip is then placed in a series of positions, of which the first two and the last are shown in Figure 21.2. In each position, each coefficient of G_x is multiplied by the coefficient of G_y directly beneath it, and the products are added. In this way each position of the strip yields one

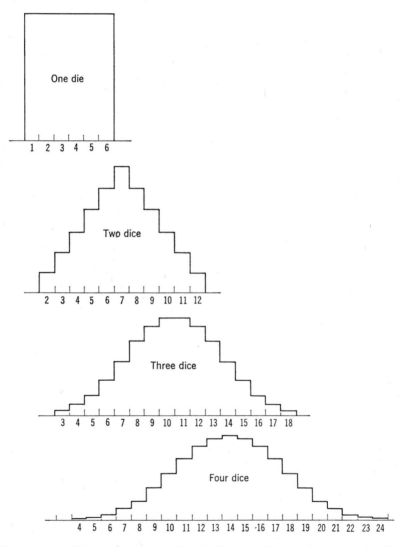

FIGURE 21.1. Histograms for sampling distributions of sums of 1, 2, 3, and 4 dice.

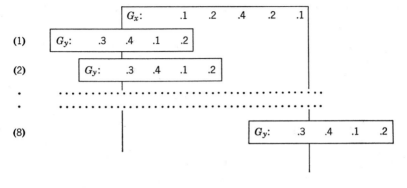

FIGURE 21.2

coefficient of the product $G_x \cdot G_y$. A calculating machine is especially helpful because the series of products for each position of the strip can be readily totaled on the machine.

EXERCISE 21

21.1 Urns U_x and U_y have the following distributions:

U_x:

x	0	1	2	3
p	.4	.2	.1	.3

U_y:

y	1	2	3
p	.3	.6	.1

A ball is withdrawn from each urn and the results are added. Find the distribution of $X + Y$, using the generating function method.

21.2. Write the generating function G_1 for a random variable X whose distribution is

x	1	2	3
p	.2	.5	.3

Find $G_2 = (G_1)^2$, $G_3 = (G_1)^3$, and $G_4 = (G_1)^4$, and hence find the sampling distributions for sums of 2, 3, and 4 independent values from the given distribution. Draw histograms corresponding to G_1, G_2, G_3, G_4.

21.3. Write the generating function G_1 for a random variable X whose distribution is

x	1	2	3
p	.4	.2	.4

Find $G_2 = (G_1)^2$, $G_3 = (G_1)^3$, and $G_4 = (G_1)^4$, and hence find the sampling distributions for sums of 2, 3, and 4 independent values from the given distribution. Draw histograms corresponding to G_1, G_2, G_3, G_4.

21.4. The generating function for a single die is

$$G_1 = \tfrac{1}{6}(s + \cdots + s^6) = \frac{s(1 - s^6)}{6(1 - s)}.$$

Hence the generating function for the sum of n dice is

$$G_n = (G_1)^n = \frac{s^n}{6^n}(1 - s^6)^n(1 - s)^{-n}.$$

In order to find G_5, for example, we can expand $(1 - s^6)^5$ and $(1 - s)^{-5}$ by means of the binomial theorem. Without finding the entire generating function, use this method to find the probability of obtaining a sum of 17 when 5 dice are thrown. (Note that only three terms are required in the expansion of $(1 - s)^{-5}$.)

21.5. Consider again the carnival game of Exercise 7.22. Form the generating function of the random variable of this game, and use it in order to obtain the complete probability distribution for the sum of 3 trials.

22. ASYMPTOTIC NORMALITY OF SAMPLING DISTRIBUTIONS

The central limit theorem asserts, as has already been stated, that for many commonly used statistics (mean, median, variance, etc.) the form of the sampling distribution of the statistic becomes normal as n, the sample size, increases without limit. The limiting form of a sampling distribution as $n \to \infty$ is referred to as its *asymptotic distribution*. Thus we say that the distributions of the mean, median, variance, etc., are *asymptotically normal*. The proofs of these results are rather difficult; some particular cases will be considered in Chapter 5. For the present we shall be content with *illustrating* the tendency toward normality, continuing with the example of dice, already considered in Section 21.

In Figure 21.1 histograms were shown for the distributions of the sums of 1, 2, 3, and 4 dice. In addition to the evident tendency toward normality there is a tendency for the center of the distribution to move progressively to the right and for the distribution to spread out as n increases. This increase of both mean and variance of the sum of n identically distributed random variables, with increase of n, will be systematically studied in Section 27. There the following theorem will be proved:

(22.1) THEOREM. *If $X_1, \cdots, X_n$ are independently distributed, each having mean μ and variance σ^2, then the sum $S = X_1 + \cdots + X_n$ has mean $\mu_S = n\mu$ and variance $\sigma_S{}^2 = n\sigma^2$, and the mean $\overline{X} = \dfrac{1}{n}(X_1 + \cdots + X_n)$ has mean $\mu_{\overline{X}} = \mu$ and variance $\sigma_{\overline{X}}{}^2 = \sigma^2/n$.*

Since the mean and variance for a single die are $\mu = 3.5$, $\sigma^2 = 35/12$, we may conclude that for the sum S of n dice $\mu_S = 3.5n$, $\sigma_S{}^2 = 35n/12$.

The sequence of distributions will be stabilized if we make a transformation to standard units, that is, make use of the variable

(22.2)
$$Z = \frac{(S - \mu_S)}{\sigma_S} = \frac{(S - 3.5n)}{1.708\sqrt{n}}.$$

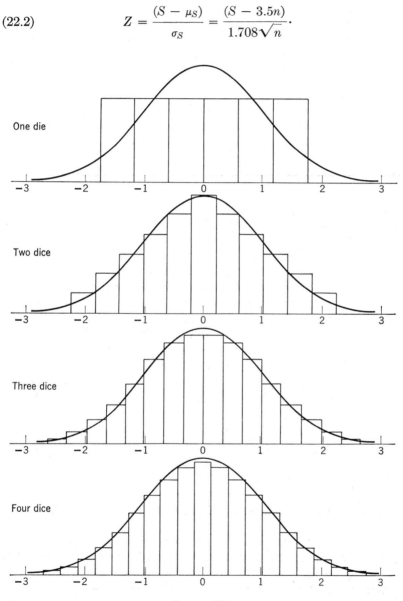

One die

Two dice

Three dice

Four dice

FIGURE 22.1

TABLE 22.1

S	p	Z	$p\sigma_S$	$f_N(z)$	$d = p\sigma_S - f_N(Z)$	
14	.1127	0	.3848	.3989	−.0141	
15	.1080	.2928	.3690	.3822	−.0132	
16	.0964	.5855	.3294	.3361	−.0067	$\mu_4 = 14.0$
17	.0822	.8763	.2741	.2713	.0028	$\sigma_4{}^2 = 11.667$
18	.0617	1.1711	.2108	.2009	.0099	$\sigma_4 = 3.416$
19	.0432	1.4638	.1476	.1366	.0110	
20	.0270	1.7566	.0922	.0853	.0069	
21	.0154	2.0494	.0527	.0489	.0038	
22	.0077	2.3422	.0264	.0245	.0019	
23	.0032	2.6349	.0105	.0124	−.0019	
24	.0008	2.9277	.0026	.0055	−.0029	

In Figure 22.1, the 4 histograms of Figure 21.1 are redrawn, using the variable Z of (22.2) on the horizontal scale. In order to insure that the histograms have unit area, the ordinate used in each histogram is $p\sigma_S$, where p is the height of the histogram in Figure 21.1. In each of the 4 histograms of Figure 22.1, a unit normal curve is shown in order to make the progress toward normality more evident. The necessary computations are shown in Table 22.1 for the case of 4 dice. Since the distribution is symmetrical, only the values for the right half of the figure are shown. The column labeled $f_N(z)$ gives the ordinate of the normal curve, and the value $d = p\sigma_S - f_N(z)$ gives the distance between the histogram and the normal curve. For any one of the 4 histograms we may measure the discrepancy between the histogram and the normal curve by a suitable average of the values of d. Since both positive and negative values are present, the root mean square is a suitable average. Denoting the rms of the d-values of the nth histogram of the sequence by $\tilde{d}_n$, we find the following 4 values for the 4 histograms of Figure 22.1:

$$\tilde{d}_1 = .1026, \quad \tilde{d}_2 = .0232, \quad \tilde{d}_3 = .0114, \quad \tilde{d}_4 = .0077.$$

The tendency for $\tilde{d}_n$ to decrease as $n \to \infty$ is apparent.

The approach toward normality may be quite slow with some distributions, quite rapid with others. A distribution which approaches normality quite rapidly is given in the following example.

Example 22.1.   Consider the distribution whose g.f. is $G_x = .2s + .5s^2 + .3s^3$. When this g.f. is raised to the powers 2, 3, 4, 5, 6 and the rms discrepancy $\tilde{d}_n$ between the histogram and the normal curve is calculated as in the previous example, we find the following sequence of values of $\tilde{d}_n$:

$$\tilde{d}_1 = .0358, \quad \tilde{d}_2 = .0136, \quad \tilde{d}_3 = .0089, \quad \tilde{d}_4 = .0065, \quad \tilde{d}_5 = .0058, \quad \tilde{d}_6 = .0046.$$

A distribution for which the sampling distributions of the sums of samples of size n approaches normality slowly with increase of n is the following:

Example 22.2.   Let $G_x = .4s + .2s^2 + .4s^3$.   The sequence of values of $\tilde{d}_n$ is $\tilde{d}_1 = .1732, \tilde{d}_2 = .0834, \tilde{d}_3 = .0487, \tilde{d}_4 = .0286, \tilde{d}_5 = .0175, \tilde{d}_6 = .0112.$

In general, the approach of the histogram to the normal curve tends to be more rapid near the center of the distribution than in the tails of the distribution.   For this reason, an over-all measure of the closeness of approach, such as the quantity $\tilde{d}_n$ used above, must be interpreted with caution.   We shall find, in Chapter 4, that in the use of sampling distributions for the purposes of statistical inference, the part of the curve of greatest interest lies in the extremes of the tails.

EXERCISE 22

22.1.   Verify that when a histogram is constructed using the values Z given by (22.2) on the horizontal scale and the quantity $p\sigma s$ on the vertical scale, the histogram has unit area.

22.2.   In Exercise 21.2 the generating function G_1 corresponding to a given distribution was raised to the second, third, and fourth powers.   For each of the distributions corresponding to G_1, G_2, G_3, and G_4, make a table like Table 22.1, and thus compute the values of d in each case.   Check with Example 22.1.

22.3.   Apply the same procedure as in Exercise 22.3, to the distributions found in Exercise 21.2.   Check with Example 22.2.

23. THE BINOMIAL DISTRIBUTION

A dichotomy was defined, in Section 2, as a random experiment with just 2 outcomes.   A few examples are: the sex of a new-born baby, the acceptance or rejection of an industrial product, the occurrence or non-occurrence of rain on a particular day.   It is convenient to define a random variable X associated with a dichotomy in the following way. We first designate one of the outcomes as a "success," the other as a "failure."   Then we define X to be the number of successes on a single trial; obviously the sample space for X is the set $\{0, 1\}$.   In a series of trials the total of the values of X will give the number of successes, and the sample mean $\overline{X}$ will be the proportion of successes.   A single trial of such a random experiment is frequently called a *Bernoullian trial,* and a sequence of such trials is called a *Bernoullian sequence* of trials, after James Bernoulli (1654–1705), who wrote the first major treatise on probability, *The Art of Conjecture* (*Ars conjectandi*), published posthumously in 1713.

The probability distribution of the sum of n drawings from a dichotomy is called the binomial or Bernoullian distribution. In Section 7 the binomial distribution was obtained by two methods: first, as the limiting form of the hypergeometric distribution when the number of balls in the urn becomes infinite; second, by considering the sample space associated with n values from a dichotomy. Here we shall use the method of generating functions to derive the binomial distribution. We shall use p for the probability that a single trial will yield "success," and $\hat{p}$ for the proportion of successes in a sample of size n. We shall also use $q = 1 - p$ and $\hat{q} = 1 - \hat{p}$. Hence the population and sample distributions are:

	x	0	1
Population probabilities		q	p
Sample proportions		$\hat{q}$	$\hat{p}$

The g.f. for the number of successes on a single trial is $G_1 = q + ps$, so that by (21.4) the g.f. for the number of successes in a sample of size n is

$$(23.1) \qquad G_n = (G_1)^n = (q + ps)^n.$$

If we expand the binomial by means of the binomial theorem (7.7), we find, for the probability of x successes in n trials,

$$(23.2) \qquad P(X = x) = \binom{n}{x} p^x q^{n-x}.$$

The mean and variance for the distribution of a single trial are readily found to be $\mu_1 = p$, $\sigma_1{}^2 = p - p^2 = pq$. Hence, by (22.1), the mean and variance of the number of successes in n trials is

$$(23.3) \qquad \mu_n = np, \quad \sigma_n{}^2 = npq.$$

Since the proportion of successes in n trials is $\overline{X} = \hat{p}$, we may use (22.1) to find the mean and variance of this proportion:

$$(23.4) \qquad \mu_{\hat{p}} = p, \quad \sigma_{\hat{p}}{}^2 = \frac{pq}{n}.$$

In Section 34 we shall show that for fixed p the histogram of the binomial distribution (23.2) approaches a normal curve as $n \to \infty$.

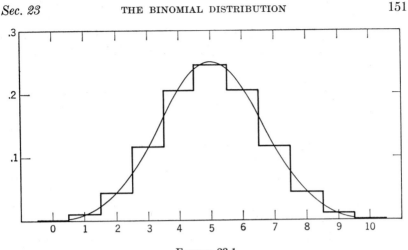

FIGURE 23.1

This is, of course, a special case of the central limit theorem. It enables us to use the normal distribution in order to estimate probabilities associated with the binomial distribution. Consider, for example, the binomial distribution for which $p = .5$ and $n = 10$, whose histogram is shown in Figure 23.1, together with a fitted normal curve, i.e., a normal curve with the same mean $\mu = np = 5$ and the same standard deviation $\sigma = \sqrt{npq} = \sqrt{2.5} = 1.581$, as the binomial distribution. The vertical scale is such that both histogram and curve have unit area. Note particularly that the value of x corresponding to a particular block of the histogram is at the *center of its base*. Thus, for the purposes of estimating probability by means of the normal distribution, we shall interpret the probability of obtaining the value x in the following way:

(23.5)

$$P(X = x), \qquad \text{for a binomial distribution}$$
$$\doteq P(x - 1/2 < X < x + 1/2), \quad \text{for the approximating normal distribution}$$

where the sign $\doteq$ means "is approximately equal to." Similarly,

(23.6)

$$P(X > x), \qquad \text{for a binomial distribution}$$
$$\doteq P(X > x + 1/2), \quad \text{for the approximating normal distribution;}$$

$$P(X \geqq x), \qquad \text{for a binomial distribution}$$
$$\doteq P(X > x - 1/2), \quad \text{for the approximating normal distribution.}$$

This adjustment of 1/2 unit in adapting the normal distribution to the calculation of binomial probabilities is often called the *correction for continuity*.

Example 23.1. Find the values of $P(X = 7)$, where X possesses the binomial distribution with $p = .5$, $n = 10$. Find also the estimate of this probability by (23.5).

Solution. By using (23.2),

$$P(X = 7) = \binom{10}{7}(.5)^7(.5)^3 = 120(.5)^{10} = .1172.$$

For the normal approximation, we use the distribution $N(5, 2.5)$, since the binomial distribution has mean 5, variance 2.5. According to (23.5) we need to calculate $P(6.5 < X < 7.5)$ for this normal distribution. We re-express the limits in terms of the standard units given by $z = (x - 5)/\sqrt{2.5}$ and find

$$P(6.5 < X < 7.5) = P(.949 < Z < 1.581), \quad \text{where } Z \text{ has the unit normal} $$
$$\text{distribution,}$$
$$= .4430 - .3287 = .1143.$$

This compares fairly well with the correct value, $P = .1172$.

Example 23.2. If X has the binomial distribution of Example 23.1, find $P(X > 9)$ and $P(X > 8)$.

Solution. Using the binomial distribution (23.2), we find

$$P(X > 9) = P(X = 10) = \binom{10}{10}(.5)^{10} = .0009766,$$
$$P(X > 8) = P(X = 9) + P(X = 10) = .009766 + .0009766 = .01074.$$

Using the normal distribution $N(5, 2.5)$, we must calculate $P(X > 8.5)$ and $P(X > 7.5)$. Transforming these x-values into z-values (standard units) as in Example 23.1, we find

$$P(X > 9.5) = P(Z > 2.846) = .0022, \quad P(X > 9.5) = P(Z > 2.214) = .0134.$$

Thus the normal distribution considerably overestimates these probabilities, illustrating the fact that the normal approximation to the binomial distribution tends to be unreliable in the extreme tails of the distribution, unless n is sufficiently large. The next example suggests that $n = 20$ may be sufficiently large if $p = .5$. But much larger values of n are required for values of p as small as .2, for example.

Example 23.3. If X has a binomial distribution with $p = .5$ and $n = 20$, find $P(X > 15)$ using the binomial distribution (23.2) and also using the normal approximation.

Solution. With the binomial distribution we find

$$P(X > 15) = P(X = 16) + \cdots + P(X = 20) = .005914.$$

The approximating normal distribution is $N(10, 5)$. Hence, using (23.6), we calculate

$$P(X > 15.5) = P(Z > 2.460) = .005947.$$

Thus the agreement between the binomial probability and its normal estimate is much better than in Example 23.2, although the z-values are comparable in these two examples.

The following example illustrates the deterioration of the approximation for small values of p. Note that the value of z is comparable with those encountered in Examples 23.2 and 23.3.

Example 23.4. If $n = 20$, $p = .2$, we find, using the binomial distribution, that $P(X > 9) = .0026$. Using the normal distribution we find $P(X > 8.5) = P(Z > 2.515) = .0060$.

In order that the binomial probabilities may be satisfactorily approximated by means of the normal distribution, it is necessary that neither np nor nq be too small. A rule of thumb frequently used to insure that this is the case is the requirement that the smaller of np and nq be larger than 5.

Various tables of the binomial distribution are in print. Two of the most useful are: *Tables of the Binomial Probability Distribution*, National Bureau of Standards, Washington, D. C., and *50–100 Binomial Tables*, by H. G. Romig, John Wiley and Sons, 1953. The first gives the complete binomial distribution for every value of n from $n = 2$ to $n = 49$, and for values of p from .01 to .50, in steps of .01. The second gives the complete binomial distribution for values of n from 50 to 100 in steps of 5, and for values of p from .01 to .50 in steps of .01. Both books give individual terms, and the cumulative distributions.

EXERCISE 23

23.1. Assuming that 65% of the citizens in a town favor a sewer bond proposal, find the probability that in a random sample of 10 citizens:
(a) Exactly 8 will favor the proposal.
(b) 8 or more will favor the proposal.

23.2. If it is true that 35% of all cigarette smokers prefer brand A, what is the probability that in a random sample of 12 smokers
(a) Exactly 10 will prefer brand A?
(b) 10 or more will prefer brand A?

23.3. In a certain manufacturing process there are 2% defectives. What is the probability that in a random sample of 20 there are (a) 3 defectives, (b) 3 or more defectives?

23.4. The recovery rate for a certain critical operation is .70. What is the probability that of a random group of 20 patients submitting to this operation
(a) 15 will recover?
(b) 15 or more will recover?

23.5. In Pascal's triangle, shown at the right, each number is the sum of those above it, to the right and left. The numbers in the nth row are the binomial coefficients in the expansion of $(a + b)^n$ (here we are not counting the single "1" at the apex of the triangle as a row). The sum of the numbers in the nth row is 2^n; this serves as a check on the computation. Construct the triangle down to the 10th row, thus obtaining the coefficients in the expansion of $(a + b)^{10}$.

```
         1
        1 1
       1 2 1
      1 3 3 1
     1 4 6 4 1
    . . . . . . . . . .
    . . . . . . . . . .
```

23.6. (a) Using the coefficients obtained in Exercise 23.5, find the complete binomial distribution for $n = 10$, $p = .5$.

(b) Use the normal distribution, with the correction for continuity, in order to approximate the binomial probabilities obtained in (a).

(c) For what value of x is the discrepancy greatest between the binomial probabilities and the normal approximations?

23.6. For what value is the discrepancy greatest, when expressed as a per cent of the binomial probability?

23.7. Same as Exercises 23.5 and 23.6, with $p = .2$.

23.8. Use the approximating normal distribution to estimate the probabilities in Exercise 23.1.

23.9. Use the approximating normal distribution to estimate the probabilities in Exercise 23.2.

23.10. Use the approximating normal distribution to estimate the probabilities in Exercise 23.3.

23.11. Use the approximating normal distribution to estimate the probabilities in Exercise 23.4.

24. BIVARIATE NORMAL DISTRIBUTION

In Section 15 it was pointed out that the sampling distributions associated with a normal population are, in general, simpler than those for other populations. In this section and the next we shall derive some of the more elementary normal sampling distributions.

Let X and Y be independent values from $N(\mu_x, \sigma_x^2)$ and $N(\mu_y, \sigma_y^2)$, respectively. Thus their densities are

$$f_1(x) = \frac{1}{\sigma_x \sqrt{2\pi}} e^{-(x-\mu_x)^2/2\sigma_x^2}, \quad f_2(y) = \frac{1}{\sigma_y \sqrt{2\pi}} e^{-(y-\mu_y)^2/2\sigma_y^2},$$

and their joint density, by (20.14), is

$$(24.1) \quad f(x, y) = f_1(x) f_2(y) = \frac{1}{2\pi\sigma_x\sigma_y} e^{-[(x-\mu_x)^2/2\sigma_x^2 + (y-\mu_y)^2/2\sigma_y^2]}.$$

Consider the probability surface $z = f(x, y)$ associated with this bivariate distribution. A section of this surface parallel to the yz-plane will be obtained by putting x equal to a constant, say $x = x_0$. Then we obtain $z = f(x_0, y) = f_1(x_0) f_2(y)$. Since $f_1(x_0)$ is a constant, we find that the section is a normal curve. Similarly sections parallel to the xz-plane will likewise be normal curves. On the other hand every horizontal section is an ellipse, as may be seen by taking logarithms of both sides of (24.1):

(24.2) $\log_e z = - \log_e 2\pi\sigma_x\sigma_y - (x - \mu_x)^2/2\sigma_x^2 - (y - \mu_y)^2/2\sigma_y^2.$

or

$$\frac{(x - \mu_x)^2}{-2\sigma_x^2 \log_e (2\pi\sigma_x\sigma_y z)} + \frac{(y - \mu_y)^2}{-2\sigma_y^2 \log_e (2\pi\sigma_x\sigma_y z)} = 1.$$

If z is made constant in Equation (24.2), we have the equation of an ellipse with center (μ_x, μ_y) and with semi-axes $\sigma_x\sqrt{-2 \log_e (2\pi\sigma_x\sigma_y z)}$ and $\sigma_y\sqrt{-2 \log_e (2\pi\sigma_x\sigma_y z)}$. The semi-axes decrease as z is increased, until the ellipse vanishes for $z = 1/2\pi\sigma_x\sigma_y$ which is the maximum height of the probability surface.

The case of greatest interest is that for which both X and Y have the distribution $N(0, 1)$. In this case the probability surface reduces to

(24.3) $$z = f(x, y) = \frac{1}{2\pi} e^{-(x^2+y^2)/2}.$$

It is immediately seen that the ellipses of (24.2) have become circles, so that we have a surface of revolution. In this case we call the joint distribution the *circular normal distribution* or the *symmetrical normal distribution*. We shall first consider a series of problems connected with this distribution.

Example 24.1. If X and Y are independent values from $N(0, 1)$, find $P(X^2 + Y^2 < R^2)$, that is, the probability that the random point (X, Y) shall fall within a circle of radius R about the origin.

Solution. By (20.11) the required probability is the volume under the surface (24.3) and above the interior of the circle $x^2 + y^2 = R^2$. Let us integrate by means of cylindrical shells. A cylindrical shell of radius r is readily found to have height $(1/2\pi)e^{-r^2/2}$. If its thickness is dr, its volume is $dV = e^{-r^2/2}r\, dr$. Integrating from $r = 0$ to $r = R$, we find the required probability to be

(24.4) $$P(X^2 + Y^2 < R^2) = 1 - e^{-R^2/2}.$$

Thus, for example, $P(X^2 + Y^2 < 4) = 1 - e^{-2} = .8647$.

If in (24.4) we let $R \to \infty$, we obtain the total volume under the surface as unity, which is a requirement for a probability surface.

Example 24.2. Show that $\int_{-\infty}^{\infty} e^{-x^2/2}\, dx = \sqrt{2\pi}.$

Solution. Put $A = \int_{-\infty}^{\infty} e^{-x^2/2}\, dx$. The total volume under the surface (24.3) may be written

$$\frac{1}{2\pi} \int_{-\infty}^{\infty} \int_{-\infty}^{\infty} e^{-(x^2+y^2)/2}\, dx\, dy = \frac{1}{2\pi} \int_{-\infty}^{\infty} e^{-x^2/2}\, dx \int_{-\infty}^{\infty} e^{-y^2/2}\, dy = A^2/2\pi = 1.$$

Hence $A = \sqrt{2\pi}$.

Example 24.3. Show that $\Gamma(1/2) = \sqrt{\pi}$.

Solution. Using the definition (17.1) for the gamma function and making the substitution $x = z^2/2$, we obtain

$$\Gamma(1/2) = \int_0^{\infty} x^{-\frac{1}{2}} e^{-x}\, dx = \sqrt{2} \int_0^{\infty} e^{-z^2/2}\, dz.$$

But from the result of Example 24.2, $\int_0^{\infty} e^{-z^2/2}\, dz = \sqrt{\pi/2}$. Hence $\Gamma(1/2) = \sqrt{\pi}$.

Example 24.4. Show that, if X and Y are independent values from $N(0, 1)$, then $Z = X^2 + Y^2$ has the chi-square distribution with 2 d.f. (degrees of freedom).

Solution. By using (24.4), the distribution function of Z is found to be

$$F(z) = P(X^2 + Y^2 < z) = 1 - e^{-z/2}.$$

Hence the density of Z is $dF(z)/dz = \frac{1}{2}e^{-z/2}$, which according to (18.1) is the density of a chi-square distribution with 2 d.f.

Example 24.5. If X and Y are independent values from $N(0, 1)$, find the probability that the line joining (X, Y) to the origin makes an angle with the x-axis which is less than $\pi/6$ in absolute value.

Solution. We require the probability that (X, Y) shall lie in the sector AOD or the sector BOC (Figure 24.1), where AOC and BOD both make $30°$ angles

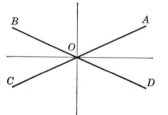

FIGURE 24.1

with the x-axis. Since the probability surface is a surface of revolution, the volume above the two sectors is $1/3$ the volume of the whole surface. Thus the required probability is $1/3$.

Example 24.6. If X and Y are independent values from $N(0, 1)$, find the probability that (X, Y) will fall in the rectangle whose vertices are $A(.5, .5)$, $B(1.0, .5)$, $C(1.0, 1.5)$, $D(.5, 1.5)$.

Solution. The interior of the rectangle consists of all points (X, Y) for which $.5 < X < 1.0$, $.5 < Y < 1.5$. Since X and Y are independent, the required probability is

$$P(.5 < X < 1.0, .5 < Y < 1.5) = P(.5 < X < 1.0) P(.5 < Y < 1.5)$$
$$= (.1498)(.2417) = .0362.$$

Example 24.7. If X and Y are independent values from $N(0, 1)$, find the probability that (X, Y) lies between the lines $3x + 4y = 7$ and $3x + 4y = 8$.

Solution. These 2 lines are parallel to each other but not to either axis. As a result of the rotary symmetry of (24.3), the required probability is the same as the probability that (X, Y) will fall between 2 lines parallel to the y-axis and at the same distances from the origin as the given lines. In order to find their distances from the origin, we write the equations of the lines in normal form:

$$\frac{3x + 4y - 7}{5} = 0,$$

$$\frac{3x + 4y - 8}{5} = 0.$$

Hence the distances from the origin are 1.4 and 1.6, and the required probability is $P(1.4 < X < 1.6) = .0260$.

Example 24.8. If X and Y are independent values from $N(0, 1)$, find the probability that (X, Y) will fall in the rectangle whose vertices are $A(1.2, .8)$, $B(1.6, .6)$, $C(1.9, 1.2)$, $D(1.5, 1.4)$.

Solution. The equations of the 4 sides are AB: $x + 2y = 2.8$; BC: $2x - y = 2.6$; CD: $x + 2y = 4.3$; DA: $2x - y = 1.6$. The parallel sides AB and CD are distant from the origin $2.8/\sqrt{5}$ and $4.3/\sqrt{5}$, on the same side of the origin; the parallel sides BC and AD are distant from the origin $2.6/\sqrt{5}$ and $1.6/\sqrt{5}$, on the same side of the origin. Hence the required probability is

$$P(2.8/\sqrt{5} < X < 4.3/\sqrt{5}) P(1.6/\sqrt{5} < Y < 2.6/\sqrt{5}) = (.0781)(.1146)$$
$$= .00895.$$

Example 24.9. If X and Y are independent values from $N(0, 9)$, find the probability that (X, Y) will lie between the lines $5x + 2y = 7$ and $5x + 2y = -2$.

Solution. The probability surface is no longer (24.3), but

$$z = \frac{1}{18\pi} e^{-(x^2 + y^2)/18}.$$

This is still a surface of revolution, and the method of Example 24.7 will work. We note that the parallel lines are distant $7/\sqrt{29}$ and $-2/\sqrt{29}$ units from the origin, the signs indicating that they are on opposite sides of the origin. Hence we require $P(-2/\sqrt{29} < X < 7/\sqrt{29})$, where X is from $N(0, 9)$. By the usual methods this is found to be .2169.

Example 24.10. If X and Y are independent values from $N(0, 9)$, find $P(2X + 3Y > 5)$.

Solution. The line $2x + 3y = 5$ is distant $5/\sqrt{13}$ units from the origin. We require the probability that the point (X, Y) will fall on the side of this line remote from the origin, which (using the rotary principle) is $P(X > 5/\sqrt{13})$, where X is from $N(0, 9)$. Hence the required probability is .3221.

Example 24.11.   If X and Y are independent values from $N(0, 9)$, find $P(X^2 + Y^2 < 16)$.

Solution.   If X and Y are from $N(0, 9)$, then $U = X/3$ and $V = Y/3$ are from $N(0, 1)$. We may now employ (24.4) in the following way:

$$P(X^2 + Y^2 < 16) = P(9(U^2 + V^2) < 16) = P(U^2 + V^2 < 16/9) = 1 - e^{-16/18}$$
$$= .5889.$$

EXERCISE 24

24.1. If X_1 and X_2 are independently distributed, the first according to $N(5, 9)$, the second according to $N(2, 16)$, find the joint density of (X_1, X_2).

24.2. If X and Y are independent values from $N(0, 1)$, what is the probability that the point (X, Y) lies between the lines $3x + y - 5 = 0$ and $3x + y - 10 = 0$?

24.3. If X and Y are independent values from $N(0, 9)$, what is the probability that the point (X, Y) lies between the lines $5x + 2y - 3 = 0$ and $5x + 2y + 4 = 0$?

24.4. If X and Y are independent values from $N(0, 1)$, what is the probability that the point (X, Y) lies in the rectangle whose vertices are $(-2, 1)$, $(4, 1)$, $(4, 3)$, $(-2, 3)$?

24.5. If X and Y are independent values from $N(0, 15)$, what is the probability that the point (X, Y) lies in the rectangle whose vertices are $(2, 5)$, $(10, 5)$, $(10, -3)$, $(2, -3)$?

24.6. If X and Y are independent values from $N(0, 1)$, what is the probability that the point (X, Y) lies within the rectangle bounded by $x + 3y = 2$, $x + 3y = -1$, $3x - y = 1$, $3x - y = -2$?

24.7. If X and Y are independent values from $N(0, 25)$, what is the probability that the point (X, Y) lies within the sector of a circle bounded by the lines $x - 2y = 0$ and $x - 3y = 0$ and the circle $x^2 + y^2 = 10$, and in the first quadrant?

25. THE NORMAL REPRODUCTIVE LAW

In the light of the discussion of the central limit theorem in Section 22 and elsewhere, it should perhaps seem reasonable that, if samples of size n are drawn from a normal distribution, the sampling distribution of their sums is itself normal. This result is a special case of a more general principle known as the normal reproductive law. Several different modes of proof of this result will be indicated as we proceed. The one given in this section involves no integration and prepares the way for later work.

The operation of sampling from a normal population can always be approximated by sampling from an urn whose distribution is nearly normal. With this in mind, we shall sometimes use the phrase "X is a value from $N(\mu, \sigma^2)$" in place of the phrase "X is a random variable with the distribution $N(\mu, \sigma^2)$." The new phraseology will sometimes enable us to state theorems more concisely.

The proofs of theorems in this section all rest on the following simple result, which is closely related to several of the examples of the previous section. (A review of those examples will prepare the way for the methods of this section.) We recall, from elementary analytic geometry, that a directed line is a line with a positive direction specified upon it. A directed segment AB on a directed line is positive if the direction from A to B is the positive direction on the line, negative otherwise.

(25.1) THEOREM. *Let X and Y be independent values from $N(0, 1)$, and let L be a directed line through the origin O. Let P be the foot of the perpendicular from (X, Y) to the line L. Then the directed segment OP has the distribution $N(0, 1)$.*

Proof. Let $OP = X'$. Let u be any real number. To prove that X' has the distribution $N(0, 1)$, we shall show that $P(X' \leqq u) = F_N(u)$. Assume $u > 0$, let $OQ = u$ (Figure 25.1), and let QR be a line perpendicular to OQ. Then $P(X' \leqq u)$ is the probability that (X, Y) lies on the same side of QR as the origin. This probability is given by the volume under the probability surface (24.3) and on the origin side of RQ. But, since (24.3) is a surface of revolution, the volume in question is equal to the volume under the surface and to the left of the line $x = u$. But this is simply $P(X \leqq u) = F_N(u)$. Hence $P(X' \leqq u) = F_N(u)$, and it follows that $X' = OP$ has the distribution $N(0, 1)$. If $u < 0$, the proof will be similar, except that $P(X' = u)$ will be the

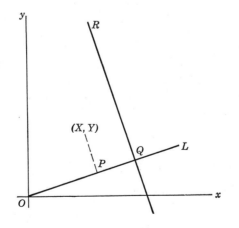

FIGURE 25.1

probability that (X, Y) lies on the side of QR remote from the origin. If $u = 0$, $P(X' \leq u) = .5 = F_N(0)$. Thus the proof is complete.

If the positive direction on OQ makes an angle θ with the positive direction on the x-axis, it is proved in analytic geometry that $X' = OP = X \cos \theta + Y \sin \theta$. Hence we have

(25.2) THEOREM. *If X and Y are independent values from $N(0, 1)$, and θ is an arbitrary angle, then $X' = X \cos \theta + Y \sin \theta$ has the distribution $N(0, 1)$.*

The simplest version of the normal reproductive law is the following:

(25.3) THEOREM. *If X and Y are independent values, the first from $N(\mu_x, \sigma_x^2)$, the second from $N(\mu_y, \sigma_y^2)$, then $X + Y$ has the distribution $N(\mu_x + \mu_y, \sigma_x^2 + \sigma_y^2)$.*

Proof. Since X and Y possess the specified distributions, $U = (X - \mu_x)\sigma_x$ and $V = (Y - \mu_y)/\sigma_y$ are independent values from $N(0, 1)$. Now consider the quantity

$$Z = X + Y = \sigma_x U + \sigma_y V + \mu_x + \mu_y$$

$$= \sqrt{\sigma_x^2 + \sigma_y^2} \left[\frac{\sigma_x}{\sqrt{\sigma_x^2 + \sigma_y^2}} U + \frac{\sigma_y}{\sqrt{\sigma_x^2 + \sigma_y^2}} V \right] + \mu_x + \mu_y$$

$$= \sqrt{\sigma_x^2 + \sigma_y^2} \, (U \cos \theta + V \sin \theta) + \mu_x + \mu_y,$$

where θ is the first-quadrant angle such that $\tan \theta = \sigma_y/\sigma_x$. From (25.2) the quantity $W = U \cos \theta + V \sin \theta$ has the distribution $N(0, 1)$, and as a result the quantity $Z = X + Y = \sqrt{\sigma_x^2 + \sigma_y^2} \, W + \mu_x + \mu_y$ has the distribution $N(\mu_x + \mu_y, \sigma_x^2 + \sigma_y^2)$.

A more general form of the normal reproductive law is the following:

(25.4) THEOREM. *If X_1 and X_2 are independently distributed, the first from $N(\mu_1, \sigma_1^2)$, the second from $N(\mu_2, \sigma_2^2)$, and if a_1 and a_2 are real numbers, then $a_1X_1 + a_2X_2$ has the distribution $N(a_1\mu_1 + a_2\mu_2, a_1^2\sigma_2^2 + a_2^2\sigma_2^2)$.*

Proof. The proof is similar to that for (25.3), the angle θ now being chosen as the smallest angle (first or second quadrant) for which $\tan \theta = a_2\sigma_2/a_1\sigma_1$.

An expression such as $a_1X_1 + a_2X_2$ is called a *linear combination* of X_1 and X_2. Thus (25.4) asserts that a linear combination of two normally and independently distributed quantities is itself normally distributed. The extension of this result to n normally and independently distributed quantities is contained in the following theorem. We shall only remark that the manner of proof is entirely similar to that used in (21.3).

(25.5) THEOREM. NORMAL REPRODUCTIVE LAW. *If $X_1, \cdots, X_n$ are independent random values, with distributions $N(\mu_1, \sigma_1{}^2), \cdots, N(\mu_n, \sigma_n{}^2)$, respectively, and if $a_1, \cdots, a_n$ are arbitrary real numbers, then $a_1X_1 + \cdots + a_nX_n$ has the distribution $N(a_1\mu_1 + \cdots + a_n\mu_n, a_1{}^2\sigma_1{}^2 + \cdots + a_n{}^2\sigma_n{}^2)$.*

EXERCISE 25

25.1. X, Y, and Z are independent random values, the first from $N(-3, 4)$, the second from $N(10, 16)$, the third from $N(2, 25)$. Find the probability
  (*a*) That $X + Y + Z$ is greater than 17.
  (*b*) That $2X - 3Y + Z$ is less than -50.

25.2. Prove Theorem (25.5).

25.3. Prove that, if X has the distribution $N(\mu_x, \sigma_x{}^2)$ and Y has the distribution $N(\mu_y, \sigma_y{}^2)$, then $X - Y$ has the distribution $N(\mu_x - \mu_y, \sigma_x{}^2 + \sigma_y{}^2)$.

25.4. Prove that, if a sample of n independent values $(X_1, \cdots, X_n)$ is drawn from $N(\mu, \sigma^2)$, the sample mean $\overline{X}$ has the distribution $N(\mu, \sigma^2/n)$. Use (25.5), with a suitable choice of $a_1, \cdots, a_n$.

25.5. Let $(X_1, \cdots, X_n)$ be a sample of n independent values from $N(\mu_x, \sigma_x{}^2)$, and $(Y_1, \cdots, Y_m)$ a second sample of m independent values from $N(\mu_y, \sigma_y{}^2)$. Show that, if $\overline{X}$ is the mean of the first sample and $\overline{Y}$ the mean of the second sample, then $\overline{X} - \overline{Y}$ has the distribution

$$N\left(\mu_x - \mu_y, \frac{\sigma_x{}^2}{n} + \frac{\sigma_y{}^2}{m}\right).$$

26. THE t DISTRIBUTION—CONFIDENCE INTERVALS

We shall find, in Chapter 4, that it is of great advantage to be able to make probability statements concerning a normal population without explicit reference to the population variance σ^2. The means by which this may be done is the ratio t defined by

(26.1)
$$t = \frac{\overline{X} - \mu}{s/\sqrt{n}},$$

where μ is the population mean, and $\overline{X}$ and s are the mean and variance of a sample of size n. The distribution of t was first derived by W. S. Gosset ("Student"). For this reason, the distribution is often referred to as Student's distribution, and the quantity t of (26.1) is sometimes called Student's ratio.

In Section 41 we shall prove that the quantity t defined by (26.1) possesses the t distribution with $n - 1$ d.f. The density of this distribution is

$$(26.2) \quad f(t) = \frac{\Gamma\left(\dfrac{m+1}{2}\right)}{\sqrt{n\pi}\ \Gamma\left(\dfrac{m}{2}\right)}\left(1 + \frac{t^2}{m}\right)^{-(m+1)/2} , \quad -\infty < t < \infty,$$

where $m = n - 1$ is the number of degrees of freedom. This is the distribution that was discussed in Example 18.8. For 1 d.f. ($n = 2$), it is identical with the Cauchy distribution (Example 18.5); for large n, the distribution approaches $N(0, 1)$. The t distribution for 11 d.f. is shown in Figure 26.1, together with a normal density curve for comparison. It will be noted that the t-curve approaches the horizontal axis more slowly than does the normal curve.

In order to illustrate the use of the t distribution in statistical inference, consider a sample of size n, with mean $\overline{X}$ and standard deviation s. Let us suppose that we are satisfied that the sample is drawn from a normal distribution, whose mean μ we do not know. Let $t_{.975}$ denote the 97.5 percentile of the t distribution with $n - 1$ d.f. Then we may state

$$P\left(\left|\frac{\overline{X} - \mu}{s/\sqrt{n}}\right| \leq t_{.975}\right) = P(|t| \leq .975) = .95,$$

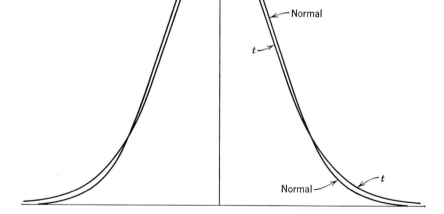

FIGURE 26.1. Comparison of normal distribution with the t distribution with 11 d.f.

since 95% of the area under the curve will lie between $-t_{.975}$ and $t_{.975}$. Thus

$$P(|\overline{X} - \mu| \leq st_{.975}/\sqrt{n}) = .95.$$

Now the inequality $|\overline{X} - \mu| \leq st_{.975}/\sqrt{n}$ is equivalent to $-st_{.975}/\sqrt{n} \leq \mu - \overline{X} \leq st_{.975}/\sqrt{n}$, which is again equivalent to

(26.3) $$\overline{X} - st_{.975}/\sqrt{n} \leq \mu \leq \overline{X} + st_{.975}/\sqrt{n}.$$

Although (26.3) is derived from a probability statement, we avoid saying that the probability is .95 that (26.3) is true, since such a statement would seem to imply that μ is a random variable. Equation (26.3) actually states that μ lies in a certain interval; but μ is fixed, and the two boundaries of the interval are random variables. Under these circumstances we say that we are *95% confident* that (26.3) is true. The quantities $\overline{X} \pm st_{.975}/\sqrt{n}$ are called *confidence limits*, and the interval (26.3) is called a *confidence interval*. Confidence intervals are systematically considered in Section 31.

Example 26.1. A sample of size $n = 15$ has mean $\overline{X} = 27.80$ and variance $s^2 = 37.2$. Find the 95% confidence limits for the population mean μ.

Solution. From Table 4 we find the 97.5 percentile of t, with 14 d.f. is $t_{.975} = 2.145$. The confidence limits are, from (26.3),

$$27.80 \pm 2.145 \sqrt{37.2/15} = 27.80 \pm 3.38 = 24.42 \text{ and } 31.18.$$

We therefore may assert, with 95% confidence, that the population mean μ lies in the interval 24.42 to 31.18.

EXERCISE 26

26.1. Plot the t distribution with 3 d.f. and, for comparison, the unit normal distribution. Note that this t distribution is farther from the normal distribution than is the t distribution depicted in Figure 26.1.

26.2. A sample of size $n = 25$ has mean $\overline{X} = 135.4$ and variance $s^2 = 26.4$. Find the 90% confidence limits for the population mean μ.

26.3. A sample of size $n = 16$ has mean $\overline{X} = 315.2$ and variance $s^2 = 75.8$. Find the 95% confidence limits for the population mean μ.

26.4. $\overline{X}$ is the mean of a sample of size $n = 25$, and s^2 is its variance. The sample is drawn from a normal distribution with mean $\mu = 50$. Find $P(\overline{X} > 50 + .4s)$.

26.5. A sample of size $n = 10$ is drawn from a normal distribution whose mean is $\mu = 250$. If $\overline{X}$ and s^2 are the sample mean and variance, find $P(s > 5\overline{X} - 1250)$.

27. PARAMETERS OF BIVARIATE AND SAMPLING DISTRIBUTIONS

It is proved in more advanced treatments of statistical theory that a distribution is completely specified if we know its complete series of moments μ_1', μ_2', μ_3', $\cdots$. In the case of the commonly used distributions (normal, binomial, Poisson, etc.), one or two moments suffice to determine the distribution. Thus a powerful approach to the problem of sampling distributions is to find the relationships which exist between the moments of a sampling distribution and the moments of the parent population. The derivation of such relations is a primary goal of this section.

The results of this section will be true for both discrete and continuous variables. The proofs for the discrete case and the continuous case are always strictly parallel, so that one can be converted into the other by replacing the operation of summation by the operation of integration, or vice versa. We shall usually present only a single proof; the student is urged to obtain the other proof by exchanging the operations of summation and integration.

Let X and Y be a pair of random variables. For the discrete case we assume that the joint frequency function is $P(X = x_i, Y = y_j) = p_{ij}$; for the continuous case we assume the joint density is $f(x, y)$. Then we have the following pair of definitions for the expected value of a function $g(X, Y)$:

$$E(g(X, Y)) = \Sigma p_{ij}\, g(x_i, y_j)$$

(27.1)

$$E(g(X, Y)) = \iint f(x, y)\, g(x, y)\, dx\, dy$$

The summation will always extend over the complete range of the subscripts i and j; the integration will likewise always extend over the complete range of x and y. For this reason it will not be necessary to indicate the range of summation or integration. Such parameters as $E(X^n)$, $E(Y^n)$, σ_x^2, σ_y^2, $E(XY)$ may all be regarded as special cases of (27.1). For example, the mean and variance of X are given by

$$\mu_x = E(X) = \Sigma p_{ij}x_i \qquad \mu_x = E(X) = \iint f(x, y)x\, dx\, dy$$

(27.2) $\sigma_x^2 = E(X^2) - (E(X))^2$, for both cases where

$$E(X^2) = \Sigma p_{ij}x_i^2 \qquad E(X^2) = \iint f(x, y)x^2\, dx\, dy.$$

If X and Y are random variables, their sum $X + Y$ is a random variable. Since for many purposes the distribution of $X + Y$ is adequately specified by its mean and variance, we shall be primarily interested in these two parameters and in the extent to which they can be predicted from a knowledge of the mean and variance of X and Y. The following theorem enables us to obtain the mean of $X + Y$ from the means of X and of Y.

(27.3)   THEOREM.   *Let X and Y be random variables with means μ_x and μ_y. Then the mean of the random variable $X + Y$ is $\mu_x + \mu_y$.*

Proof. We shall provide parallel proofs for the discrete and continuous cases. For the discrete case, let $P(X = x_i, Y = y_j) = p_{ij}$; for the continuous case, let the density be $f(x, y)$. The mean of $X + Y$ is the same as $E(X + Y)$. We find

$$E(X + Y) = \Sigma p_{ij}(x_i + y_j) \qquad E(X + Y) = \iint f(x, y)(x + y)\, dx\, dy$$

$$= \Sigma p_{ij}x_i + \Sigma p_{ij}y_j \qquad = \iint f(x, y)x\, dx\, dy$$

$$+ \iint f(x, y)y\, dx\, dy$$

$$= E(X) + E(Y) \qquad = E(X) + E(Y)$$

$$= \mu_x + \mu_y \qquad = \mu_x + \mu_y$$

The preceding theorem is readily extended to n variables, using mathematical induction.

(27.4)   THEOREM.   *Let $X_1, \cdots, X_n$ be random variables with means $\mu_1, \cdots, \mu_n$. Then the mean of the random variable $X_1 + \cdots + X_n$ is $\mu_1 + \cdots + \mu_n$.*

Proof. The proof is quite similar to that of Theorem (21.3). From (27.3) we first conclude that the mean of the random variable $X_1 + X_2$ is $\mu_1 + \mu_2$. Now consider the random variable $X_1 + X_2 + X_3 = (X_1 + X_2) + X_3$. This is the sum of two random variables $(X_1 + X_2)$ with mean $\mu_1 + \mu_2$ and X_3 with mean μ_3. Hence by (27.3) its mean is $\mu_1 + \mu_2 + \mu_3$. The proof is now completed by mathematical induction.

Since the mean of a random variable is identical with its mathematical expectation, (27.4) may be put in the following form:

(27.5)   *If $X_1, \cdots, X_n$ are random variables*

$$E(X_1 + \cdots + X_n) = E(X_1) + \cdots + E(X_n).$$

Thus the expectation of a sum is the sum of the individual expectations.

Example 27.1.   Consider the bivariate distribution of Example 20.2, in which X and Y are drawings without replacement from an urn.   We readily find the marginal distributions

x	1	2	3
p	.2	.5	.3

y	1	2	3
p	.2	.5	.3

Thus $E(X) = E(Y) = 2.1$.   On the other hand the distribution of $X + Y$ is

$x+y$	2	3	4	5	6
p	2/90	20/90	32/90	30/90	6/90

from which we find $E(X + Y) = 4.2$, thus illustrating (27.5).   Let us now investigate $E(XY)$.   The distribution of XY is

xy	1	2	3	4	6	9
p	2/90	20/90	12/90	20/90	30/90	6/90

,

so that $E(XY) = 392/90 = 4.356$.   Thus $E(XY)$ is not the same as $E(X) E(Y) = 2.1^2 = 4.41$.   One is led to ask under what circumstances $E(XY) = E(X) E(Y)$.   Theorem (27.6) will show that $E(XY) = E(X) E(Y)$ if X and Y are independently distributed.   The converse is not true, however, as is demonstrated by the following example.

Example 27.2.   For the bivariate distribution specified by the table, we readily find $E(X) = E(Y) = 2.0$ and $E(XY) = 4.0$, so that $E(XY) = E(X) E(Y)$. Nevertheless the variables X and Y are not independently distributed since the equation $P(X = x_i, Y = y_j) = P(X = x_i) P(Y = y_j)$ is not satisfied for all i, j.

y \ x	1	2	3	
1	.2	0	.2	.4
2	0	.2	0	.2
3	.2	0	.2	.4
	.4	.2	.4	1.0

(27.6)   THEOREM.   *If X and Y are independent random variables, then $E(XY) = E(X) E(Y)$.*

Proof.   Since X and Y are independent, $p_{ij} = p_i p_j'$, where $p_i = P(X = x_i)$, $p_j' = P(Y = y_j)$.   Hence

$$E(XY) = \sum_i \sum_j p_i p_j' x_i y_j = \sum_i p_i x_i \sum_j p_j' y_j = E(X) E(Y).$$

In order to see clearly that $\sum_i \sum_j p_i p_j' x_i x_j$ actually factors into $\sum_i p_i x_i \sum_j p_j' y_j$, it may be helpful to write out the summations in full for a modest example, say that for which $i = 1, 2, 3$ and $j = 1, 2, 3$.

Theorem (27.6) asserts that, if X and Y are independent, the expectation of their product is the product of their expectations.

We may use (27.6) to show that, if X and Y are independently distributed, the variance of their sum is equal to the sum of their variances.

(27.7) THEOREM. *If X and Y are independently distributed with variances $\sigma_x{}^2$ and $\sigma_y{}^2$, then the variance of $X + Y$ is $\sigma_x{}^2 + \sigma_y{}^2$.*

Proof. We first find the expectation of $(X + Y)^2$.

$$E(X + Y)^2 = E(X^2 + 2XY + Y^2)$$
$$= E(X^2) + 2E(XY) + E(Y^2), \quad \text{using (27.5)}$$
$$= E(X^2) + 2E(X)\,E(Y) + E(Y^2), \quad \text{using (27.6).}$$

Thus

$$\sigma_{x+y}^2 = E(X + Y)^2 - [E(X + Y)]^2$$
$$= E(X^2) + 2E(X)\,E(Y) + E(Y^2) - [E(X) + E(Y)]^2$$
$$= E(X^2) - (E(X))^2 + E(Y^2) - (E(Y))^2 = \sigma_x{}^2 + \sigma_y{}^2.$$

Using mathematical induction in the same manner as in (27.4), we may readily extend (27.7) to the case of n independent random variables. This result may conveniently be combined with that of (27.5) in the following form:

(27.8) THEOREM. *If $X_1, \cdots, X_n$ are independent random variables with means $\mu_1, \cdots, \mu_n$ and variances $\sigma_1{}^2, \cdots, \sigma_n{}^2$, then the mean and variance of their sum S are*

$$\mu_S = \mu_1 + \cdots + \mu_n, \quad \sigma_S{}^2 = \sigma_1{}^2 + \cdots + \sigma_n{}^2.$$

More generally, consider the linear combination $Z = a_1X_1 + \cdots + a_nX_n$ of the independent random variables $X_1, \cdots, X_n$, where $a_1, \cdots, a_n$ are constants. The following result can be proved in the same manner as (27.8), beginning with 2 variables and extending to n variables by induction. The proof is left as an exercise.

(27.9) THEOREM. *If $X_1, \cdots, X_n$ are independent random variables with means $\mu_1, \cdots, \mu_n$ and variances $\sigma_1{}^2, \cdots, \sigma_n{}^2$ and if $a_1, \cdots, a_n$ are arbitrary real numbers, then the random variable $Z = a_1X_1 + \cdots + a_nX_n$ has mean and variance*

$$\mu_z = a_1\mu_1 + \cdots + a_n\mu_n, \quad \sigma_z{}^2 = a_1{}^2\sigma_1{}^2 + \cdots + a_n{}^2\sigma_n{}^2.$$

Consider now the important case in which $X_1, \cdots, X_n$ all possess the same distribution, so that the set $(X_1, \cdots, X_n)$ constitutes a random sample from some population. We wish to find the mean and variance of the sample sum $S = X_1 + \cdots + X_n$ and of the sample mean $\overline{X} = (1/n)(X_1 + \cdots + X_n)$. The mean and variance of S are given directly by (27.8), while the mean and variance of $\overline{X} = (1/n)X_1 + \cdots + (1/n)X_n$ are given by (27.9) with $a_1 = \cdots = a_n = 1/n$. We thus obtain

(27.10)   THEOREM. *If $X_1, \cdots, X_n$ are independent random values from a population with mean μ and variance σ^2, then the mean and variance of $S = X_1 + \cdots + X_n$ are*

$$\mu_S = n\mu, \quad \sigma_S{}^2 = n\sigma^2,$$

and the mean and variance of $\overline{X} = (1/n)(X_1 + \cdots + X_n)$ are

$$\mu_{\overline{X}} = \mu, \quad \sigma_{\overline{X}}{}^2 = \frac{1}{n}\sigma^2.$$

The fact that $\mu_{\overline{X}} = \mu$ implies that, if we form all possible samples of size n from a given population, calculate the mean of each, and average these means, we obtain the mean of the original population. This is the justification for the assertion, made in Section 8, that the mean of a sample provides an unbiased estimate of the mean of the population from which the sample was drawn. We noted, also in Section 8, that the sample variance as given by $\text{var}(X)$ *is not* an unbiased estimate of the population variance, but that

$$s^2 = \frac{n}{n-1} \, \text{var}(X)$$

is an unbiased estimate. We are now in a position to prove the latter assertion.

(27.11)   THEOREM. *If $X_1, \cdots, X_n$ are independent random values from a population with variance σ^2 and if*

$$s^2 = \frac{n\Sigma X^2 - (\Sigma X)^2}{n(n-1)},$$

then $E(s^2) = \sigma^2$.

Proof. From (27.10), $E(\overline{X}) = \mu$, where μ is the mean of the population. Since $X_1, \cdots, X_n$ are from a population with mean μ and variance σ^2,

$$E(X_i{}^2) = \sigma^2 + \mu^2, \quad i = 1, \cdots, n.$$

On the other hand $\overline{X}$ may be regarded as a random variable from a population with mean μ and variance σ^2/n, so that

$$E(\overline{X}^2) = \frac{\sigma^2}{n} + \mu^2.$$

Now

$$\frac{n-1}{n} s^2 = \frac{1}{n}(X_1{}^2 + \cdots + X_n{}^2) - \overline{X}^2.$$

Hence

$$E\left(\frac{n-1}{n} s^2\right) = \frac{1}{n}(E(X_1{}^2) + \cdots + E(X_n{}^2)) - E(\overline{X}^2)$$

$$= \sigma^2 + \mu^2 - \left(\frac{\sigma^2}{n} + \mu^2\right) = \frac{n-1}{n} \sigma^2.$$

Hence $E(s^2) = \sigma^2$.

This theorem implies that the quantity var(X), when calculated for a sample, has a systematic tendency to underestimate the population variance, which is corrected by the factor $n/(n-1)$.

The *covariance* of the pair of variables X and Y is denoted by cov(X, Y) and defined by

$$(27.12) \quad \text{cov}(X, Y) = E(X - \mu_x)(Y - \mu_y) = E(XY) - E(X)\,E(Y).$$

We have seen, in (27.6), that $E(XY) = E(X)\,E(Y)$, or equivalently, cov(X, Y) = 0, when X and Y are independently distributed. This suggests the possibility of using cov(X, Y) as a measure of the "degree of dependence" of X and Y, since it is zero when they are independent. In order to get a suitable "scale of dependence," we shall assume that a linear relationship $Y = aX + b$, where $a \neq 0$, represents "complete dependence" of Y upon X. Then, remembering that $\sigma_x{}^2 = E(X^2) - \mu_x{}^2$, $\sigma_y{}^2 = E(Y^2) - \mu_y{}^2$, we find

$$E(Y) = a\mu_x + b, \quad E(Y^2) = E(a^2X^2 + 2abX + b^2)$$

$$= a^2(\sigma_x{}^2 + \mu_x{}^2) + 2ab\mu_x + b^2,$$

$$\sigma_y{}^2 = E(Y^2) - \mu_y{}^2 = a^2\sigma_x{}^2, \quad \sigma_y = \pm a\sigma_x,$$

$$E(XY) = E(aX^2 + bX) = a(\sigma_x{}^2 + \mu_x{}^2) + b\mu_x,$$

$$\text{cov}(X, Y) = E(XY) - E(X)\,E(Y) = a\sigma_x{}^2 = \pm\sigma_x\sigma_y.$$

The covariance cov(X, Y) thus ranges from zero for independence to $\pm\sigma_x\sigma_y$ for "complete dependence." We would prefer to have a measure which ranges from 0 to ± 1, and so we divide by $\sigma_x\sigma_y$. We thus arrive at the "index of dependence,"

$$(27.13) \quad \rho = \frac{\text{cov}(X, Y)}{\sigma_x\sigma_y} = \frac{E(XY) - E(X)\,E(Y)}{\sigma_x\sigma_y}$$

The quantity defined in (27.13) is called the *coefficient of correlation*. Here it is defined for a bivariate population; in Chapter 6 we shall see that a corresponding statistic exists, defined for a bivariate sample.

Example 27.3. In Example 27.1 we found the following parameters of the joint distribution of 2 drawings without replacement from the urn of Example 20.2: $E(X) = E(Y) = 2.1$, $E(XY) = 392/90$. Thus we obtain $\mathrm{cov}(X, Y) = 392/90 - 4.41 = -49/900$. It is readily verified, also, that $E(X^2) = E(Y^2) = 4.9$, $\sigma_x^2 = \sigma_y^2 = \sigma_x \sigma_y = .49$. Hence

$$\rho = \frac{\mathrm{cov}(X,\ Y)}{\sigma_x \sigma_y} = \frac{\dfrac{-49}{900}}{.49} = -1/9.$$

This is a special, and very simple, case of the general result stated in Exercise 27.7.

In Example 27.2 we saw that $E(XY) = E(X)\,E(Y)$, even though the variables were not independently distributed. It follows that $\rho = 0$ is a necessary, but not a sufficient, condition for the independence of two variables.

We may now state the following generalization of (27.7) for the case in which X and Y need not be independent:

(27.14)   THEOREM.   *If the random variables X and Y possess variances σ_x^2 and σ_y^2, and correlation ρ, then $\sigma_{x+y}^2 = \sigma_x^2 + 2\rho\sigma_x\sigma_y + \sigma_y^2$.*

Proof. In the proof of (27.7) we replaced $E(XY)$ by the product $E(X)\,E(Y)$. In the general case when the variables X and Y need not be independent, we should according to (27.13) replace $E(XY)$ by $E(X)\,E(Y) + \rho\sigma_x\sigma_y$. When this adjustment is made in the proof of (27.7), we readily obtain the result stated in (27.14).

The extension of (27.14) to n variables is straightforward.

(27.15)   THEOREM.   *If the variables $X_1, \cdots, X_n$ have variances $\sigma_1^2, \cdots, \sigma_n^2$ and if the correlation between X_i and X_j is ρ_{ij}, then the variance of the random variable $Z = X_1 + \cdots + X_n$ is*

$$\sigma_z^2 = \sigma_1^2 + \cdots + \sigma_n^2 + 2 \sum_{ij} \rho_{ij}\sigma_i\sigma_j,$$
$$= \sigma_1^2 + \cdots + \sigma_n^2 + 2 \sum_{ij} \mathrm{cov}(X_i, X_j)$$

where the summation is over all pairs i, j for which $i \neq j$.

The proof, which will not be given, proceeds by induction.

Up to this point we have been mainly concerned with sampling from an infinite population or, equivalently, with sampling with replacement from a finite population. The basic tool in the treatment of sampling without replacement is the generalized hypergeometric distribution (7.12). The sample space here consists of the possible ordered sets $(x_1, \cdots, x_k)$, subject to the restrictions mentioned in connection with (7.12). It should be emphasized that the numbers $x_1, \cdots, x_k$ are here to be understood as *sample frequencies* and that each of these numbers may vary from sample to sample.

Let us now make a slight alteration in (7.12). Instead of labeling the balls in the urn 1, 2, $\cdots$, k, let us label them $u_1, \cdots, u_k$, where the u_i are arbitrary real numbers, fixed once and for all when the original finite population is formed. Then the frequency distribution for the sample corresponding to the sample point $(x_1, \cdots, x_k)$ is

$$\text{Value} \qquad u_1 \cdots u_k$$

$$\text{Frequency} \quad x_1 \cdots x_k.$$

Let us use $X_1, \cdots, X_k$ for the random variables corresponding to $x_1, \cdots, x_k$. The sample mean, $\overline{U} = \dfrac{1}{n}\Sigma X_i u_i$, is also a random variable. We shall state without proof the essential facts concerning the parameters of the distributions of the X_i and $\overline{U}$. Suggested methods of proof are outlined in Exercises 27.12 to 27.16.

$$(27.16) \qquad E(X_i) = np_i$$

$$(27.17) \qquad \text{var}(X_i) = \frac{n(N-n)}{N-1}\, p_i(1-p_i)$$

$$(27.18) \quad \text{cov}(X_i, X_j) = \frac{-n(N-n)}{N-1}\, p_i p_j$$

$$(27.19) \qquad E(\overline{U}) = \mu = \Sigma p_i u_i$$

$$(27.20) \qquad \text{var}(\overline{U}) = \frac{N-n}{n(N-1)}\, \sigma^2, \quad \text{where } \sigma^2 = \Sigma p_i(u_i - \mu)^2.$$

The concepts of generating function (g.f.) and moment generating function (m.g.f.) are readily extended to bivariate distributions. If $g(x, y)$ is any function, the g.f. of the random variable $g(X, Y)$ is

$$(27.21) \qquad G_{g(x,y)}(t) = F(t^{g(X,Y)}),$$

and the m.g.f. of $g(X, Y)$ is

$$(27.22) \qquad M_{g(x,y)}(t) = E(e^{tg(X,Y)}),$$

provided that these expectations exist.

The usefulness of these functions becomes evident when we consider the case $g(x, y) = x + y$ and assume that the variables X and Y are continuous and independent, with densities $f_1(x)$ and $f_2(y)$. Then $f(x, y) = f_1(x) f_2(y)$, and

$$(27.23) \quad G_{x+y}(t) = E(t^{X+Y}) = \iint t^{x+y} f_1(x) f_2(y) \, dx \, dy$$

$$= \int t^x f_1(x) \, dx \int t^y f_2(y) \, dy = G_x(t) \, G_y(t).$$

This is the result we obtained in (21.2) for the discrete case, which we may state in the form: the g.f. of the sum of 2 independent random variables is the product of their g.f.'s.

A similar result holds for the m.g.f. of $x + y$ when X and Y are independent. We find

$$(27.24) \quad M_{x+y}(t) = E(e^{t(X+Y)}) = \iint e^{t(x+y)} f_1(x) f_2(y) \, dx \, dy$$

$$= \int e^{tx} f_1(x) \, dx \int e^{ty} f_2(y) \, dy = M_x(t) M_y(t).$$

Thus the m.g.f. of a sum of 2 independent random variables is the product of their m.g.f.'s.

Example 27.4. Let X and Y be independently distributed normal variates, X possessing the distribution $N(\mu_1, \sigma_1^2)$, Y the distribution $N(\mu_2, \sigma_2^2)$. According to Example 19.2, their m.g.f.'s are $M_x(t) = e^{(\sigma_1^2 t^2 + 2\mu_1 t)/2}$, $M_y(t) = e^{(\sigma_2^2 t^2 + 2\mu_2 t)/2}$. The m.g.f. of $X + Y$ is thus, according to (27.24)

$$M_{x+y}(t) = M_x(t) M_y(t) = e^{((\sigma_1^2 + \sigma_2^2) t^2 + 2(\mu_1 + \mu_2) t)/2}.$$

But this is the m.g.f. of a random variable with distribution $N(\mu_1 + \mu_2, \sigma_1^2 + \sigma_2^2)$. Hence, if we assume that only this particular normal distribution can possess this m.g.f. (a fact proved at a more advanced level), we can conclude that, if X has the distribution $N(\mu_1, \sigma_1^2)$ and Y the distribution $N(\mu_2, \sigma_2^2)$ and if X and Y are independent, their sum has the distribution $N(\mu_1 + \mu_2, \sigma_1^2 + \sigma_2^2)$. This is a form of the normal reproductive law, proved otherwise in (25.3).

Example 27.5. Suppose X and Y are independent variables with chi-square distributions, the first with m d.f., the second with n d.f. Then according to Example 19.4 the m.g.f.'s of X and Y are $M_x(t) = (1 - 2t)^{-m/2}$ and $M_y(t) = (1 - 2t)^{-n/2}$. Hence from (27.24) the m.g.f. of $X + Y$ is $M_{x+y}(t) = (1 - 2t)^{-(m+n)/2}$. This is the m.g.f. of a chi-square distribution with $m + n$ d.f. We conclude that if 2 independently distributed quantities have chi-square distributions with m and n d.f., their sum likewise possesses the chi-square distribution with $m + n$ d.f. This is the so-called reproductive law for the chi-square distribution. See (37.3).

EXERCISE 27

27.1. The random variables X and Y possess the joint distribution given in the table. Find:

$\quad$ (*a*) $E(X)$, $\qquad$ (*b*) $E(Y)$, $\qquad$ (*c*) $E(X^2)$, $\quad$ (*d*) $E(Y^2)$,

$\quad$ (*e*) σ_x^2, $\qquad\quad$ (*f*) σ_y^2, $\qquad$ (*g*) $E(XY)$, $\quad$ (*h*) $\mathrm{cov}(X, Y)$,

$\quad$ (*i*) $E(2X + 3Y)$, $\;$ (*j*) $E(X^2Y)$, $\;$ (*k*) ρ.

y \ x	1	2	3
1	.12	.05	.13
2	.21	.15	.09
3	.03	.14	.08

27.2. An urn possesses the distribution

x	1	2	3
ϕ	3	3	4

Find, as in Example 20.2, the joint frequency distribution for pairs of drawings from this urn, without replacement. Then determine all the parameters (*a*) through (*k*) listed in Exercise 27.1, for this distribution.

27.3. The random variables X and Y possess the joint density $f(x, y) = 4xy$ over the region $0 \leq x \leq 1$, $0 \leq y \leq 1$. Determine, for this example, the parameters *a* through *k* listed in Exercise 27.1.

27.4. Let X be a random variable with density $f(x) = 2x$, $0 \leq x \leq 1$, and Y be a second random variable, independent of X, with a uniform density over the interval $0 \leq y \leq 1$. Find the mean and variance of $X + Y$ and of $2X - 5Y$.

27.5. Let X and Y have the joint density $f(x, y) = 3y$ over the region $x < 1$, $y > 0$, $x - y > 0$; and $f(x, y) = 3x$ over the region $x > 0$, $y < 1$, $x - y < 0$. Find the marginal densities of X and Y, the mean and variance of X and Y, and the correlation between X and Y.

*27.6. Show that, if an urn has the distribution

u	u_1	u_2	$\cdots$	u_k
p	p_1	p_2	$\cdots$	p_k

then 2 drawings X and Y, without replacement, will have the joint distribution:

y \ x	u_1	u_2		u_k
μ_1	$p_1^2 - p_1/N$	p_1p_2	$\cdots$	p_1p_k
μ_2	p_1p_2	$p_2^2 - p_2/N$	$\cdots$	p_2p_k
.				
.				
.				
μ_k	p_1p_k	p_2p_k		$p_k^2 - p_k/N$

*27.7. Use the result of Exercise 27.6 in order to prove that, for the joint distribution of 2 drawings X and Y, without replacement, from the urn of Exercise 27.6:

(a) $E(X) = E(Y) = \Sigma p_i u_i = \mu$.

(b) $\operatorname{var}(X) = \operatorname{var}(Y) = \Sigma p_i u_i^2 - \mu^2 = \sigma^2$.

(c) $\operatorname{cov}(X, Y) = -\sigma^2/(N - 1)$.

(d) $\rho = -1/N - 1$.

*27.8. Prove (27.9).

*27.9. The term "bivariate normal distribution" includes all densities of the form $f(x, y) = ke^{-Q}$, where Q is a quadratic function in x and y, with certain additional restrictions. Suppose $Q = ax^2 + hxy + cy^2$, where a and c are positive, and $b^2 - 4ac$ is negative. Find, in terms of a, b, and c, the mean and variance of X, the mean and variance of Y, and the correlation between X and Y. (Use appropriate integrals from Exercise 17.)

*27.10. Prove that, if the random variables X and Y have variances σ_x^2 and σ_y^2 and covariance $\operatorname{cov}(X, Y)$ and if a and b are real numbers, the variance of the random variable $Z = aX + bY$ is $\sigma_z^2 = a^2\sigma_x^2 + b^2\sigma_y^2 + 2ab \operatorname{cov}(X, Y)$.

*27.11. Extend the result of Exercise 27.10 to show that, if the random variables X_1, $\cdots$, X_n have variances σ_1^2, $\cdots$, σ_n^2 and if the covariance of the pair X_i, X_j is $\operatorname{cov}(X_i, X_j)$, the variance of $Z = a_1X_1 + \cdots + a_nX_n$ is

$$\sigma_2^2 = a_1^2\sigma_1^2 + \cdots + a_n^2\sigma_n^2 + 2\Sigma a_i a_j \operatorname{cov}(X_i, X_j),$$

where a_1, $\cdots$, a_n are real numbers, and the summation extends over all pairs i, j for which $i \neq j$.

*27.12. A population of size N has the distribution

$$\left\{ \begin{matrix} u_1 \cdots u_k \\ p_1 \cdots p_k \end{matrix} \right\}.$$

[See (7.12).] A random sample of size n, drawn without replacement, has the frequency distribution

$$\left\{ \begin{matrix} u_1 \cdots u_k \\ X_1 \cdots X_k \end{matrix} \right\},$$

where the joint frequency function of the random variables X_1, $\cdots$, X_k is given by (7.12). Using the approach of Exercise 11.10, show that $E(X_i) = np_i$, $i = 1$, $\cdots$, k. Note that the range of the random variable X_i is from 0 to the smaller of n and Np_i.

*27.13. Let X_1, $\cdots$, X_k be random variables with the distribution specified in Exercise 27.12. Show, using the method of Exercise 11.11, that

$$\operatorname{var}(X_i) = \frac{n(N - n)}{N - 1} p_i(1 - p_i).$$

*27.14. Let X_1, $\cdots$, X_k be random variables with the distribution specified in Exercise 27.12. Adapt the method of Exercises 11.10 and 11.11 to show that

$$E(X_i X_j) = \frac{Nn(n - 1)p_i p_j}{N - 1},$$

and thus that

$$\operatorname{cov}(X_i, X_j) = \frac{-n(N - n)p_i p_j}{N - 1}.$$

*27.15. Let $X_1, \cdots, X_k$ be random variables with the distribution specified in Exercise 27.12. Then the mean $\overline{U}$ of the random sample with frequencies $X_1, \cdots, X_k$ is $\overline{U} = (1/n)(u_iX_i)$. Show that the expectation of $\overline{U}$ is $\mu = p_1u_1 + \cdots + p_ku_k$.

*27.16. Let $\overline{U}$ be the random variable defined in Exercise 27.15. Using (27.15), show that the variance of $\overline{U}$ is

$$\mathrm{var}(\overline{X}) = \frac{N-n}{n(N-1)}\, \sigma^2,$$

where

$$\sigma^2 = \sum_{i=1}^{k} p_i(u_i - \mu)^2.$$

*27.17. Let X and Y be independent random variables, X with the density $f(x) = ac^{-ax}$, $0 \leq x < \infty$, Y with the density $g(y) = be^{-by}$, $0 \leq y < \infty$, where a and b are positive. Let Z be a random variable with the density

$$h(z) = \frac{ab}{a-b}\,(e^{-bz} - e^{-az}).$$

Find the moment generating functions $M_x(t)$, $M_y(t)$, and $M_z(t)$, and show that $M_z(t) = M_x(t)\, M_y(t)$. By making use of (27.24), this strongly suggests, but does not quite prove, that the sum $X + Y$ of the random variables X and Y has the density $h(z)$.

*27.18. The random variables X and Y possess the joint probability distribution given in the table. Find the generating function and the moment generating function of (a) XY, (b) $X + Y$, (c) $X^2 + Y^2$, (d) X/Y.

x $\backslash$ y	1	2
1	.1	.4
2	.3	.2

*27.19. X and Y are independent random variables, each with the distribution $N(0, 1)$. Find the moment generating function of XY.

CHAPTER 4

Statistical Inference

28. THE CONCEPT OF STATISTICAL INFERENCE

There are, broadly speaking, two ways in which the data of a sample can be made to yield information concerning the parameters of the population from which the sample is drawn. They are known as the methods of *estimation* and of *hypothesis testing*. For example, suppose that one is interested in information concerning the mean μ of a certain population and that one has a random sample from that population. From the sample one may compute the sample mean $\overline{X}$, which we have earlier shown to be an unbiased estimate of the parameter μ. Such a statistic as $\overline{X}$, used as an estimate of μ, is called a *point estimate*, in order to distinguish it from an *interval estimate*, that is, a pair of statistics so computed that the parameter in question has known likelihood of lying between them. Interval estimates have already been briefly considered in Section 26 and will be systematically studied in Section 31. In the method of hypothesis testing, on the other hand, a statement (hypothesis) is proposed concerning some parameter of the population, and then the information contained in the sample is used to evaluate the statement. If the sample actually obtained is highly unlikely to have come from such a population as is described by the hypothesis, we reject the hypothesis. This turns out to be quite a useful method of inference, particularly in dealing with the results of a scientific investigation.

In pure mathematics we start from certain postulates or given theorems and from them deduce other theorems, by a process which does not admit of variations and exceptions. We may speak of this kind of deduction as *certain inference*. Statistical inference, as above described, is a form of *uncertain inference*, since a random sample of a population contains only a limited amount of information about the population and since the operation of chance may have produced an extreme sample rather unrepresentative of the population. A feature of statistical inference is the measuring of the degree of uncertainty that is to be attached to the statements made about the population from which the sample is drawn. Such statements are, as it were, themselves subject to sampling variability and hence liable to error. We shall need, in the course of our discussion, to specify the nature of these errors and to determine their probabilities.

We first consider hypothesis testing. A test of a hypothesis consists, essentially, of two parts: first, some *hypothesis* must be proposed; and, second, a *rule of decision* must be provided which enables us to pass judgment on the hypothesis on the basis of the information in the sample. This process is quite analogous to the evaluation of scientific theories in the light of experimental data, where the evidence of experience is said either to *confirm* or to *disconfirm* a theory. Notice that, whereas the confirmation of a theory requires the accumulation of a great body of evidence, the disconfirmation or rejection of a theory may be achieved by a single *counterexample*, that is, a single well-attested example which is in clear contradiction to the theory. Thus disconfirmatory evidence has great decisive power. In statistical inference a similar principle is employed, namely, that of rejecting a hypothesis on the basis of *a sample statistic which would very rarely be obtained if the hypothesis were true*. In the application of this principle a pair of hypotheses are specified: a so-called *null hypothesis*, which will usually be rejected if the experiment is a significant one, and an *alternative hypothesis*, which is automatically accepted when the null hypothesis is rejected. These hypotheses are known as *statistical hypotheses*, that is, statements concerning some parameter of the population involved. These concepts will be clarified by an example.

Example 28.1. A die is suspected of being loaded. An investigator wishes to test the possibility that there is a bias toward the number "6." He plans to throw the die 200 times and observe the proportion of 6's. A suitable null hypothesis, denoted by H_0, is:

$$(28.1) \qquad\qquad H_0: \quad p = 1/6,$$

where p is the probability of throwing a "6." Notice that the null hypothesis asserts that the probability for a "6" is precisely what one would expect with a perfect die, so that the null hypothesis asserts that *the suspected condition does not exist*. This suggests why the adjective "null" is appropriate. An element of judgment enters into the choice of the alternative hypothesis. If, as suggested above, the investigator has prior reason to suspect that there is a bias favoring the number "6," he will use as his alternative hypothesis:

$$(28.2) \qquad\qquad H_1: \quad p > 1/6.$$

He is thus dismissing $p < 1/6$ as being, on a priori grounds, so unlikely that it may be ignored. In the absence of prior evidence a suitable alternative hypothesis would be

$$(28.3) \qquad\qquad H_1: \quad p \neq 1/6.$$

We speak of (28.2) as specifying a *one-sided alternative* and leading to a *one-sided test*, while (28.3) specifies a *two-sided alternative* and leads to a *two-sided test*.

The formation of a rule of decision involves several steps. We must first select a statistic whose value, computed for the sample, will be the basis for our acceptance or rejection of the null hypothesis. This we shall call the *critical statistic*.* We then obtain (if possible) the distribution of the critical statistic under the assumption that the null hypothesis is true; all the standard methods of testing hypotheses are based on critical statistics whose distributions are well known. Finally we divide the range of possible values of the critical statistic into two regions, a *region of rejection* (R) and a *region of acceptance* (A), with the property that, if the critical statistic as obtained from the observed data falls in the region R, the null hypothesis is rejected, and, if it falls in the region A, the null hypothesis is accepted.

Let us return to Example 28.1. Here an obvious choice of the critical statistic is $\hat{p}$, the sample proportion of 6's. Under the null hypothesis (28.1), $\hat{p}$ has the binomial distribution

$$(28.4) \qquad P(\hat{p} = p_0) = \binom{200}{200\ p_0} \left(\frac{1}{6}\right)^{200p_0} \left(\frac{5}{6}\right)^{200-200p_0}$$

Since this distribution involves excessive computation we approximate it by the normal distribution $N(1/6, 5/7200)$ (see Section 23).

We now require a method of determining the regions R and A. Notice, first of all, that since high values of $\hat{p}$ are consistent with the alternative hypothesis (28.2), we should expect extremely high values of $\hat{p}$ to fall in the region of rejection of H_0. For this reason, we should place the region R to the right of the region A. How shall we decide on the boundary point between regions A and R? Let us denote the critical value separating the two regions by p', and let us arbitrarily select, for purposes of discussion, $p' = .2$. This leads to the decision rule:

RULE. *Reject H_0 if $\hat{p} > .2$, accept H_0 if $\hat{p} \leq .2$.*

In Figure 28.1 we show the normal curve which approximates the binomial distribution (28.4).

---

* The term *test statistic* is standard, but it is essentially unpronounceable.

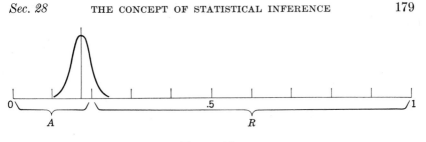

FIGURE 28.1.

In order to judge whether or not this choice of the regions R and A is a suitable one, we consider the errors of judgment that may arise in using the above decision rule. We have four possibilities: if H_0 is true, we may either accept or reject it; if H_0 is false, we may either accept or reject it. Two of these judgments are correct, two erroneous. The four possibilities, together with the probabilities, are shown in Table 28.1, which also shows the standard terminology and notation for the two possible types of error, and their probabilities. To call the null hypothesis false when it is true is called an error of Type I, or error I, and its probability is denoted by α; this probability is sometimes called the *level of significance* of the test, sometimes the *size* of the test. To call the null hypothesis true when it is false is called an error of Type II, and its probability is denoted by β. The probability $1 - \beta$ of rejecting H_0 when it is false is called the *power* of the test.

Before computing α for the choice of the regions A and R suggested above, we first consider the more general case in which samples of size n are drawn from a dichotomy with parameter p. The distribution of

TABLE 28.1

Actual Situation Regarding H_0	Decision Regarding H_0	Probability
True	Accept = Correct decision	$1 - \alpha$
	Reject = Error of Type I	α = Level of significance
False	Accept = Error of Type II	β
	Reject = Correct decision	$1 - \beta$ = Power of test

$\hat{p}$ may be approximated by a normal distribution with $\mu = p$, $\sigma^2 = p(1 - p)/n$. Thus, if p' is the critical value separating the regions A and R, the probability that $\hat{p}$ will fall in the region R is (neglecting the correction for continuity) approximately,

$$(28.5) \qquad P(\hat{p} > p') = 1 - F_N\left(\frac{p' - p}{\sqrt{\left(\dfrac{p(1 - p)}{n}\right)}}\right).$$

In the present case, by the null hypothesis, $p = 1/6$, and $p' = .2$ (arbitrary). Hence

$$\alpha = P(\hat{p} > p') = 1 - F_N(1.265) = .1029.$$

This is the level of significance of the test or the probability that, when the null hypothesis is true, we shall declare it to be false. It may be felt that this is too large a probability of error of Type I. It can be reduced in size by either of two expedients: (*a*) increase the critical value p' dividing the regions A and R; (*b*) increase n, as may be seen from the following general relation between α, p', and n:

$$(28.6) \qquad \alpha = 1 - F_N[2.684\sqrt{n}\,(p' - 1/6)], \qquad \text{or}$$

$$p' = \frac{1}{6} + \frac{1}{2.684\sqrt{n}}\,F_N^{-1}(1 - \alpha).$$

If, for example, we wish to make $\alpha = .05$ while holding $n = 200$, we substitute these values in the second equation of (28.6), and obtain $p' = .2100$.

In order to calculate the probability α, we have had to specify the null hypothesis H_0 in terms of *a particular value of the parameter* p, not a range of values. For the same reason the probability β must be calculated separately for each possible value of p. In this way we determine how our decision rule actually performs in dealing with situations for which the null hypothesis is not true. This calculation will be deferred until a later section. Meanwhile we summarize the essentials of a test of a hypothesis briefly, before considering a series of examples in the next section.

(*a*) *The null hypothesis H_0 is stated, usually in such a form that significant data will result in its rejection.* The null hypotheses that we shall consider will be of the form $\lambda = \lambda_0$, where λ is a parameter of the population being investigated. The alternative hypothesis H_1 will be either of the form $\lambda \neq \lambda_0$ (two sided) or of the forms $\lambda > \lambda_0$ or $\lambda < \lambda_0$ (one sided).

(*b*) *The critical statistic L and the sample size n are selected.* The sampling distribution of L is determined under the assumption that the null hypothesis is true. L will often be an estimate of λ, or simply related to such an estimate. Thus, when the null hypothesis is $\mu = \mu_0$, we may use $\overline{X}$ as critical statistic, or alternatively, $Z = \dfrac{\overline{X} - \mu_0}{\sigma_{\overline{X}}}$.

(*c*) *An arbitrary level of significance α is selected.* The critical value (or values) is determined in the following way:

(i) For a one-sided alternative of the form $\lambda > \lambda_0$, the critical value l' is determined from $P(L > l') = \alpha$. The region of rejection is $L > l'$.

(ii) For a one-sided alternative of the form $\lambda < \lambda_0$, the critical value l' is determined from $P(L < l') = \alpha$. The region of rejection is $L < l'$.

(iii) For a two-sided alternative, $\lambda \neq \lambda_0$, the critical values l' and l'' are determined from $P(L < l') = \alpha/2$, $P(L > l'') = \alpha/2$. The region of rejection consists of the two portions $L < l'$ and $L > l''$.

(*d*) *A random sample is obtained and the critical statistic L is calculated for the sample.* If L falls in the region of rejection, the null hypothesis is rejected at the $100\alpha\%$ level, and the experiment is said to be significant; otherwise the hypothesis is accepted, and the experiment is said to be non-significant.

It should be noted that there are other types of tests of hypotheses, particularly those which dispense with a fixed sample size (multiple sampling, sequential sampling) and those which offer other alternatives than the simple acceptance or rejection of a hypothesis. In any case it is essential that the rule of decision be formulated before the actual experiment is performed. The theory of probability, on which the process is founded, is inapplicable if, for example, the null hypothesis is selected after the data have been examined. If, as is often the case, the statistical method is not selected until the experiment is well under way, the experiment may actually be wasted, either because it is not possible to reach any conclusion or because the conclusion that is reached is not really supported by the data.

A one-sided test will be appropriate either (i) when we have prior reason to believe that the actual population mean deviates from the value λ_0 in a particular direction or (ii) when we are interested only in alternatives which lie on a particular side of λ_0. Thus, to illustrate case (i) a researcher might have reason to believe that he has produced a more effective antibiotic than one previously available. If μ is the mean performance of the new drug as measured, say, by the number of bacteria killed in a specific period of time, and μ_0 is the mean for the competing drug, then he will want to use the alternative $\mu > \mu_0$.

Case (ii) is illustrated by a manufacturer who wishes to prevent the proportion $\hat{p}$ of defectives produced in any one day from exceeding a specified maximum p_0. He will be concerned about the alternative $\hat{p} > p_0$ but probably not about the alternative $\hat{p} < p$. A two-sided test will be appropriate when one is equally concerned about possible values of the parameter λ lying on either side of λ. This will usually be the case in the absence of prior information about the outcome of the experiment.

At this point we cannot be more specific about methods of selecting a critical statistic. In the next section we shall consider the commonly used tests of significance and the critical statistics appropriate to each. In Section 33 a method will be presented which yields, for many types of problems, a critical statistic appropriate for the testing of a specified hypothesis.

The values most commonly used for the level of significance α are .05, .01, and .001. The smaller the value of α, the less risk there is of committing errors of Type I. However the reduction of α usually tends to increase β if the sample size is held constant. These matters will receive further consideration in Section 30,

EXERCISE 28

28.1. In Example 28.1, another possible choice for the critical statistic is X, the number of 6's in 200 throws. Find the distribution of X under the null hypothesis (28.1) and also the approximating normal distribution. If $\alpha = .05$ and the alternative hypothesis is $H_1: p > 1/6$, find the critical value of X, say X'. Note that this value of X' might also have been obtained by multiplying $n = 200$ by $p' = .2100$, the critical value when p was chosen as critical statistic.

28.2. Using Equation 28.6 for p' in terms of α and n and setting $n = 200$, find p' for $\alpha = .10, .05, .01$, and .005, and make a graph of p' against α. With $\alpha = .05$, find p' for $n = 10, 20, 50, 200, 500$, and 1000, and make a graph of p' against n.

29. SIMPLE TYPES OF HYPOTHESIS TESTING

The simplest types of tests of hypothesis are:

(A) Those concerning the parameter p of a dichotomy.
(B) Those concerning the mean of a continuous population.
(C) Those concerning the means of two continuous populations.

We shall deal with each of these types in turn, first stating the necessary facts concerning sampling distributions, then illustrating each type by a series of examples.

A. Dichotomies

The only essential parameter possessed by a dichotomy is p, the probability of "success." Thus the null hypothesis for a dichotomy will always take the form $p = p_0$.

Some will ask, why not use a null hypothesis of the form $p > p_0$, for example? The reason is that the whole procedure of hypothesis testing is based on the sampling distribution of some suitable statistic, and a sampling distribution is available only when p assumes some particular value rather than a range of values.

The necessary facts concerning sampling distributions derived from a dichotomy may be summarized as follows (Sections 23, 34):

(29.1) *Let samples of size n be drawn from a dichotomy for which the probability of success is p. Let the number of successes in the sample be X, and the proportion of successes be $\hat{p} = X/n$. Then*
  (a) *The distribution of X is, approximately, $N(np, np(1 - p))$.*
  (b) *The distribution of $\hat{p}$ is, approximately, $N(p, p(1 - p)/n)$.*
  (c) *The distribution of*

$$Z = \frac{X - np}{\sqrt{np(1 - p)}} = \frac{\hat{p} - p}{\sqrt{p(1 - p)/n}}$$

is, approximately, $N(0, 1)$.

Example 29.1. Survey. A newspaper claims that it is read by more than 75% of the residents of the county in which it is published. A survey is conducted on a random sample of 1000 county residents. If $\alpha = .05$, formulate null and alternative hypotheses and an appropriate decision rule.

Solution. The null and alternative hypotheses will be

$$H_0: \quad p = .75, \quad H_1: \quad p > .75.$$

The alternative $p > .75$ is here chosen on the grounds that the newspaper has some prior evidence on which to base its claim. There are 3 possible choices of critical statistic: X, $\hat{p}$, or Z, as suggested in Theorem (29.1); but the choice is of little significance, since all three are linearly related to each other (i.e., any one may be obtained from any other by means of a linear transformation).

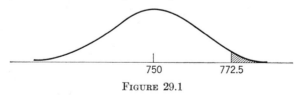

750   772.5

FIGURE 29.1

Suppose, for example, that we use X. Then, if H_0 is true, X will possess, approximately, the distribution $N(750, 187.5)$, whose form is sketched in Figure 29.1. Because of the form of H_1 we have a one-sided test, and the region of rejection will be in the right-hand tail of the distribution. To find the critical value of X, we determine the 95th percentile of the unit normal distribution: $z_{.95} = 1.645$. The 95th percentile of X is then given by $X_{.95} = 750 + \sqrt{187.5} \times 1.645 = 772.5$. The correction for continuity gives us the value $772.5 - .5 = 772.0$. Thus, if $X > 772$, the null hypothesis H_0 will be rejected, and the alternative H_1 will be accepted.

Example 29.2. *Scientific investigation.* A certain cattle disease is known to have a 40% mortality rate. If a new treatment is tried on 100 animals, under what circumstances will we declare the treatment to be successful at the 1% level of significance?

Solution. The null hypothesis here is H_0: $p = .40$, and the alternative H_1: $p < .40$ since there are presumptive grounds for expecting a lowering of the mortality rate due to the treatment. Let us use

$$Z = \frac{X - np}{\sqrt{np(1 - p)}}$$

as the critical statistic, where X will be the number of animals who die in a sample of 100. We are given $\alpha = .01$. Because of the alternative H_1: $p < .4$ we are concerned with the left tail of the distribution, so that the critical value of Z is $z_{.01} = -2.326$. The region of rejection is $Z < -2.326$. Note that, if X were the number of animals surviving, the null and alternative hypotheses would have to be H_0: $p = .6$, H_1: $p > .6$, and the region of rejection would lie in the right tail of the distribution: $Z > 2.326$.

Example 29.3. *Industrial quality control.* A manufactured product is visually inspected and has been found, in the past, to yield 3% of defective material. The manufacturer is satisfied with this state of affairs since the cost of weeding out the defectives is somewhat less than the cost of altering the process so as to reduce the number of defectives. However he feels he cannot afford to permit the proportion of defectives to increase. If he decides on $\alpha = .005$ and uses a sample of 200 pieces as a basis for decision, under what circumstances should he conclude that the process is producing more than 3% defectives?

Solution. The null hypothesis is $p = .03$; that is, the process is still producing 3% defectives on the day in question. The alternative hypothesis is $p > .03$. The test will thus be one sided, since the manufacturer is not interested in exceptionally small values of p. As critical statistic we shall use $\hat{p}$, the proportion of defectives in a sample of 200. The distribution of $\hat{p}$ will be, approximately, $N(.03, .03 \times .97/200) = N(.03, .000146)$.

Note that the rather small value of the level of significance $\alpha = .005$ means that the manufacturer will seldom make an error of Type I, that is, he will seldom conclude that $p > .03$ when in fact $p = .03$. He is thus protecting himself against unnecessary meddling with the manufacturing process. He would rather run the risk of having a few more defectives to weed out than to stop the process and adjust it when he is not certain that it needs attention. In other words, he is decreasing the probability of error I (i.e., the value of α) even though this may result in an increase in the probability of error II (i.e., the value of β), which in this case implies a failure to detect a real shift of p toward values larger than .03.

The region of rejection is in the right tail, so that we require the 99.5 percentile of the distribution of $\hat{p}$. From $z_{.995} = 2.576$ we find

$$\hat{p}_{.995} = .03 + 2.576\sqrt{.000146} = .03 + .0311 = .0611.$$

Hence, he will reject the null hypothesis when he finds more than 6.1% defective in his sample of 200. In practical terms this means that, if he obtains 13 or more defectives, he will undertake to find and correct the manufacturing condition that has led to the excessive porportion of defectives.

Example 29.4. Control chart for $\hat{p}$. A graphical device, known as a *control chart*, is usually employed to handle the decision process presented in Example 29.3. In this chart, shown in Figure 29.2, the value of $\hat{p}$ is plotted on the verti-

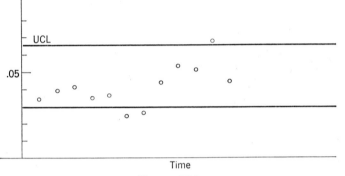

FIGURE 29.2

cal scale, time on the horizontal scale. The chart thus presents a series of points which show at a glance past and present behavior of the manufacturing process. This type of control chart is known as a *p-chart*.

Two horizontal lines are shown. The lower one is at height $p = .03$. The upper line is known as the *upper control limit* (UCL). When a random sample has been obtained, it is plotted as a point with abscissa equal to the time at which the sample was obtained, and ordinate equal to the fraction defective in the sample. Corrective action is taken whenever a point falls above the upper control limit. The control chart is essentially a graphical method of carrying out the process of statistical inference described in Example 29.3.

In industrial quality control the UCL is commonly put at a distance of 3 standard deviations above the mean. Such a UCL is referred to as the "3-sigma limit." For the present example this would give

$$\text{UCL} = .03 + 3\sqrt{.000146} = .0663.$$

In order to evaluate α, the level of significance corresponding to the use of the 3-sigma UCL, we note that $F_N(3) = .99865$, hence $\alpha = P(Z > 3) = .00135$. There is thus about 1 chance in 740 that a point will fall above the UCL if the probability for each defective remains at 3 per cent.

B. Hypotheses Concerning the Mean of a Normal Distribution

In many practical situations it is reasonable to assume an approximately normal distribution for the characteristic being measured. This is true, for example, of a great variety of biological and psychological measures and also of the measurement data commonly encountered in industrial quality control. Since a normal distribution has two parameters μ and σ, we say that all normal distributions constitute a 2-parameter family of distributions.

We shall consider here hypotheses of the form $\mu = \mu_0$. The value of σ will in some cases be available from earlier observations. Under such circumstances we speak of the assumption of normality, together with a specific value of σ, as constituting the *model* underlying the inference. The model specifies a one-parameter family of normal distributions, and the null hypothesis further narrows the consideration down to a particular member of the family. The essential sampling distributions required for tests of hypotheses of this type are summarized below (Section 25):

(29.2) *Let samples of size n be drawn from a normal distribution $N(\mu_0, \sigma^2)$, and let $\overline{X}$ be the sample mean. Then:*

  (a) *The distribution of $\overline{X}$ is $N(\mu_0, \sigma^2/n)$.*

  (b) *The distribution of $Z = \dfrac{\overline{X} - \mu_0}{\sigma/\sqrt{n}}$ is $N(0, 1)$.*

A more common situation is that in which we have no information concerning σ other than the estimates obtained from the sample at hand. Then we are obliged to use the t distribution, as suggested below:

  (c) *Let samples of size n be drawn from a normal distribution $N(\mu_0, \sigma^2)$, and let $\overline{X}$ be the sample mean. Then the quantity*

$$t = \frac{\overline{X} - \mu_0}{s/\sqrt{n}}$$

has the t distribution with $n - 1$ d.f. (Sections 26, 41.)

Example 29.5. *Comparison with an Established Norm.* A certain psychological test has been administered to a large group of "normal" children, and its mean and variance have been found to be $\mu = 82$ and $\sigma^2 = 36.5$. If this test is administered to a group of 35 children, how large will the mean $\overline{X}$ have to be in order to conclude that the group is exceptionally high in the trait measured by this test? The phrase "exceptionally high" will be taken to mean "significantly higher than the original group (the control group) to whom the test was administered."

We shall assume normality of the population from which the sample is drawn; we also assume that $\sigma^2 = 36.5$ for this population. These two assumptions together constitute the model underlying the test. The null hypothesis is $\mu = 82$, the alternative hypothesis $\mu > 82$, since the test is being used to detect exceptionally high performance. Let us use $\overline{X}$ as the critical statistic, with distribution $N(82, 36.5/35) = N(82, 1.043)$. For the level of significance we select $\alpha = .01$. Since we have a one-sided test and since $z_{.99} = 2.326$, we find the critical value of $\overline{X}$ to be $82 + 2.326\sqrt{1.043} = 84.38$. Thus we shall regard a group of 35 children as exceptionally high in the trait measured by the test if their mean exceeds 84.38.

Example 29.6.   *Before-and-After Experiment.*   In an experiment to determine the effect of a meal on heart functioning as indicated by the electrocardiograph, 12 normal young men were tested before and after a meal. Table 29.1 shows

TABLE 29.1

Before	After	Diff. $= d$
5.4	5.1	$-$ .3
6.5	6.4	$-$ .1
5.8	4.4	-1.4
5.0	3.9	-1.1
9.6	8.1	-1.5
4.2	3.1	-1.1
4.9	4.5	$-$ .4
5.0	3.6	-1.4
7.5	6.3	-1.2
3.9	2.6	-1.3
10.0	5.7	-4.3
3.1	3.5	.4
70.9	57.2	-13.7

the values of the electrocardiographic function known as ΣT, before and after the meal. The final column shows the difference. The values in the final column constitute a sample of size $n = 12$ from a hypothetical population consisting of values of d for a great many "normal young men" submitting to such an experiment. We shall assume the population of d-values to possess a normal distribution, and we consider the null hypothesis, $\mu_d = 0$, where μ_d is the mean of the population. This hypothesis implies that a meal has no effect on the particular heart performance being measured. Let us assume also that there is no prior scientific evidence on the effect of a meal on this particular type of heart performance, so that the alternative hypothesis is $\mu_d \neq 0$. By selecting $\alpha = .01$ and using both tails of the t distribution, the critical values of t will be the .5 and 99.5 percentiles, $t_{.005} = -3.106$ and $t_{.995} =$

3.106. The standard deviation of d is found to be $s_d = 1.167$, and thus the observed value of t is

$$t = \frac{\bar{d}}{s_d/\sqrt{12}} = -3.39.$$

Since this is in the region of rejection, we conclude that there is a significant effect of a meal on heart performance, as measured by this electrocardiographic variable.

Since 11 out of the 12 values of d in Table 29.1 are negative, it may be felt that the evidence very clearly supports the theory that a meal affects heart performance. It is the object of statistical inference to replace such subjective feelings about the evidence by an unambiguous rule of decision which will take care of all cases, those on the border line as well as those whose interpretation seems crystal clear.

Example 29.7. *Industrial Quality Control.* A manufacturer has been producing a cylindrical shaft. Measurements on 200 shafts have shown a mean diameter of .751 inch, with a standard deviation of .012 inch. A sample of 10 shafts is drawn from the production process; they may be 10 shafts produced consecutively, or they may be a random sample from a bin containing a day's production. How large or how small should the sample mean be in order to conclude that the process has shifted significantly?

Solution. The model will assume normality of the underlying population, and the value $\sigma = .012$ inch for the standard deviation. The null hypothesis is $\mu = .751$ inch, with the alternative $\mu \neq .751$, since in this case the manufacturer may wish to guard against either oversized or undersized shafts. A suitable critical statistic is $\bar{X}$, with distribution $N(.751, .012^2/10)$. Let us use $\alpha = .005$ and a two-sided test. We first find $z_{.0025} = -2.813$, $z_{.9975} = 2.813$, and thus the critical values of $\bar{X}$: $.751 \pm 2.813 \times .012/10 = .751 \pm .0107$.

The test described in Example 29.7 is essentially a test of the *stability* of the manufacturing process. A process such as that described is said to be *in a state of control* if repeated tests of significance of the above type reveal no shift in the population mean. It may sometimes be necessary to investigate whether the population standard deviation as well as the population mean remains constant; properly speaking, the process is in a state of control if both mean and standard deviation are stabilized. These tests are most frequently performed graphically, by means of a control chart similar to that of Example 29.4. The control chart for the sample mean, known as the $\bar{X}$-chart, is described in the following example.

Example 29.8. *$\bar{X}$-Chart.* In order to adapt a test of the kind discussed in Example 29.7 to typical industrial situations, a chart is used similar to the $\hat{p}$-chart of Example 29.4. If used in a systematic way, the chart effectively prevents the process from deviating from a "state of control" and has the added advantage of presenting the situation vividly and in a form that can be immediately grasped by the machine operator. In addition to the mean line, at height $\mu = .751$ for the previous example, the upper control limit (UCL), and the lower control limit (LCL) are shown as horizontal lines. A widely used practice places these lines 3 standard deviations above and below the mean line; the limits are then known as "3-sigma limits." The standard deviation to be used here is that of $\overline{X}$, that is, $\sigma_{\overline{X}} = \sigma_x/\sqrt{n}$. The significance level is then $\alpha = 2[1 - F_N(3)] = .0027$. The control chart corresponding to Example 29.8 is shown in Figure 29.3. If we assume that samples of 5 are used, the control limits are $.751 \pm 3 \times .012/\sqrt{5} = .751 \pm .016 = .767$ and $.735$. Of

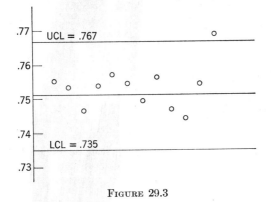

FIGURE 29.3

the 12 points plotted on the chart, one is shown beyond the UCL line; standard practice would call for corrective action to be taken when such a point is discovered.

In practice, we say that the process is under control, or in a state of control, when the plotted points continue to fall inside the control limits; the process is out of control whenever a point falls outside the control limits, and corrective action is normally taken under such circumstances. However, it should be noted that it is perfectly possible for points to fall outside the control limits without any shift in the manufacturing process because of chance alone. We have seen that this will occur with a probability of .0027, so that approximately 1 out of 370 samples drawn from a process which is under control can be expected to fall outside the control limits. When a point falls outside the control limits, it may be due either to a real change in the process or to a random fluctuation of the stabilized process. Only very rarely will the latter be the case, so that we run little risk of being wrong if we treat every point falling outside the control limits as an indication of a genuine shift in the process.

C. Hypotheses Concerning the Means of Two Normal Populations

A type of experiment that is used in many fields of science involves a comparison of the effect of two conditions or treatments. Suppose that

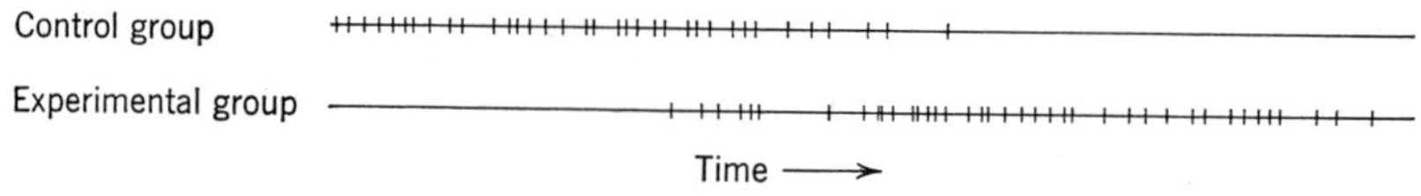

Control group

Experimental group

Time ⟶

FIGURE 29.4

a psychological experiment is designed to determine the effect of a certain drug on the rate of learning in rats. The animals (say 100 of them) are divided into two equal groups, the control group and the experimental group; only the latter receives the drug. The time taken to learn to run a certain maze is then recorded for each of the 100 rats. The results may appear as shown in Figure 29.4. A problem of interpretation is presented by the lack of clear-cut differentiation between the groups. Although the time taken by the experimental group is, on the average, longer than the time taken by the control group, the result is somewhat obscured by the overlapping of the two groups. We now indicate how a test of significance may be used to evaluate the results of an experiment of this kind.

We may regard each set of 50 values as a random sample from a population, namely, the population of "all possible" results obtained by measuring the rate of learning of rats under identical conditions. Thus we conceive of two populations, which we may name the "control" and the "experimental" populations. The question which the experiment is designed to answer really is: does the experimental population differ from the control population? More specifically, does the mean of the experimental population differ from the mean of the control population?

In order to apply a test of significance to this type of experiment, we set up the null hypothesis that the average rate of learning of drugged rats is the same as the average rate of learning of normal rats. Using μ_c for the mean of the control population and μ_e for the mean of the experimental population, the null hypothesis is $\mu_c = \mu_e$.

The basic distribution we shall employ in order to test a hypothesis of the above type is the t distribution (Sections 26, 41).

(29.3) *Let two samples of sizes n_1 and n_2 be respectively drawn from populations with distributions $N(\mu_1, \sigma^2)$ and $N(\mu_2, \sigma^2)$. Let the mean and variance of the first be $\overline{X}_1$ and $s_1{}^2$, of the second, $\overline{X}_2$ and $s_2{}^2$. Let $s_p{}^2$ denote the pooled variance defined by*

$$s_p{}^2 = \frac{(n_1 - 1)s_1{}^2 + (n_2 - 1)s_2{}^2}{n_1 + n_2 - 2}.$$

Then the quantity

$$t = \frac{\overline{X}_1 - \overline{X}_2 - (\mu_1 - \mu_2)}{s_p \sqrt{\dfrac{1}{n_1} + \dfrac{1}{n_2}}}$$

possesses the t distribution with $n_1 + n_2 - 2$ *d.f.*

Example 29.9. Comparison of Two Conditions. Let us assume that for the control group of 50 rats in the experiment described above, the mean time required to learn to run the maze is $\overline{X}_c = 29.6$ minutes with a variance of $s_c^2 = 9.6$. For the experimental group of 50, the mean learning time is $\overline{X}_e = 35.2$ minutes with a variance of $s_e^2 = 12.2$. Hence we find, for the pooled variance,

$$s_p^2 = \frac{49 \times 9.6 + 49 \times 12.2}{98} = 10.9.$$

Under the hypothesis $\mu_e = \mu_c$, the quantity

$$t = \frac{(\overline{X}_e - \overline{X}_c)}{s_p \sqrt{\dfrac{1}{n_1} + \dfrac{1}{n_2}}}$$

will have the t distribution with $n_1 + n_2 - 2 = 98$ d.f. We shall suppose that there is no prior knowledge to indicate which of $\overline{X}_c$ and $\overline{X}_e$ should be greater, so that a two-sided test is indicated. With $\alpha = .01$ and 98 d.f. the critical values of t are ± 2.627. The value of t for the experimental data is found to be

$$t = \frac{35.2 - 29.6}{\sqrt{10.9 \times .04}} = 8.48.$$

Thus the null hypothesis is rejected. The conclusion is that the drug has indeed affected the rate of learning.

EXERCISE 29

Exercises 29.1 through 29.8 involve testing a variety of hypotheses. In each case a series of steps similar to those outlined in Section 28 should be followed. One should state clearly both the null and the alternative hypotheses; the exercise will always give the sample size, but the critical statistic must be selected and its sampling distribution determined under the assumption that the null hypothesis is true; the level of significance must be selected (unless given in the exercise), and the critical value or values must be determined. Finally, we determine whether to accept or reject the null hypothesis on the basis of the observed data, and we ordinarily rephrase this decision in the language of the experiment.

29.1. A seed distributor guarantees 95% germination of the seeds he supplies. A retailer has an agreement with the distributor, under which he may test a random sample of 200 seeds for germination and send the whole lot back to the manufacturer if the proportion of germinating seeds is significantly below

95%. With a level of significance of .001, what is the smallest number of germinating seeds in a sample of 200 that would be acceptable?

29.2. Certain electrical gadgets are required to work for 1000 hours before failure. A sample of 100 is randomly drawn from a lot of several thousand, and each item in the sample is tested. The buyer will be satisfied if no more than 5% of the lot are defective. If $\alpha = .005$, how many defectives will the buyer tolerate in the sample?

29.3. A candidate for political office needs the support of the county organization of his party. They decide to support him if a poll of 1000 members of the party, selected at random, indicates that 50% of the party members in the county favor him. How many in the sample should favor him if he is to be backed by his party?

29.4. Charles Darwin compared the effects of cross-fertilization versus self-fertilization using 15 pairs of seedlings of *Zea mays*, each pair being grown in the same pot. The heights of all 30 plants, measured in inches at the same time, are shown in the table. Are the cross-fertilized plants significantly taller than the self-fertilized? Use $\alpha = .05$.

Cross	Self
23.5	17.4
12.0	20.4
21.0	20.0
22.0	20.0
19.1	18.4
21.5	18.6
22.1	18.6
20.4	15.2
18.2	16.5
21.6	18.0
23.2	16.2
21.0	18.0
22.1	12.8
23.0	15.5
12.0	18.0

29.5. 32 young men volunteered for an experiment in semi-starvation. Their average height was 178.6 cm. The average height of 99,172 white selective service registrants was 173.9 cm., with a standard deviation of 7.1 cm. Is the difference in height significant?

29.6. How would the treatment of Exercise 29.2 be altered if we did not know the standard deviation of height of the group of 99,172 men but did know that the standard deviation for the group of 32 men was 5.9 cm.?

29.7. A group of inducted basic airmen at Lackland Air Force Base were given a test for anxiety. On the basis of this test, 178 subjects were classified as anxious, 159 as non-anxious. These 337 were given the Army Clerical Speed Test, with the following results:

	Anxious Group	Non-anxious Group
n	178	159
Mean	70.70	63.34
Standard deviation	27.75	26.47

Test for significance of the difference between the means of the two groups.

29.8. Basalt minerals may be visually classified into 2 groups, A and B, according to "texture." In an investigation to see whether the same result might be accomplished chemically by means of the "pyroxene ratio," 155 specimens of texture A were found to have a mean of 42.54 and a standard deviation of 6.25; while 82 specimens of texture B had a mean of 28.73 and a standard deviation of 7.10, all measured by means of the pyroxene ratio. Are minerals A and B significantly different in regard to pyroxene ratio?

30. THE PERFORMANCE OF A TEST OF SIGNIFICANCE

The effectiveness of a test of significance as a rule of decision may be measured by the probabilities α and β of the errors of judgment we may commit when using the test. In all the tests considered in the preceding two sections the probability α of errors of Type I was specified in advance and used in the determination of the region of rejection. Thus such tests include a "built-in" control of the probability of error I at a prespecified level. We must now investigate the probability β of errors of Type II.

To fix our ideas, suppose we are considering a test of the hypothesis $H_0: \lambda = \lambda_0$ against the alternative $H_1: \lambda > \lambda_0$, where λ is some parameter of the population under consideration. Suppose that L is the critical statistic and that $R: L > l'$ is the region of rejection. If $\lambda > \lambda_0$ (i.e., H_0 is false) but the sample value of L falls in the region of acceptance $L \leq l'$, we accept H_0, thus committing an error of Type II. For each value of λ we have a distribution function of L, say $F(l \mid \lambda)$, which we may use to compute the probability β of accepting H_0. This will simply be the probability that L falls in the region of acceptance $L \leq l'$, that is,

$$(30.1) \qquad \beta = F(l' \mid \lambda).$$

The functional relationship between β and λ will be our basic means of judging the performance of the test. The graph of β against λ is called the *operating characteristic* (OC) of the test of significance. A closely related curve, called the *power curve* of the test, is obtained by graphing $1 - \beta$ against the parameter λ.

A suitable illustration is provided by Example 28.1, which was concerned with a die suspected of being loaded. In that example a test was devised for deciding whether or not a die is biased toward the number "6." Imagine the test applied to a great many dice with varying degrees of bias toward "6." The OC curve can be regarded as depicting the performance of the test when these various dice are submitted to it. In the following example we shall show how the OC curve is obtained.

Example 30.1. In Example 28.1 we considered the hypothesis $p = 1/6$ against the alternative $p > 1/6$, where p is the probability of throwing a "6." The critical statistic was $\hat{p}$, the proportion of 6's in a sample of $n = 200$ throws. With a level of significance $\alpha = .05$ the region of rejection turned out to be $\hat{p} > .2100$. For a particular value of p, $\hat{p}$ has the binomial distribution

$$(30.2) \qquad P(\hat{p} = p_0) = \binom{200}{200p_0} p^{200p_0}(1 - p)^{200-200p_0}.$$

According to (30.1), the value of β may be obtained by the use of the distribution function derived from the frequency function (30.2). Since excessive calculation would be involved in this procedure, we use the normal approximation with $\mu = p$ and $\sigma^2 = p(1 - p)/200$. Here we shall neglect the continuity correction. Thus the probability that $\hat{p}$ will fall in the region of acceptance is approximately

$$(30.3) \qquad \beta = F_N \left(\frac{.2100 - p}{\sqrt{p(1 - p)/200}} \right).$$

In Table 30.1 values of β are computed using this formula for values of p ranging from .12 to .30, and the OC curve is graphed in the solid curve of

TABLE 30.1

p	.12	.14	.16	.18	.20	.22	.24	.26	.28	.30
β	1.000	.998	.973	.865	.641	.366	.160	.054	.014	.003
$1-\beta$	0·000	·002	·027	·135	·359	·634	·840	·946	·986	·997

Figure 30.1. The vertical line at $p = .167$ cuts the curve at a point whose ordinate is $.95 = 1 - \alpha$, as follows from Equations (28.6) and (30.3). The effectiveness of the test in discriminating between dice for which $p = 1/6$ and those for which $p > 1/6$ depends on the steepness of the OC curve. The present test, for example, would accept 64.1% of dice for which $p = .20$. If this is regarded as too high a probability of acceptance for dice with $p = .20$, the curve can be made more steep by increasing n. If, for example, we wish to make $\beta = .10$ when $p = .20$ and to retain $\alpha = .05$ when $p = 1/6$, we may determine both p' and n from the simultaneous equations

$$\alpha = .05 = 1 - F_N(2.684\sqrt{n}(p' - 1/6)) \quad \text{or} \quad 2.684\sqrt{n}(p' - 1/6) = 1.645$$

$$\beta = .10 = F_N \left[\frac{p' - .20}{\sqrt{.2 \times \frac{.8}{n}}} \right] \quad \text{or} \quad 2.5\sqrt{n}(p' - .2) = -1.282.$$

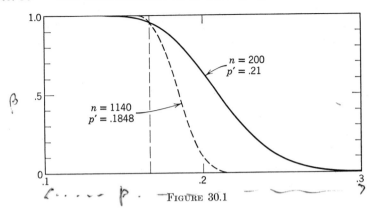

β

FIGURE 30.1

Solving these equations for n and p', we find $n = 1140$ and $p' = .1848$. The OC curve for these values of n and p' is shown in Figure 30.1 by means of a broken line.

We must now consider the power curve for a two-sided test. Example 30.1 will deal with the case in which σ is assumed to be known, which is often an appropriate assumption in dealing with control charts of the type discussed in Example 29.7. The computation of β for the case of sampling from a normal distribution with unknown variance, as in Example 29.6, is considerably more complicated and will not be discussed in this book.

Example 30.2. Consider a two-sided test of the hypothesis that the mean of a population is $\mu = \mu_0$, under the assumption that the population is normal with known variance σ^2. For concreteness, let us assume that the population variance is $\sigma^2 = 16$ and samples of size $n = 25$ are drawn. With a significance level of $\alpha = .05$ the critical values for the sample mean will be determined from the equation

$$\left| \frac{X - \mu_0}{\sigma/\sqrt{n}} \right| = \left| \frac{\overline{X} - \mu_0}{.8} \right| = z_{.975} = 1.96.$$

Thus we shall accept the null hypothesis if $|\overline{X} - \mu_0| < .8 \times 1.96 = 1.57$. Now let μ_1 be the actual value of the population mean. Then the quantity $Y = 1.25(\overline{X} - \mu_1)$ has the distribution $N(0, 1)$, and the probability of accepting the hypothesis is

$$\beta = P(|\overline{X} - \mu_0| < 1.57).$$

The random variables $\overline{X}$ and Y are related by $\overline{X} = .8Y + \mu_1$. Making this substitution in the above equation, we find

$$\beta = P(|.8Y + \mu_1 - \mu_0| < 1.57) = P(|Y + 1.25(\mu_1 - \mu_0)| < 1.96)$$

$$= P(1.25(\mu_0 - \mu_1) - 1.96 < Y < 1.25(\mu_0 - \mu_1) + 1.96)$$

$$= F_N(1.25(\mu_0 - \mu_1) + 1.96) - F_N(1.25(\mu_0 - \mu_1) - 1.96).$$

This is the operating characteristic function, which gives β as a function of μ_1. Its graph, the OC curve, is shown in Figure 30.2. The same curve, with the use of the inverted scale shown on the right, is the power curve of the test.

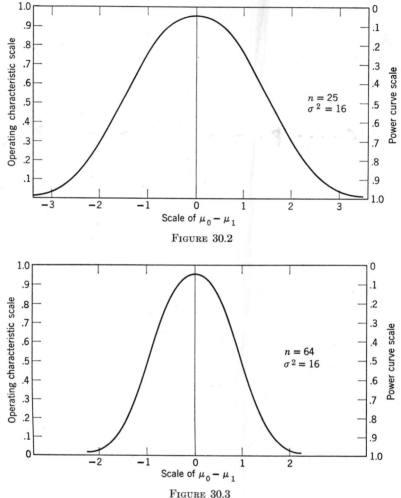

FIGURE 30.2

FIGURE 30.3

The effect on the curve of an increase in the value of n is shown in Figure 30.3, which gives the OC curve for $n = 64$, $\sigma^2 = 16$, $\alpha = .05$. In both of these curves we have taken $\mu_0 = 0$, for convenience.

In the field of industrial quality control the OC curve serves as a means of telling how well an inspection plan discriminates between acceptable and unacceptable material. This may be illustrated in connection with *acceptance sampling*, that is, the process of deciding whether or not to accept a lot on the basis of the number of defectives in the lot, as illustrated in the following example.

Example 30.3.   A receiving inspection scheme has the following specifications: parts come in lots of 100; from each lot a random sample of 20 is drawn and inspected; if more than 3 defectives are found, the lot is rejected.   The purchaser of the material will want his inspection scheme to protect him adequately from defective material, but he will prefer not to have a scheme so stringent that material which he can quite satisfactorily use is rejected most of the time.   We shall see how the OC curve enables him to decide whether the plan is performing as he wishes.

By means of the hypergeometric distribution, given in (7.10), we can compute the probability of accepting a lot of material of any specified proportion defective.   In fact, if p is the proportion defective in the lot, according to (7.10) the probability of drawing a sample of size $n = 20$ containing x defectives from a lot of size $N = 100$ is

$$P(X = x) = \frac{\binom{100p}{x}\binom{100 - 100p}{20 - x}}{\binom{100}{20}}.$$

But β, the probability of accepting the lot, is given by the probability of obtaining less than 4 defectives.   Hence

$$\beta = P(X < 4) = \sum_{x=0}^{3} \frac{\binom{100p}{x}\binom{100 - 100p}{20 - x}}{\binom{100}{20}}.$$

Probabilities such as these may be computed using logarithms of factorials (Table 6); they may be obtained more conveniently by using a table of logarithms of binomial coefficients, such as that found in *Statistical Tables and Formulas,*

TABLE 30.2

.03	1.0000
.04	.9988
.05	.9947
.06	.9862
.10	.8903
.15	.6521
.20	.3911
.25	.1957
.30	.0823
.40	.0086
.50	.0004

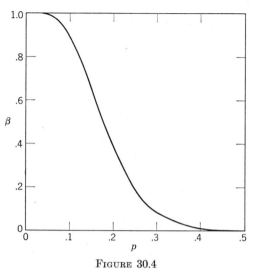

FIGURE 30.4

by A. Hald (John Wiley and Sons, 1952). By this means, Table 30.2 was computed, and Figure 30.4 was constructed from the table.

Does this sampling scheme do what the purchaser of the incoming material wants it to do? We note, first of all, that material which is 5% defective is accepted 99.47% of the time. Let us assume, therefore, that the purchaser is content with material which is 5% defective; probably his manufacturing process can cope with this many defective items without undue strain. Note, however, that incoming material which is 10% defective runs an 89.0% chance of being accepted, while material 20% defective has a 39.1% chance of being accepted. In view of these facts we can say that, although the plan readily accepts good material, it provides little protection against bad material. That protection can be bought at the price of increased inspection.

The power of an inspection scheme to discriminate between good and bad incoming material is reflected in the *steepness* of its OC curve. An ideal scheme would accept all lots with $p < p_0$, reject all lots with $p > p_0$, where p_0 is the maximum proportion of defectives the purchaser will tolerate. The OC curve for such an ideal plan would appear as in Figure 30.5. As long as samples are used, this ideal is unattain-

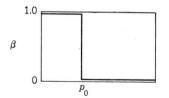

FIGURE 30.5

able. It can be approached by increasing the sample size n as indicated in Figure 30.1.

EXERCISE 30

30.1. Show that, if the correction for continuity (Section 23) is used, then (30.3) takes the form

$$\beta = F_N \left(\frac{42.00 - 200p + .5}{\sqrt{200p(1 - p)}} \right).$$

30.2. Recompute the values in Table 30.1 using the formula in Exercise 30.1, and graph the result.

30.3. Rework Example 30.1 using X, the number of 6's in 200 throws, as the critical statistic. Show that the formula that we then obtain for β can be reduced to the formula (30.3).

30.4. Consider a two-sided test of the hypothesis H_0: $\mu = \mu_0$, under the assumption that the parent population is normal with variance σ^2. Suppose that the significance level is α and that $z_{1-\alpha/2}$ is the $100(1 - \alpha/2)$ percentile of the unit normal distribution. Show that the relation between β, the error of the second kind, and the true population mean μ is

$$\beta = F_N \left[\frac{\sqrt{n}}{\sigma} (\mu_0 - \mu) + z_{1-\alpha/2} \right] - F_N \left[\frac{\sqrt{n}}{\sigma} (\mu_0 - \mu) - z_{1-\alpha/2} \right].$$

30.5. Show that Figures 30.2 and 30.3 can be transformed into each other by simply changing the units of the horizontal scale.

30.6. Show that Figure 30.2 can be used for the OC curve of the general type of test described in Exericse 30.4, with a proper change of the unit of the horizontal scale, provided that $\alpha = .05$. In view of this, use Figure 30.2 to find the value of β when $\mu_0 = 25$, $\mu_1 = 24$, $\sigma = 10$, $n = 100$, $\alpha = .05$.

30.7. In view of Exercise 30.6, use Figure 30.2 to find the value of n, given that $\alpha = .05$, $\beta = .10$, $\mu_0 - \mu_1 = 20$, and $\sigma = 30$.

30.8. Let the receiving inspection plan of Example 30.3 be altered by stipulating that the lot of 100 is rejected if more than 2 defectives are found in a sample of 20. Compute the values of β corresponding to the values of p given in Table 30.2, and construct the OC curve.

31. CONFIDENCE INTERVALS

Statistical inference includes, along with the methods of testing hypotheses discussed earlier in this chapter, various methods of estimation. When a single statistic obtained from a sample is used to estimate a parameter, we refer to the statistic as a *point estimate* of the parameter. Thus, for example, the sample mean is a point estimate of the population mean. Confidence intervals, which have been briefly referred to in Section 26, form a second type of estimate known as an *interval estimate.* An interval estimate (or a confidence interval) for the parameter λ will be given by a pair of statistics L_1 and L_2, computed from the same sample, such that the inequality $L_1 < \lambda < L_2$ will hold for a known proportion of randomly drawn samples. Thus we shall say that L_1 and L_2 are *99% confidence limits for* λ if, when such limits are computed for a great many samples from the same population, 99% of the pairs of limits include λ between them. The concept employed here is quite similar to that of probability but differs in that here a *random interval* may be predicted to cover or include a fixed (though unknown) parameter with specified confidence, whereas the probability concept has been applied to the statement that a fixed interval contains some random variable (statistic). The number that expresses our degree of confidence that the random interval (L_1, L_2) includes λ is called the *confidence coefficient* or simply the *confidence* associated with the statement and is usually expressed as a per cent.

The virtue of a test of significance is that it provides a clear-cut decision for or against a proposed hypothesis, and in many experimental situations this is precisely what is wanted. However, the yes-or-no answer provided by the test of significance conveys relatively little numerical information about the population. Confidence intervals, on the other hand, extract from the sample a good deal of pertinent information about the population.

We shall approach the construction of confidence intervals by showing how they are related to simple tests of significance. Consider, for example, a two-sided test of the hypothesis H_0: $\mu = \mu_0$, based on a sample of size n from a normal population. Suppose that the level of significance is α and that $\overline{X}$ and s are the sample mean and variance. Under the null hypothesis the quantity $t = (\overline{X} - \mu_0)\sqrt{n}/s$ has the t distribution with $n - 1$ d.f. If $t_{1-\alpha/2}$ is the $100(1 - \alpha/2)$ percentile of the t distribution, the acceptance region for t is $|t| < t_{1-\alpha/2}$, so that H_0 will be accepted if

$$(31.1) \qquad\qquad |\overline{X} - \mu_0| < \frac{s t_{1-\alpha/2}}{\sqrt{n}}.$$

No matter what value of μ_0 is employed in the null hypothesis, the null hypothesis will be accepted if (31.1) is satisfied. Thus, given the values of $\overline{X}$ and s from a particular sample, we may, from (31.1), obtain the complete *range of values of* μ_0 *which would be accepted if employed as hypothetical values of* μ_0. In fact, (31.1) leads to the inequality

$$\frac{-s}{\sqrt{n}} t_{1-\alpha/2} < \mu_0 - \overline{X} < \frac{s}{\sqrt{n}} t_{1-\alpha/2},$$

and this in turn to

$$(31.2) \qquad \overline{X} - \frac{s}{\sqrt{n}} t_{1-\alpha/2} < \mu_0 < \overline{X} + \frac{s}{\sqrt{n}} t_{1-\alpha/2}.$$

The interval, specified by (31.2), within which μ_0 may be said to lie with $100(1 - \alpha)\%$ confidence is called a *$100(1 - \alpha)\%$ confidence interval* for the population mean. If a great many such intervals are constructed from samples from the same population, then we may expect that approximately $100(1 - \alpha)\%$ of these intervals will contain the population mean.

Example 31.1. In Example 29.6, which had to do with the effect of a meal upon the heart performance of young men, as measured by the EKG, we had a sample of 12 values of the difference d between the before-meal performance and the after-meal performance of young men. For these 12 values, $\overline{d} = -1.142$, $s_d = 1.167$. Let us form a 99% confidence interval for μ_d, the mean of the population of all similar values of d. We find $t_{.995} = 3.106$, whence

$$\frac{s_d}{\sqrt{n}} t_{.995} = \frac{1.167}{\sqrt{12}} \times 3.106 = 1.046$$

and the confidence interval is

$$-1.142 - 1.046 < \mu_d < -1.142 + 1.046$$

or

$$-2.188 < \mu_d < -.096.$$

The conclusion is that, with 99% confidence, we can declare that μ_d lies in the specified interval. Thus we have at least this degree of confidence that μ_d is not zero, a result in agreement with that of Example 29.6. Note that in this type of application of a confidence interval, essentially the same kind of conclusion is obtained as is gotten from a test of significance.

Consider now a two-sided test for the parameter p of a dichotomy, as discussed in Section 29. Since $Z = (\hat{p} - p)/\sqrt{p(1 - p)/n}$ is approximately normally distributed, the acceptance region of the hypothesis $p = p_0$ is

$$(31.3) \qquad \frac{|\hat{p} - p_0|}{\sqrt{\dfrac{p_0(1 - p_0)}{n}}} < z_{1-\alpha/2},$$

where α is the level of significance and $z_{1-\alpha/2}$ is the $100(1 - \alpha/2)$ percentile of the unit normal distribution. Thus, given an observed value of p, all hypothetical values of p_0 which will be accepted are those which satisfy the inequality (31.3). Let us now, for compactness, replace $z_{1-\alpha/2}$ by z^*. If we square both sides of (31.3), clear of fractions, and transpose all terms to the left, we obtain

$$(31.4) \qquad n(p_0 - \hat{p})^2 - z^{*2}p_0(1 - p_0) < 0.$$

Now consider the left side of (31.4) as a function of p_0:

$$f(p_0) = n(p_0 - \hat{p})^2 - z^{*2}p_0(1 - p_0).$$

The graph of $f(p_0)$ against p_0 will be a parabola opening upwards since the coefficient of $p_0{}^2$, namely, $n + z^{*2}$, is positive. Hence the values of p_0 which satisfy (31.4) lie between the 2 roots of the quadratic equation $f(p_0) = 0$, namely,

$$(31.5) \qquad \frac{2n\hat{p} + z^{*2} \pm z^*\sqrt{z^{*2} + 4n\hat{p}(1 - \hat{p})}}{2(n + z^{*2})}.$$

Since any value of p_0 lying between these roots will satisfy (31.4), the two values given by (31.5) are the confidence limits for p_0.

Example 31.2. A sample of $n = 200$ items from a manufacturing process is found to contain 6 defectives. What are the 99% confidence limits for p, the population fraction defective? Here $z^* = z_{1-\alpha/2} = z_{.995} = 2.576$, $\hat{p} = .03$, and (31.5) yields

$$\frac{18.63 \pm 2.576\sqrt{29.91}}{413.3}.$$

Thus the confidence limits turn out to be .0110 and .0792. The manufacturer will be primarily interested in the larger limit, and he may claim with 99% confidence that his proportion defective does not exceed 7.92%.

For most practical purposes the 95% confidence limits for a proportion can be obtained graphically from Figure 31.1. The observed proportion p is located on the horizontal scale. The sample size determines a pair of curves, say C_1 and C_2, each labeled with the same value of n. A vertical line through the point $\hat{p}$ on the horizontal scale will cut C_1 and C_2 in 2 points whose ordinates, as determined on the vertical scale, give the confidence limits.

Example 31.3. What are the 95% confidence limits for p if a sample of $n = 250$ contains 100 defectives? Here $\hat{p} = 100/250 = .4$. A vertical line through the point $\hat{p} = .4$ on the horizontal scale cuts the curves for $n = 250$ at points whose ordinates are .34 and .47; they are the required confidence limits. If formula (31.5) is employed to determine the confidence limits in this example, we obtain .341 and .462; they are somewhat inaccurate because (31.5) was obtained using the normal approximation to the binomial distribution.

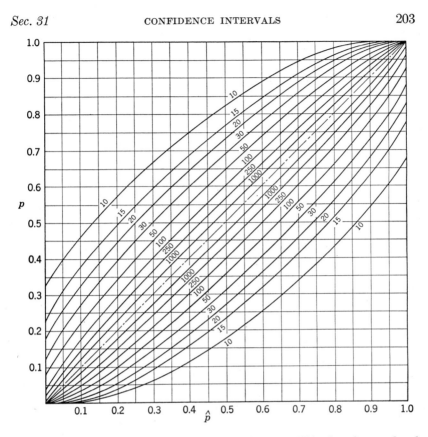

FIGURE 31.1. Chart of 95% confidence intervals for p. This chart is reproduced with the permission of Professor E. S. Pearson from C. J. Clopper and E. S. Pearson, "The use of confidence or fiducial limits illustrated in the case of the binomial," *Biometrika*, vol. 26 (1934), p. 404.

EXERCISE 31

31.1. Let μ_d be the mean difference in height for an infinite population of pairs of plants grown under the circumstances described in Exercise 29.4. Find a 95% confidence interval for μ_d. Here, $n = 15$.

31.2. The 32 volunteers mentioned in Exercises 29.5 and 29.6 had a mean height of 178.6 cm. with a standard deviation of 5.9 cm. Form a 99% confidence interval for the mean height μ of the population from which these men are drawn.

31.3. Show that, if z^{*2} is negligible in comparison with $2n\hat{p}$ and n, then the confidence limits given by (31.5) reduce to $\hat{p} \pm (z^*/n)\sqrt{np(1 - \hat{p})}$.

31.4. A buyer tests a random sample of 100 of the electrical devices discussed in Exercise 29.2 and finds that 94% of them pass the test. Form a 95% confidence interval for the population proportion, p, which will pass the test.

31.5. Suppose a customer of the seed distributor of Exercise 29.1 finds that 182 seeds germinate in a random sample of 200 seeds. Form a 99% confidence interval for the population proportion, p, of viable seeds.

31.6. Suppose that it is known that the standard deviation of a normal population is 13.7. How large should a sample be in order that a 95% confidence interval for the population mean should be no larger than 10 units in length?

32. ESTIMATION OF PARAMETERS— MAXIMUM LIKELIHOOD

Having in the previous section dealt with interval estimates, we now return to the consideration of point estimates and probe more deeply into their properties. It will be recalled that a point estimate (or an *estimator*) is a single statistic (i.e., a function of the sample values) which is expected to be "close to" the parameter it is said to estimate. To express the matter more accurately, consider the sampling distribution of the statistic in question. Then an estimate $\hat{\theta}$ of a parameter θ will be "good" if it possesses such properties as the following:

(*a*) Its expected value equals the parameter: $E(\hat{\theta}) = \theta$. This is the property of *unbiasedness* which we have already encountered several times.

(*b*) If the sample size becomes infinite, so that the sample becomes indistinguishable from the population, the estimate should become identical with the parameter. To this property R. A. Fisher gives the name of *consistency*. Alternatively we may define a consistent estimate $\hat{\theta}$ as one whose distribution becomes more and more closely concentrated about the parameter as $n \to \infty$.

(*c*) The variance of the sampling distribution of $\hat{\theta}$ should be small. If $\hat{\theta}_1$ and $\hat{\theta}_2$ are two estimates of the parameter θ, with variances $\sigma_1{}^2$ and $\sigma_2{}^2$, the *efficiency of $\hat{\theta}_2$ relative to $\hat{\theta}_1$* is defined by Fisher to be $\sigma_1{}^2/\sigma_2{}^2$. The ratio is usually expressed in percentage form. In some cases an estimate $\hat{\theta}_1$ can be found whose variance is smaller than that of any other estimate of the parameter. Such an estimate is said to be *efficient*. Then, for any other estimate $\hat{\theta}_2$ the quantity $100\,\sigma_1{}^2/\sigma_2{}^2$ is called the efficiency of $\hat{\theta}_2$. Thus an efficient estimator has an efficiency of 100%.

(*d*) The statistic should convey as much as possible of the information about the parameter which is contained in the sample, so that little additional information will be supplied if other estimates are reported. Fisher discovered a class of statistics which he called *sufficient* and which in his own words "summarize the whole of the relevant information supplied by the sample." They are such that no additional information about the parameter is supplied by any other statistic. An estimator $\hat{\theta}_1$ of a parameter θ is said to be sufficient if for every other estimator $\hat{\theta}_2$ the conditional distribution of $\hat{\theta}_2$ given $\hat{\theta}_1$ is independent of θ.

The foregoing definitions may be illustrated in terms of the mean $\bar{X}$ of a sample. It possesses, first of all, the property of being unbiased (Section 27). Second, since $\mu = E(x)$ is the direct extension to an infinite population of the averaging process involved in the sample mean, it follows that $\bar{X}$ is consistent. Third, the mean $\bar{X}$ of a sample from a normal population is efficient since it can be shown that any other estimate of μ has larger variance. For example, if $\tilde{X}$ is the median of a sample, it can be shown that $E(\tilde{X}) = \mu$ so that $\tilde{X}$ is an unbiased estimate of μ. We know that the variance of $\bar{X}$ is $\sigma_{\bar{X}}^2 = \sigma^2/n$; it can be shown that the variance of $\tilde{X}$ is $\sigma_{\tilde{X}}^2 = \sigma^2/nE$, where E is a function of n, ranging from 1.00 when $n = 2$ to an asymptotic value of .637 as $n \to \infty$. Thus the relative efficiency of $\tilde{X}$ with respect to $\bar{X}$ is $\sigma_{\bar{X}}^2/\sigma_{\tilde{X}}^2 = E$.

We shall not pursue further the systematic study of the properties of estimates listed above since such a study goes beyond the level assumed in this book. Instead we shall consider an important method of obtaining estimates which, under certain circumstances, will possess many of the desirable properties just considered. This is the method of maximum likelihood, due to R. A. Fisher.

Consider a typical density function, such as the normal density

$$(32.1) \qquad f_N(x \,|\, \mu, \sigma^2) = \frac{1}{\sigma\sqrt{2\pi}}\, e^{-(x-\mu)^2/2\sigma^2}.$$

The variables upon which this function depends are of two kinds: the letter x represents the random variable whose density this is; the letters μ and σ are the parameters of the distribution. If $(x_1, \cdots, x_n)$ * is a sample from this distribution, the random variables $x_1, \cdots, x_n$ have the joint distribution

$$(32.2) \qquad f(x_1, \cdots, x_n \,|\, \mu, \sigma^2) = \frac{1}{\sigma^n (2\pi)^{n/2}} \exp \frac{-\Sigma(x_i - \mu)^2}{2\sigma^2}.$$

Generalizing these ideas, we consider a sample $(x_1, \cdots, x_n)$ from a population whose distribution depends on certain parameters $\theta_1, \cdots, \theta_r$.

---

* In this section and in Section 33 we shall drop the practise of using capital letters for sample values.

The joint density of the x's will be a function of $x_1, \cdots, x_n$ and also of $\theta_1, \cdots, \theta_r$ which may be written

(32.3) $$f(x_1, \cdots, x_n \,|\, \theta_1, \cdots, \theta_r).$$

If we wish to estimate one of the parameters, say θ_i, the problem is that of selecting a suitable statistic, or estimator, which will be a function of the sample values, say $\hat{\theta}_i(x_1, \cdots, x_n)$.

Up to this point, in considering the general density (32.3) or the particular case (32.2), we have thought of the parameters $\theta_1, \cdots, \theta_r$ as fixed, while the random variables $x_1, \cdots, x_n$ vary from sample to sample. The density is thus regarded as a function of the point $(x_1, \cdots, x_n)$ of the sample space. We now change our point of view and consider that we have a fixed sample $(x_1, \cdots, x_n)$ and that the function (32.3) depends on the *parameter point* $(\theta_1, \cdots, \theta_r)$. Considered in this way, the density function is rechristened the *likelihood function* or the *likelihood*, which varies with the parameter point $(\theta_1, \cdots, \theta_r)$ of the *parameter space*. When considered as a likelihood we shall often use the letter L to denote the density function $f(x_1, \cdots, x_n \,|\, \theta_1, \cdots, \theta_r)$.

The concept of the likelihood function is as useful and important for discrete random variables as for continuous. We may, in fact, regard (32.3) as the joint frequency function of a discrete multivariate distribution. If, in such a function, the $x_1, \cdots, x_n$ are regarded as fixed so that (32.3) is a function of $\theta_1, \cdots, \theta_n$, the function is called the likelihood of the parameter point $(\theta_1, \cdots, \theta_r)$.

Given a likelihood function $f(x_1, \cdots, x_n \,|\, \theta_1, \cdots, \theta_r)$, for either the discrete or continuous case, we may be able to find a set of functions $\hat{\theta}_1 = \hat{\theta}_1(x_1, \cdots, x_n), \cdots, \hat{\theta}_r = \hat{\theta}_r(x_1, \cdots, x_n)$ such that the values $\theta_1 = \hat{\theta}_1, \cdots, \theta_r = \hat{\theta}_r$ maximize the function $f(x_1, \cdots, x_n \,|\, \theta_1, \cdots, \theta_r)$. In this case we call the functions $\hat{\theta}_1, \cdots, \hat{\theta}_r$ a set of *maximum likelihood estimates* of the parameters $\theta_1, \cdots, \theta_r$. In many such cases the maximum likelihood estimates can be found by the simple expedient of setting the partial derivatives of the likelihood with respect to $\theta_1, \cdots, \theta_r$ equal to zero. One must then verify by one means or another that a maximum point rather than a minimum point, or a point which is neither a maximum nor a minimum, has been obtained.

It is often more convenient to use the logarithm of the likelihood function rather than the likelihood itself in order to obtain maximum likelihood estimates. This is especially true in the important case in which each of the random variables is independently distributed, with a common density function (or frequency function) $f(x; \theta_1, \cdots, \theta_r)$.

Then the joint likelihood function, say L, is the product of the likelihood functions of the individual values:

$$L(x_1, \cdots, x_n; \theta_1, \cdots, \theta_r)$$
$$= f(x_1; \theta_1, \cdots, \theta_r) \, f(x_2; \theta_1, \cdots, \theta_r) \cdots f(x_n; \theta_1, \cdots, \theta_r).$$

By taking logarithms,

$$\log L(x_1, \cdots, x_n; \theta_1, \cdots, \theta_r) = \sum_{i=1}^{n} \log f(x_i; \theta_1, \cdots, \theta_r).$$

This function is somewhat easier to differentiate and therefore to maximize than the original likelihood functions; and the set of values of $\theta_1, \cdots, \theta_r$ which maximize $\log L$ will also maximize L.

As an illustration of the application of the method of maximum likelihood to the case of a continuous random variable, consider:

Example 32.1.   Let X_1 and X_2 each possess the distribution $N(\mu, \sigma^2)$. Find the maximum likelihood estimates of μ and σ^2.

Solution.   The joint likelihood is

$$L = \frac{1}{2\pi\sigma^2} \exp - \frac{1}{2\sigma^2} [(x_1 - \mu)^2 + (x_2 - \mu)^2],$$

and its logarithm is

$$\log L = -\log 2\pi - 2 \log \sigma - \frac{1}{2\sigma^2} [(x_1 - \mu)^2 + (x_2 - \mu)^2].$$

Taking the partial derivative with regard to μ and equating to zero, we find the maximum likelihood estimator of μ to be $\hat{\mu} = \frac{1}{2}(x_1 + x_2)$. Taking the partial derivative with regard to σ and equating to zero, we obtain for the maximum likelihood estimator of σ^2, $\hat{\sigma}^2 = \frac{1}{2}[(x_1 - \mu)^2 + (x_2 - \mu)^2]$. If we now consider these two equations simultaneously, we may substitute the maximum likelihood estimate of μ into $\hat{\sigma}^2$, obtaining $\hat{\sigma}^2 = \frac{1}{4}(x_1 - x_2)^2$. Note that this is not an unbiased estimate of σ^2. It is, in fact, simply the value of $\text{var}(x)$, as calculated for the sample, which must be multiplied by the ratio $n/(n-1) = 2$ in order to produce the unbiased estimate s^2.

It is a characteristic of maximum likelihood estimates that, although they may be biased as in the above example, the bias can usually be removed by some such simple modification as was used in the example.

To illustrate the application of the method to a case involving discrete random variables we consider a dichotomous variable:

Example 32.2.   Let $x_1, \cdots, x_n$ be independent values from the binomial distribution whose frequency function is

$$f(x) = \binom{m}{x} p^x (1 - p)^{m-x}.$$

Find the maximum likelihood estimate of p.

Solution. The joint frequency function of $x_1, \cdots, x_n$ is the product

$$f(x_1) f(x_2) \cdots f(x_n) = \binom{m}{x_1} p^{x_1}(1 - p)^{m-x_1} \binom{m}{x_2} p^{x_2}(1 - p)^{m-x_2}$$

$$\cdots \binom{m}{x_n} p^{x_n}(1 - p)^{m-x_n}$$

$$= \binom{m}{x_1}\binom{m}{x_2} \cdots \binom{m}{x_n} p^{\Sigma x}(1 - p)^{mn-\Sigma x},$$

where $\Sigma x = x_1 + \cdots + x_n$. We now regard this as a function of the parameter p and consider $x_1, \cdots, x_n$ to be fixed numbers. This function of p is the likelihood function L. The logarithm of the likelihood is

$$\log L = \sum_{i=1}^{n} \log \binom{m}{x_i} + (\Sigma x) \log p + (mn - \Sigma x) \log (1 - p).$$

Differentiating, we find

$$\frac{\partial \log L}{\partial p} = \frac{\Sigma x}{p} - \frac{mn - \Sigma x}{1 - p}.$$

Setting the partial derivative equal to zero, we conclude that the maximum likelihood estimator of p is $\hat{p} = \Sigma x/mn$.

In more advanced works on mathematical statistics it is shown that maximum likelihood estimates are always efficient and consistent. Furthermore, if θ is a parameter which possesses a sufficient estimate, the maximum likelihood estimate of that parameter will be sufficient. When we add to these useful properties the fact that in most cases maximum likelihood estimates are obtainable by a very direct process (partial differentiation), we can understand why their discovery marked a very significant advance in mathematical statistics.

EXERCISE 32

32.1. Specify the parameter space for Example 32.2.

32.2. The random variables $X_1, \cdots, X_n$ are independently drawn from a population with density $f(x) = ae^{-ax}$, $0 \leq x < \infty$, $a > 0$. Find the maximum likelihood estimate of the parameter a.

32.3. A single value X_1 is drawn from the distribution $N(\mu, \sigma_1^2)$, in which σ_1 is presumed to be known. Find the maximum likelihood estimate of μ.

32.4. A sample of n values $(X_1, \cdots, X_n)$ is drawn from the distribution $N(\mu, \sigma_1^2)$, in which σ_1 is regarded as known. Find the maximum likelihood estimate of μ.

32.5. A single value X_1 is drawn from the rectangular distribution

$$f(x) = k, \quad 0 \leq x \leq 1/k$$

$$f(x) = 0, \quad \text{elsewhere.}$$

Show that the maximum likelihood estimate of k is $1/X_1$.

32.6. Let two values X_1, X_2 be drawn from the rectangular distribution

$$f(x) = k, \quad 0 \leqq x \leqq 1/k$$

$$f(x) = 0, \quad \text{elsewhere.}$$

Show that the maximum likelihood estimate of k is the smaller of $1/X_1$ and $1/X_2$. Extend the result to the case in which a sample of n values $(X_1, \cdots, X_n)$ is drawn from the rectangular distribution specified above.

*33. LIKELIHOOD RATIO TEST OF A HYPOTHESIS

A serious defect in the approach to tests of hypotheses presented in Section 28 is that no rule is given for the selection of a suitable critical statistic. The types of tests that have been considered in this chapter were of the simplest kind, depending on the direct application of the normal distribution or of the t distribution. For such tests there are one or two rather obvious possibilities for the critical statistic, and it makes little difference which is chosen. In the more complex types of tests of significance it becomes important to have a systematic method of selecting a suitable critical statistic. For this purpose, the likelihood ratio method, about to be described, often supplies the need.

Example 33.1. Let us use the illustration of Example 32.1. Now x_1 and x_2 are regarded as fixed, and the function

$$(33.1) \qquad L = \frac{1}{2\pi\sigma^2} \exp - \frac{1}{2\sigma^2} [(x_1 - \mu)^2 + (x_2 - \mu)^2]$$

is to be regarded as a likelihood function ranging over the parameter space consisting of the upper half of the μ, σ^2 plane (see Figure 33.1). Suppose we

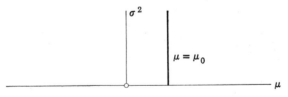

FIGURE 33.1

wish to test the hypothesis that $\mu = \mu_0$. This hypothesis corresponds to a set of points in the parameter space, namely, those on the vertical line $\mu = \mu_0$. The *likelihood ratio* is defined, in this case, to be

$$\lambda = \frac{\text{Maximum of } L \text{ along the line } \mu = \mu_0}{\text{Maximum of } L \text{ over the whole parameter space}}.$$

Up to this point the sample values x_1 and x_2 are held fixed. We now regard λ as a function of x_1 and x_2. This function will be positive since L is $\geqq 0$ for all values of μ, σ^2, x_1, x_2. Speaking intuitively, we may say that a low value of

λ implies a lack of consistency between the sample values and the null hypothesis. Let the density of λ be $g(\lambda)$, and let $\int_0^{\alpha} g(\lambda)\, d\lambda = \alpha$, where α is some arbitrarily chosen level of significance. Then the critical region (region of rejection) for the hypothesis is the interval $0 \leqq \lambda \leqq \lambda_{\alpha}$.

Let us find the value of λ as a function of x_1 and x_2 for the example with which we began this discussion. According to Example 32.1, the maximum of L over the whole parameter space occurs at the point $\mu = \frac{1}{2}(x_1 + x_2)$, $\sigma^2 = \frac{1}{4}(x_1 - x_2)^2$. Substituting these values in (33.1) we find that the maximum value is

$$\frac{2}{\pi e (x_1 - x_2)^2}.$$

On the other hand we readily find that along $\mu = \mu_0$ the maximum of L occurs when $\sigma^2 = \frac{1}{2}[(x_1 - \mu_0)^2 + (x_2 - \mu_0)^2]$, and that the value of the maximum is

$$\frac{1}{\pi e [(x_1 - \mu_0)^2 + (x_2 - \mu_0)^2]}.$$

Hence the likelihood ratio is

(33.2)
$$\lambda = \frac{(x_1 - x_2)^2}{2[(x_1 - \mu_0)^2 + (x_2 - \mu_0)^2]}.$$

We shall see, in Section 41, that the quantity λ in (33.2) is closely related to Student's t-statistic. This suggests a justification for the use of the t-statistic in tests of significance, and it provides a means for obtaining the sampling distribution of λ.

We may now describe the general concept of a likelihood ratio test. Let $f(x_1, \cdots, x_n; \theta_1, \cdots, \theta_r)$ be a likelihood function for the sample $(x_1, \cdots, x_n)$ over the parameter space whose coordinates are $\theta_1, \cdots, \theta_r$. We shall usually be interested in hypotheses of the type that specify values for certain of the parameters, say $\theta_1 = \theta_1{}^*$, $\theta_2 = \theta_2{}^*$, $\cdots$, $\theta_p = \theta_p{}^*$. These conditions together specify a certain subregion of the parameter space which we may call the hypothetical subregion. The hypothetical subregion may also be specified by means of inequalities rather than equalities. The likelihood ratio statistic may now be defined quite generally by

(33.3) $\lambda = \dfrac{\text{Maximum of the likelihood over the hypothetical subregion}}{\text{Maximum of the likelihood over the whole parameter space}}.$

EXERCISE 33

33.1. Extend the result of Example 33.1 to a sample of size n: $(X_1, \cdots, X_n)$ by showing that the likelihood ratio statistic λ for the hypothesis $\mu = \mu_0$ is, assuming that each of the values $x_1, \cdots, x_n$ is independently distributed according to $N(\mu, \sigma^2)$:

$$\lambda = \left[\frac{\Sigma(x - \bar{x})^2}{\Sigma(x - \mu_0)^2}\right]^{n/2}.$$

CHAPTER 5

Sampling Distributions II

In Chapter 3, only a few sampling distributions were considered, primarily in order to provide a basis for the discussion of statistical inference in Chapter 4. The present chapter will provide proofs for some of the results used without proof in Chapters 3 and 4. It will also consider a much wider range of sampling distributions. Most of them will have some relation to the normal distribution, either because they tend to approach the normal distribution under certain circumstances or because they are in some way derived from the normal distribution. Somewhat removed from these classes of distributions are the distributions of order statistics, of which the distribution of the median is a typical example.

The chart on page 212 shows the relations between a number of these distributions. The reader will find it helpful to refer to this chart frequently in his reading of the chapter. A number of the distributions referred to in the chart have not yet been encountered. The letter k, as used in the upper half of the chart, refers to the parameter k in the hypergeometric distribution (7.12). In the lower half of the chart the symbol k^* has been used for the parameter of the Poisson distribution, which is denoted by k in Section 35.

34. THE NORMAL DISTRIBUTION AS A LIMITING FORM OF THE BINOMIAL DISTRIBUTION

This section will be devoted to a proof of the important result that the limiting form of the histogram of the binomial distribution is that of the normal curve. In order to state this result somewhat more accurately, we shall use the term *point graph* of the binomial to refer to the set of points which form the upper terminals of the vertical lines of the line graph. In this terminology the result to be proved is that the point graph of the binomial distribution tends toward the normal curve as n, the number of independent drawings associated with the binomial dis-

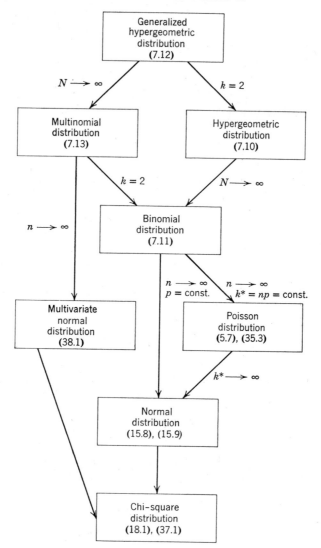

tribution, tends toward infinity. This result is a special case of the central limit theorem, already referred to several times, which states that, if n independent drawings are made from any distribution having finite variance and if the distribution of the sum of the n drawings is formed, this latter distribution will tend toward the normal distribution as n approaches infinity.

Consider the sequence of histograms associated with the binomial distribution

$$(34.1) \qquad f(x) = \binom{n}{x} p^x q^{n-x},$$

for $n = 2, 3, 4, \cdots$, p and q fixed. Each of the histograms has unit area, since the successive x-values are one unit apart and the sum of the probabilities is unity. We wish to consider the limiting form of the histograms as $n \to \infty$. However, since the mean and variance of (34.1) are $\mu = np$ and $\sigma^2 = npq$, these quantities will both increase without limit as $n \to \infty$, and the series of graphs will move to the right, spread out over a larger portion of the x-axis, and therefore tend to flatten down as $n \to \infty$ (see Section 22). In order to stabilize these tendencies, it is reasonable to use standard units defined by

$$(34.2) \qquad t = \frac{x - np}{\sqrt{npq}}.$$

However, if we now draw the histograms over a fixed t-scale, the areas will decrease with increase of n since the width of each bar of the histogram will now be $1/\sqrt{npq}$. In order to stabilize the area of the histograms, we multiply the ordinate by $\sqrt{npq}$. Thus we shall show that the function

$$(34.3) \qquad y = \sqrt{npq} \binom{n}{x} p^x q^{n-x}$$

will tend toward the normal curve

$$y = \frac{1}{\sqrt{2\pi}} e^{-t/2}$$

as $n \to \infty$, where x and t are connected by the relationship

$$(34.4) \qquad x = np + t\sqrt{npq}.$$

There is a slight complication which we shall take steps to avoid. If we hold t, p, and q fixed and let $n \to \infty$ through integral values, the quantity x in (34.4) will, in general, assume a non-integral series of values with the result that $\binom{n}{x}$ is meaningless. In order to avoid this complication we shall use, instead of $\binom{n}{x}$, the continuous quantity

$\begin{bmatrix} n \\ x \end{bmatrix}$ defined by equation (17.10), whose value is $\dbinom{n}{x}$ for integral values of n. We are thus led to consider the function

(34.5) $$y^* = \sqrt{npq}\, \begin{bmatrix} n \\ x \end{bmatrix} p^x q^{n-x}.$$

We may now state the result to be proved in the following form. Let t be an arbitrary fixed real number, and let p and q be arbitrary positive quantities such that $p + q = 1$. Let n approach infinity by a series of integral values. Then x will likewise approach infinity by a series of values given by (34.4). When these values for n and the corresponding values for x are substituted in (34.5), we obtain a series of values of y^* whose limit is the normal density.

Using Stirling's approximation to the gamma function, we find that $\begin{bmatrix} n \\ x \end{bmatrix}$ is approximated as follows:

(34.6) $$\begin{bmatrix} n \\ x \end{bmatrix} \doteq \left[\frac{n}{2\pi x(n-x)} \right]^{\frac{1}{2}} \left(\frac{n}{x} \right)^{x} \left(\frac{n}{n-x} \right)^{n-x}.$$

When this value is inserted in (34.5), we obtain

$$y^* \doteq \sqrt{npq}\, \sqrt{\frac{n}{2\pi x(n-x)}} \left(\frac{n}{x} \right)^{x} \left(\frac{n}{n-x} \right)^{n-x} p^x q^{n-x}$$

$$= \underbrace{\sqrt{\frac{n^2 pq}{2\pi x(n-x)}}}_{A} \underbrace{\left(\frac{np}{x} \right)^{x} \left(\frac{nq}{n-x} \right)^{n-x}}_{B}$$

$$= \qquad A \qquad \times \qquad B$$

where A and B are the expressions indicated by the brackets. We shall show that, as $n - \infty$, $A \rightarrow (2\pi)^{-\frac{1}{2}}$ and $B \rightarrow e^{-x^2/2}$ so that the product $A \cdot B$ approaches the ordinate of the unit normal curve.

The expressions A and B can be simplified by means of the substitutions

$$a = t\sqrt{\frac{q}{np}}, \quad b = t\sqrt{\frac{p}{nq}},$$

in which t is given by (34.2). We find

$$x = np + t\sqrt{npq} = np + npa = np(1 + a),$$

$$n - x = nq - t\sqrt{npq} = nq - nqb = nq(1 - b).$$

Thus

$$A = [2\pi(1 + a)(1 - b)]^{-\frac{1}{2}}.$$

As $n \to \infty$, both a and b will approach 0. Hence $A \to (2\pi)^{-\frac{1}{2}}$.

Again,

$$B = (1 + a)^{-np(1+a)}(1 - b)^{-nq(1-b)}.$$

We shall evaluate $\log B$, making use of the series expansion

$$(34.7) \qquad \log (1 + x) = x - \frac{x^2}{2} + \frac{x^3}{3} - \frac{x^4}{4} + \cdots,$$

which is convergent provided that $|x|$ is sufficiently small. We find

$$\log B = -np(1 + a)\left(a - \frac{a^2}{2} + \frac{a^3}{3} - \cdots\right)$$

$$+ nq(1 - b)\left(b + \frac{b^2}{2} + \frac{b^3}{3} + \cdots\right)$$

$$= -np\left(a + \frac{a^2}{2} - \frac{a^3}{6} + \cdots\right) + nq\left(b - \frac{b^2}{2} - \frac{b^3}{6} + \cdots\right).$$

We now use the definitions of a and b in order to expand this series in powers of n; it turns out that all such powers are either zero or negative. In fact we obtain

$$\log B = -\frac{t^2}{2} + \frac{t^3}{6\sqrt{pq}}(q^2 - p^2)n^{-\frac{1}{2}} + \cdots,$$

where the omitted terms all involve negative powers of n. Hence, as $n \to \infty$, $\log B \to -t^2/2$, and $B \to e^{-t^2/2}$. Finally, as $n \to \infty$,

$$y = A \cdot B \to \frac{1}{\sqrt{2\pi}} e^{-t^2/2},$$

which is what we set out to prove.

Under the assumption that Stirling's approximation involves no error in the limit as $n \to \infty$, we have proved that the smooth curve whose equation is (34.5) possesses the normal curve as its limit, as $n \to \infty$. On the other hand we know that the point graph of the quantity y, defined by (34.3), lies entirely on the smooth curve (34.5). Hence $y \to (1/\sqrt{2\pi}) e^{-t^2/2}$. But y differs from the binomial point graph only in the factor $\sqrt{npq}$, which merely affects the vertical scale. Thus we conclude that the point graph of the binomial distribution tends toward the form of the normal curve as $n \to \infty$.

EXERCISE 34

The following exercises outline an alternative proof that the limiting form of the binomial distribution, as $n \to \infty$, is the normal distribution, making use of moment generating functions.

*34.1. Let X be a random variable with the binomial frequency function (34.1). According to Exercise 19.18 the moment generating function of X is $M_x(t) = (q + pe^t)^n$. Let a new random variable Z be defined by $Z = (X - np)/\sqrt{npq}$. Using Exercise 19.16, show that Z has the m.g.f.

$$M_z(t) = e^{-\sqrt{np/q}\, t}(q + pe^{t/\sqrt{npq}})^n.$$

*34.2. If $M_z(t)$ is the function given in Exercise 34.1, use the power series expansion for $e^{t/\sqrt{npq}}$ in order to show that $\log M_z(t)$ may be written

$$\log M_z(t) = -\sqrt{\frac{np}{q}}\, t + n \log \left(1 + t\sqrt{\frac{p}{nq}} + \frac{t^2}{2nq} \right.$$
$$\left. + \text{ terms involving } n^{-2}, n^{-\delta}, \cdots \right).$$

*34.3. Use the power series expansion (34.7) for $\log (1 + x)$ to show that the expression for $\log M_z(t)$ in Exercise 34.2 may be reduced to

$$\log M_z(t) = \frac{t^2}{2} + \text{ terms involving } n^{-1}, n^{-2}, \cdots.$$

Thus, as $n \to \infty$, $M_z(t) \to e^{t^2/2}$, the moment generating function of the unit normal distribution (see Example 19.1). We conclude that the binomial distribution approaches the normal distribution as $n \to \infty$.

35. THE POISSON DISTRIBUTION AS A LIMITING FORM OF THE BINOMIAL DISTRIBUTION

The Poisson distribution has already been encountered in Section 5 (formula (5.7)). It has applications in such diverse fields as biology, radioactive decay, traffic studies, and the extent of usage of telephone facilities. A somewhat different type of use arises from the fact that the Poisson distribution provides a convenient approximation to the binomial distribution in certain cases. This fact is especially useful in industrial quality control.

As an illustration of the way in which this distribution arises in biological applications, suppose that bacteria are rather sparsely distributed through a volume of liquid. Let the average number of bacteria per cubic centimeter be k. Suppose that each cubic centimeter is divided into n parts, where n is very much greater than k. Since there are k bacteria randomly distributed among n equal volumes, we may use the relative frequency definition of probability in order to conclude that the probability that a volume of $1/n$ cc. taken at random will contain a single bacterium is given by

$$(35.1) \qquad p = k/n.$$

If we take n small volumes, each of $1/n$ cc. and regard the presence or absence of a bacterium in each as a dichotomous experiment, we may use the binomial distribution in order to obtain the probability of finding exactly x bacteria in 1 cc.:

$$(35.2) \qquad f^*(x) = \binom{n}{x} p^x q^{n-x} = \binom{n}{x}\left(\frac{k}{n}\right)^x \left(1 - \frac{k}{n}\right)^{n-x}.$$

We wish to investigate the behavior of this expression as $n \to \infty$. In order to do this, we rewrite (35.2) in the form

$$f^*(x) = \frac{n(n-1)\cdots(n-x+1)}{x!} k^x n^{-x} \left(1 - \frac{k}{n}\right)^n \left(1 - \frac{k}{n}\right)^{-x}.$$

We now use the factor n^{-x} in order to divide each term in the numerator of the first fraction by n, obtaining

$$f^*(x) = \frac{1\left(1 - \frac{1}{n}\right)\cdots\left(1 - \frac{x-1}{n}\right)}{x!} k^x \left(1 - \frac{k}{n}\right)^n \left(1 - \frac{k}{n}\right)^{-x}.$$

Now letting $n \to \infty$, we find

$$(35.3) \qquad f(x) = \lim_{n\to\infty} f^*(x) = \frac{k^x e^{-k}}{x!}.$$

This is the Poisson distribution. We note that a single number, namely k, is sufficient to specify the distribution. Such a quantity is called the *parameter* of the distribution.

We shall next find the mean and variance of the Poisson distribution. It is reasonable to use the definitions

$$(35.4) \qquad \mu = \sum_{x=1}^{\infty} x f(x), \quad \sigma^2 = \sum_{x=1}^{\infty} x^2 f(x) - \mu^2.$$

They are the generalizations of the definitions of Section 11 for the case in which the sample space has an infinite number of points. Inserting in (35.4) the value of $f(x)$ from (35.3), we have

$$\mu = \sum_{x=1}^{\infty} \frac{xk^x e^{-k}}{x!} = e^{-k} \sum_{x=1}^{\infty} \frac{k^x}{(x-1)!} = ke^{-k} \sum_{x=1}^{\infty} \frac{k^{x-1}}{(x-1)!} = ke^{-k}e^k = k.$$

$$\sigma^2 = \sum_{x=1}^{\infty} x^2 \frac{k^x e^{-k}}{x!} - \mu^2 = \sum_{x=1}^{\infty} [x(x-1) + x] \frac{k^x e^{-k}}{x!} - \mu^2$$

$$= e^{-k} \left[k^2 \sum_{x=1}^{\infty} \frac{k^{x-2}}{(x-2)!} + k \sum_{x=1}^{\infty} \frac{k^{x-1}}{(x-1)!} \right] - \mu^2$$

$$= e^{-k}[k^2 e^k + ke^k] - k^2 = k^2 + k - k^2 = k.$$

Thus both mean and variance of the Poisson distribution are equal to the parameter k.

The Poisson distribution approximates the binomial distribution if n is large and p is small, while the product np is moderate in size. This is illustrated in the following example.

Example 35.1. Use the Poisson distribution in order to approximate the binomial distribution for $n = 20$, $p = .05$, $q = .95$.

Solution. From (35.1) it follows that

(35.5) $$k = np.$$

For the example, $k = 20 \times .05 = 1.0$. Putting this value in (35.3), we have

$$f(x) = \frac{1^x e^{-1}}{x!}.$$

For $x = 5$, this yields

$$f(5) = \frac{e^{-1}}{5!} = \frac{.36788}{120} = .00307.$$

This is not a close approximation to the true binomial probability of .002245, but it is far better than the normal approximation. Table 35.1 shows the binomial probability distribution compared with the Poisson probability distribution for such values of x as give us sizeable probabilities.

A more suitable example for approximation by means of the Poisson distribution is the following:

Example 35.2. Let us find the binomial probability for $n = 100$, $p = .02$, $q = .98$, and $x = 5$.

$$P(x = 5) = \binom{100}{5} .02^5 .98^{95} = .03535.$$

Here we have $k = np = 2$. Hence the Poisson approximation is

$$\frac{2^5 e^{-2}}{5!} = .03609.$$

This illustrates the fact that the approximation tends to improve as n increases.

TABLE 35.1

COMPARISON OF BINOMIAL WITH POISSON DISTRIBUTION FOR $n = 20$, $p = .05$, $q = .95$

x	Binomial Probability	Poisson Probability
0	.358486	.367879
1	.377354	.367879
2	.188677	.183940
3	.059582	.061313
4	.013328	.015328
5	.002245	.003066
6	.000295	.000511
7	.000031	.000073
8	.000003	.000009
9	.000000	.000001
	1.000001	.999999

Note that the percentage error grows greater as x increases, while the absolute error grows smaller.

The Poisson distribution is applicable to many situations in which the probability of a single occurrence of a random event is proportional to a continuous variable y: $p = ky$. The variable y may be length (as when we study the probability of finding a car on a given stretch of highway), or area (as in considering the probability of encountering a bacterium in a particular square of a haemacytometer), or volume (as in the random experiment of drawing a given volume of a culture and determining whether or not it contains an organism), or time (as when we consider the probability that a specimen undergoes radioactive decay in a given interval of time), or indeed any continuous quantity. The preceding discussion implies that in all these cases the probability of x occurrences of the event in a unit interval of y is

$$P(X = x) = f(x) = \frac{k^x e^{-k}}{x!}.$$

The haemacytometer data of Section 4 conform rather closely to the Poisson distribution (see Exercise 35.10).

EXERCISE 35

35.1. Find the Poisson distribution for $k = 2$, for $x = 0, 1, 2, \cdots, 9$, given $e^{-2} = .13534$. Compare these probabilities with the corresponding binomial probabilities as obtained in Exercise 23.7.

35.2. Let us assume that the probability of catching a fish in a certain spot is proportional to the time spent fishing and that the probability of landing exactly one fish in 1 hour is .65. Find, using the Poisson distribution, the probability of catching 5 fish in 1 hour.

35.3. Let X be the number of successes in n Bernoullian trials, where the probability of success on a single trial is p. Let μ and σ^2 be the mean and variance of X. Show that, if $n \to \infty$ while np is fixed, then $\mu \to np$, $\sigma^2 = np$.

35.4. It is reasonable to define generating function and moment generating function, when the sample space is infinite, by means of (12.1) and (12.2) where the sums are infinite. In this way show that the g.f. and m.g.f. for the Poisson distribution are

$$G_x = e^{k(t-1)}, \quad M_x = e^{k(e^t-1)}.$$

35.5. Let X_1 and X_2 be independently distributed random variables, each with a Poisson distribution, the first with parameter k_1, the second with parameter k_2. Show that $X_1 + X_2$ possesses a Poisson distribution with parameter $k_1 + k_2$. Assume that (21.2) holds when the sample space is infinite.

35.6. Find the joint frequency function of the independent variables X_1, $\cdots, X_n$, given that each variable has a Poisson distribution, X_1 with parameter k_1, X_2 with parameter k_2, $\cdots, X_n$ with parameter k_n.

35.7. $X_1, \cdots, X_n$ are independent random values, each possessing a Poisson distribution with parameter k. Find the joint frequency function of $X_1, \cdots, X_n$. Find the maximum likelihood estimate of k.

35.8. In a sampling plan for industrial inspection a manufacturer uses a sample of size 100 and takes corrective action when the number of defectives is greater than 4. Regard this as a test of significance based on the Poisson distribution, with null hypothesis $k = 2$. Find the level of significance of the test.

35.9. The following table * gives the number of senders busy (x) in 3754 observations of a machine switching telephone exchange.

x	f	x	f	x	f	x	f
0	0	7	278	14	219	21	8
1	5	8	378	15	145	22	3
2	14	9	418	16	109		
3	24	10	461	17	57		
4	57	11	433	18	43		
5	111	12	413	19	16		
6	197	13	358	20	7		

* From T. C. Fry (7), p. 295.

(a) Find the relative frequency distribution.

(b) Find the mean $\overline{X}$.

(c) Find the theoretical probabilities for this distribution, using (35.3) with $\overline{X}$ in place of k. Compare with the relative frequencies of (a).

35.10. In Exercise 4.3 a frequency distribution and a relative frequency distribution were computed for the haemacytometer data of Table 4.2, and in Exercise 8.15 the mean, variance, and standard deviation of this distribution were obtained. Use the mean of the distribution $\overline{X} = 4.68$ as an estimate of the parameter k of a Poisson distribution. Form the Poisson distribution with parameter $k = 4.68$, and compare this distribution with the relative frequency distribution obtained in Exercise 4.3.

35.11 Let us apply the linear transformation $x = \mu + \sigma z = k + \sqrt{k}\, z$ to the frequency function (35.3). We thus obtain for the frequency function of the standardized variable z: $f(z) = k^{k+\sqrt{k}z}e^{-k}/(k + \sqrt{k}\, z)!$. Show that if we construct an "infinite histogram" on the z-axis, with blocks whose heights are equal to $\sqrt{k}\, f(z)$, the total area of the histogram will be unity. Show, using methods similar to those of Section 34, that $\sqrt{k}\, f(z) \rightarrow f_N(z)$ as $k \rightarrow \infty$. Work with $\log \sqrt{k}\, f(z)$, and use Stirling's formula (17.6).

36. DISTRIBUTION OF A FUNCTION OF RANDOM VARIABLES

The principal result of this section will be a method of deriving the distribution of a function of two random variables, both of the continuous type. We shall also indicate how the method may be generalized, enabling one to find the distribution of an arbitrary function of n random variables whose joint distribution is known. As a preliminary we shall briefly review the methods which have been used to obtain sampling distributions earlier in this book:

(a) In Section 5 a few sampling distributions were obtained by subdividing the (discrete) sample space into distinct events and finding the probability of each event. In this way we found the distribution of $X + Y$ and of $X^2 + Y^2$ when X and Y were random values arising from throwing 2 dice. Here the sample space may be represented either by a two-way table or geometrically by a rectangular array of points.

(b) In Section 7 the hypergeometric and the binomial distributions were deduced from the fact that in drawing samples of size n without replacement from an urn with N balls, there are $\binom{N}{n}$ equally likely samples; these latter were taken as the points of the sample space of the experiment.

(c) In Section 21 generating functions were used to find the distribution of $X + Y$, given the distributions of the independent discrete variables X and Y. In Section 27 this method was extended to continuous random variables.

(*d*) Sections 24 and 25 made use of a geometrical approach to sampling distributions which are related to the bivariate normal distribution. It was found that, if X and Y are independent values with the distribution $N(0, \sigma^2)$, the linear combination $aX + bY$ is normally distributed, while $(X^2 + Y^2)/\sigma^2$ has the chi-square distribution.

The method of obtaining sampling distributions described above under (*d*) is capable of immediate generalization. Let X and Y be a pair of continuous random variables with the joint density $f(x, y)$ over the region R of the x, y plane. In Section 20 we saw that the volume under the probability surface $z = f(x, y)$ and above a region R' interior to R is to be interpreted as the probability that the random point (X, Y) shall fall in the region R'.

Suppose we are given an arbitrary function $g(x, y)$. Corresponding to the random point (X, Y) we obtain the random quantity $g(X, Y)$ which we shall denote by U. We wish to find the distribution of $U = g(X, Y)$. In the x, y plane the function $u = g(x, y)$ defines a family of curves, each curve corresponding to a particular value of u. What is the geometrical interpretation of $P(U \leq u)$ where u is an arbitrary fixed value? The curve $g(x, y) = u$ shown in Figure 36.1 divides the plane into regions, in one of which $g(x, y) < u$ and in the other $g(x, y) > u$. The probability $P(U \leq u)$ is simply the volume under the surface $z = f(x, y)$ and above the region for which $g(x, y) \leq u$. This volume is, of course, the distribution function of $u = g(x, y)$. Let us denote it by $\Phi(u)$. The density will be obtained by differentiating $\Phi(u)$ with respect to u. Thus our problem is primarily the evaluation of the volume $\Phi(u) = P(U \leq u)$. Let us assume that $u = g(x, y)$ can be solved in the form $y = h(x, u)$ and that the partial derivatives $\partial h/\partial x$ and $\partial h/\partial u$ exist.

We imagine the x, y plane covered by a network of curvilinear quadri-

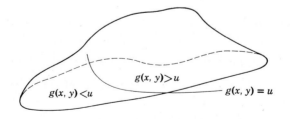

FIGURE 36.1

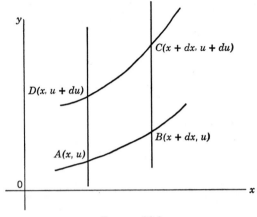

FIGURE 36.2

laterals by lines $u = g(x, y)$ = const. and lines x = const. Let us obtain the area of one of these quadrilaterals, shown in Figure 36.2, with vertices $A(x, u)$, $B(x + dx, u)$, $C(x + dx, u + du)$, $D(x, u + du)$. To a first approximation the area is $AD \cdot dx$, so our problem reduces to the evaluation of the length AD. As agreed earlier, let $y = h(x, u)$ denote the inverse of $u = g(x, y)$. The total differential of y is

$$dy = \frac{\partial h}{\partial x} dx + \frac{\partial h}{\partial u} du.$$

This gives, approximately, the increment in y when x and u are increased by dx and du. But, in going from A to D, $dx = 0$. Hence to a first approximation

$$AD = |dy| = \left| \frac{\partial h}{\partial u} \right| du.$$

Thus the area $ABCD$ is approximately $\left| \dfrac{\partial h}{\partial u} \right| du\, dx$. This is the *element of area*. The *element of probability* is

$$dp = f(x, y) \left| \frac{\partial h}{\partial u} \right| du\, dx.$$

It is convenient to express this entirely in terms of x and u by replacing y by $h(x, u)$. Thus

(36.1) $$dp = f(x, h(x, u)) \left| \frac{\partial h}{\partial u} \right| du\, dx.$$

Note that in formula (36.1) a change of variables has been accomplished in the probability element, from the pair of variables x, y to the pair u, x. Formula (36.1) should be compared with the similar result in (16.1), where a change of variables was considered for a univariate distribution. In the actual use of (36.1) as in the use of (16.1), it is necessary to consider separately regions where $\partial h/\partial u$ is positive and regions where $\partial h/\partial u$ is negative. Most of the exercises and examples in this book will deal with cases in which $\partial h/\partial u$ does not change sign in the sample space considered.

The distribution function of u, $\Phi(u)$, may be readily obtained from (36.1). It is

$$\Phi(u) = \int_{-\infty}^{u} \int f(x, h(x, u)) \left| \frac{\partial h}{\partial u} \right| dx\, du.$$

The inside integration, with respect to x, is with u held constant and is to be carried out over the range of values which x may assume for $u = \text{const}$. The density of u is now simply obtained by omitting the integration with respect to u. The result is the following theorem:

(36.2) THEOREM. *Let X and Y possess the joint density $f(x, y)$. Let $u = g(x, y)$ be a function such that the inverse function $y = h(x, u)$ and the partial derivative $\partial h/\partial u$ exist. Then the density of the random variable $U = g(X, Y)$ is*

$$\phi(u) = \int f(x, h(x, u)) \left| \frac{\partial h}{\partial u} \right| dx,$$

where the integration extends over the range of values which x may assume for $u = \text{const}$.

Example 36.1. Let X and Y be uniform random variables over the interval $(0, 1)$. Then the joint density is $f(x, y) = 1$ over the square $0 \leq x \leq 1$, $0 \leq y \leq 1$, zero elsewhere (see Figure 36.3). Let us find the density of the function

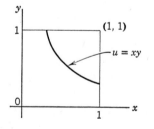

FIGURE 36.3

$u = xy$, when $0 \leq u \leq 1$. Here $u = g(x, y) = xy$, $y = h(x, u) = u/x$, and $\partial h/\partial u = 1/x$. Since the hyperbola $xy = u$ intersects the square in the points $(u, 1)$ and $(1, u)$, the integration in (36.2) will be from u to 1. Hence

$$\phi(u) = \int_u^1 \frac{1}{x}\, dx = -\log u.$$

As a check it is readily verified that $\int_0^1 (-\log u)\, du = 1.$

Our greatest interest is in the case of a sum of random variables, i.e., $g(x, y) = x + y$. For this case (36.2) assumes the following special form:

(36.3) THEOREM. *If X and Y have the joint density $f(x, y)$, then the density of $U = X + Y$ is*

$$\phi(u) = \int f(x, u - x)\, dx,$$

the integration being over the whole range of x for which $x + y = u$.

Example 36.2. Let X and Y possess the joint density $f(x, y) = e^{-(x+y)}$ over the first quadrant of the x, y plane. The line $x + y = u$ cuts the y-axis at $(0, u)$ and the x-axis at $(u, 0)$; hence, in applying (36.3), the integration will be from 0 to u. The integrand $f(x, u - x)$ will in this case become e^{-u}. Hence the density of $X + Y$ is

$$\phi(u) = \int_0^u e^{-u}\, dx = ue^{-u}.$$

Example 36.3. As in Example 36.1, let X and Y be uniform random variables over the interval $(0, 1)$. The joint density is $f(x, y) = 1$ over the square

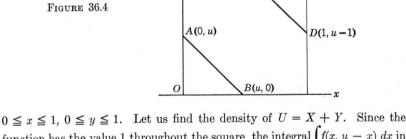

FIGURE 36.4

$0 \le x \le 1, 0 \le y \le 1$. Let us find the density of $U = X + Y$. Since the function has the value 1 throughout the square, the integral $\int f(x, u - x)\, dx$ in (36.3) becomes $\int dx$; our problem now reduces to that of determining the limits of integration. If $u < 1$, the portion of the line $x + y = u$ lying in the square sample space is the segment AB in Figure 36.4. Thus the integral, for $u < 1$, is $\int_0^u dx = u$. If $u > 1$, the portion of the line $x + y = u$ lying in the sample space is the segment CD. The integral thus assumes the form $\int_{u-1}^1 dx = 2 - u$. We have thus found the following density for $U = X + Y$:

$$\phi(u) = u, \qquad 0 \leq u \leq 1,$$

$$\phi(u) = 2 - u, \quad 1 \leq u \leq 2.$$

The density takes the form of a triangular distribution.

It is frequently necessary, in the use of the theorems of this section, to consider several portions of the sample space of u separately, as was done in Example 36.3. In many cases a careful sketch of the sample space showing a typical curve $u = g(x, y)$ is an indispensable part of the process of obtaining sampling distributions by the use of (36.2) and (36.3).

Several further illustrations of the use of Theorems (36.2) and (36.3) will be found in Sections 37 and 41.

If the proof of (36.2) is carefully reviewed, it will be found that the essential part is that which leads up to (36.1). This is an equation which expresses the probability element dp in terms of the new variable u and one of the old variables x. The variable x is finally "integrated out" to leave a density function dependent on u alone.

Let us extend this concept to the case of a trivariate distribution. Suppose that the random variables X_1, X_2, X_3 have the joint density $f(x_1, x_2, x_3)$, and suppose that we wish to find the density of the new random variable $U = g(X_1, X_2, X_3)$. We shall assume that $u = g(x_1, x_2, x_3)$ can be solved for x_3 in the form, say, $x_3 = h(x_1, x_2, u)$ and that all necessary partial derivatives exist. The probability element, in terms of the original variables, is

$$dp = f(x_1, x_2, x_3) \, dx_1 \, dx_2 \, dx_3.$$

In order to re-express dp in terms of x_1, x_2, and u, consider the sample space E_3 to be subdivided into elementary volumes by planes $x_1 = $ const. and $x_2 = $ const. and surfaces $u = $ const. In particular, consider the elementary volume bounded by the 4 planes $x_1 = x_1^*$, $x_1 = x_1^* + dx_1$, $x_2 = x_2^*$, $x_2 = x_2^* + dx_2$, and the 2 surfaces $u = u^*$, $u = u^* + du$. Let AD be the distance along the line $x_1 = x_1^*$, $x_2 = x_2^*$ from $u = u^*$ to $u = u^* + du$. The total differential of $x_3 = h(x_1, x_2, u)$ is

$$dx_3 = \frac{\partial h}{\partial x_1} dx_1 + \frac{\partial h}{\partial x_2} dx_2 + \frac{\partial h}{\partial u} du.$$

But along the line $x_1 = x_1^*$, $x_2 = x_2^*$, $dx_1 = dx_2 = 0$, so that to a first approximation

$$AD = dx_3 = \left| \frac{\partial h}{\partial u} \right| du.$$

Thus the element of volume is $\left| \dfrac{\partial h}{\partial u} \right| du \, dx_1 \, dx_2$, and the probability element is

$$dp = f(x_1, x_2, h(x_1, x_2, u)) \left| \frac{\partial h}{\partial u} \right| dx_1 \, dx_2 \, du.$$

The density of u, say $\phi(u)$, is now obtained by integrating out x_1 and x_2. Thus we obtain

(36.4)   THEOREM.   *Let X_1, X_2, X_3 possess the joint density $f(x_1, x_2, x_3)$. Let $u = g(x_1, x_2, x_3)$ be a function such that the inverse function $x_3 = h(x_1, x_2, u)$ and its partial derivative $\partial h/\partial u$ exist. Then the density of the random variable $U = g(X_1, X_2, X_3)$ is*

$$\phi(u) = \iint f(x_1, x_2, h(x_1, x_2)) \left| \frac{\partial h}{\partial u} \right| dx_1 \, dx_2,$$

where the integration extends over that portion of the sample space for which $u = const.$

Example 36.4.   Find the distribution of $U = X_1 + X_2 + X_3$ if the variables X_1, X_2, X_3 possess the joint density

$$f(x_1, x_2, x_3) = e^{-(x_1+x_2+x_3)}, \quad \text{for } x_1 \geqq 0, x_2 \geqq 0, x_3 \geqq 0,$$

$$= 0 \qquad \text{elsewhere.}$$

Solution.   Here $u = g(x_1, x_2, x_3) = x_1 + x_2 + x_3$, so that $x_3 = h(x_1, x_2, u) = u - x_1 - x_2$ and $\partial h/\partial u = 1$. Thus

$$dp = e^{-(x_1+x_2+(u-x_1-x_2))} \, dx_1 \, dx_2 \, du$$

$$= e^{-u} \, dx_1 \, dx_2 \, du.$$

According to (36.4) we must integrate out x_1 and x_2, integrating over the portion of the x_1, x_2 plane for which $x_1 + x_2 + x_3 = u$. This is a plane equally inclined to the three coordinate axes. Since the density is non-zero only for $x_1 \geqq 0$, $x_2 \geqq 0$, $x_3 \geqq 0$, the integration needs to be carried only for the portion of the first quadrant of the x_1, x_2 plane lying beneath the plane $x_1 + x_2 + x_3 = u$. This is the triangular region bounded by the x_1 and x_2 axes and the line $x_1 + x_2 = u$. Hence

$$\phi(u) = \int_0^u \int_0^{u-x_2} e^{-u} \, dx_1 \, dx_2$$

$$= e^{-u} \int_0^u (u - x_2) \, dx_2 = \tfrac{1}{2} u^2 e^{-u},$$

The result could also be obtained by noting that $\phi(u) = e^{-u} \iint dx_1\, dx_2$, where the double integral is simply the area of the triangle bounded by $x_1 = 0$, $x_2 = 0$, $x_1 + x_2 = u$, which is $\frac{1}{2}u^2$.

EXERCISE 36

36.1. Let X and Y be independent variables with densities $f_1(x) = e^{-x}$, $x > 0$, and $f_2(y) = e^{-y}$, $y > 0$. Find the density of $U = 2X + 3Y$.

36.2. For the random variables X and Y of Exercise 36.1, find the density of $U = X - Y$.

36.3. Let X and Y each possess a rectangular distribution, X over the interval $(1, 2)$, Y over the interval $(0, 1)$. Find the density of $U = Y/X$.

36.4. Suppose X and Y are independently distributed, X with the density $f(x) = 6x(1 - x)$, $0 \leq x \leq 1$, and Y with a uniform density over $(0, 1)$. Find the density of $U = X + Y$.

36.5. X and Y are independent uniform variables over the interval $(0, 1)$. Show that the density of $U = X^2 + Y^2$ is

$$\phi(u) = \pi/4, \quad 0 \leq u \leq 1$$

$$= \frac{1}{2}\left[\operatorname{arc\,sin} \frac{1}{\sqrt{u}} - \operatorname{arc\,sin} \sqrt{\frac{u-1}{u}} \right], \quad 1 \leq u \leq 2.$$

36.6. X and Y are independent variables, X distributed according to $N(0, 1)$, and Y having the density $f(y) = e^{-y}$. What is the sample space of (X, Y)? Find the family of curves along which $u = x^2/2 + y$ is constant, where $u > 0$. Find the density of the random variable $U = X^2/2 + Y$, $U > 0$.

*36.7. Prove

$$\int_{-b}^{b} \frac{dx}{(1 + x^2)(1 + (a - x)^2)}$$

$$= \frac{1}{4 + a^2}\left[2 \operatorname{arc\,tan} b + \operatorname{arc\,tan}(b - a) + \operatorname{arc\,tan}(b + a) \right.$$

$$\left. + \frac{1}{a} \log \frac{1 + (a + b)^2}{1 + (a - b)^2} \right].$$

Hint: Use partial fractions

$$\frac{1}{(1 + x^2)(1 + (a - x)^2)} = \frac{A + Bx}{1 + x^2} + \frac{C + Dx}{1 + (a - x)^2}$$

*36.8. Let X_1 and X_2 be independently distributed, each with the density $f(x) = 1/\pi(1 + x^2)$. Show, using the result of Exercise 36.7, that $U = \frac{1}{2}(X_1 + X_2)$ has the density $\varphi(u) = 1/\pi(1 + u^2)$. The conclusion is that the mean of 2 independent quantities, each with the Cauchy distribution, is a quantity also possessing the Cauchy distribution.

36.9. Extend Theorems (36.2) and (36.3) to the case in which we are given the joint density $f(x_1, \cdots, x_n)$ of the random variables $X_1, \cdots, X_n$ and we wish to find the density of the function $u = g(x_1, \cdots, x_n)$. Assume that the inverse function $x_n = h(x_1, \cdots, x_{n-1}, u)$ and its partial derivative $\partial h / \partial u$ exist.

36.10. Given that the random variables X_1, X_2, X_3 possess the joint density $(2\pi)^{-3/2} e^{-(x_1{}^2 + x_2{}^2 + x_3{}^2)/2}$, find the density of: (a) $U = X_1 + X_2 + X_3$, (b) $U = X_1{}^2 + X_2{}^2 + X_3{}^2$.

36.11. Let X and Y be uniform random variables over the interval $(0, 1)$ (see Example 15.1). According to Example 19.1, both X and Y will possess the moment generating function $(1/t)(e^t - 1)$. Show, using the result of Example 36.3, that the moment generating function of $U = X + Y$ is $(1/t^2)$ $(e^t - 1)^2$. Verify that this result is in accord with (27.24).

37. THE CHI-SQUARE DISTRIBUTION

The importance of the chi-square distribution and its intimate connection with the normal distribution have been suggested in results previously obtained. The chi-square distribution with n d.f. will be denoted by $CS(n)$. Its density is

$$(37.1) \qquad f(x) = \frac{1}{2^{n/2}\, \Gamma\left(\dfrac{n}{2}\right)}\, x^{(n/2)-1} e^{-x/2}, \quad x > 0.$$

In Example 16.6 we showed that, if X is from $N(0, 1)$, then X^2 is from $CS(1)$. Furthermore, Example 24.4 states that, if X and Y are independent values from $N(0, 1)$, then $X^2 + Y^2$ is from $CS(2)$. These are special cases of the general result which will be given in (37.3).

As a preliminary to the proof of (37.3) and as an illustration of the use of (36.3), we shall prove the following theorem, already presented in Example 16.6.

(37.2) THEOREM. *If X and Y are independent values from $CS(1)$, then $U = X + Y$ is distributed according to $CS(2)$.*

Proof. Since the quantities X and Y are from $CS(1)$, their densities are $(2\pi)^{-1/2} x^{-1/2} e^{-x/2}$ and $(2\pi)^{-1/2} y^{-1/2} e^{-y/2}$, and their joint density is $(2\pi)^{-1} x^{-1/2} y^{-1/2} e^{-(x+y)/2}$. Theorem (36.3) will now give us the density of $U = X + Y$:

$$\phi(u) = \frac{1}{2\pi} \int x^{-1/2}(u - x)^{-1/2} e^{-u/2}\, dx$$

$$= \frac{e^{-u/2}}{2\pi} \int x^{-1/2}(u - x)^{-1/2}\, dx.$$

Over what range is x to be integrated? Every chi-square distribution runs from 0 to ∞, so that the joint density extends over the first quad-

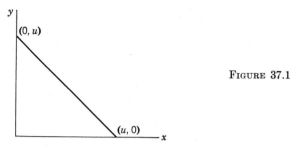

FIGURE 37.1

rant of the x, y plane.   The graph of $x + y = u$, shown in Figure 37.1, indicates that for the portion of the line in the first quadrant, x runs from 0 to u.   Hence

$$\phi(u) = \frac{e^{-u/2}}{2\pi} \int_0^u x^{-\frac{1}{2}}(u - x)^{-1/2}\,dx = \frac{e^{-u/2}}{2\pi}\left[\arcsin \frac{x - u/2}{u/2}\right]_0^u$$

$$= \tfrac{1}{2}e^{-u/2}.$$

It is readily verified, from (37.1), that this final density is that of CS(2).

We now prove the result known as the reproductive law of the chi-square distribution, of which (37.2) is a special case.

(37.3)   THEOREM.   *If X and Y are independent values from* CS(m) *and* CS(n), *respectively, their sum is distributed according to* CS($m + n$).

Proof.   The joint density of X and Y is obtained by multiplying the densities of X and Y as given by (37.1).   Thus

$$f(x, y) = \frac{1}{2^{(m+n)/2}\,\Gamma\left(\dfrac{m}{2}\right)\Gamma\left(\dfrac{n}{2}\right)}\,x^{m/2-1}y^{n/2-1}e^{-(x+y)/2}.$$

We now use (36.3) to find the density of $U = X + Y$.   Note that the joint distribution, as in (37.2), extends over the first quadrant of the x, y plane and that Figure 37.1 is applicable to this theorem as to (37.2). Hence

(37.4) $$\phi(u) = k\int_0^u x^{m/2-1}(u - x)^{n/2-1}e^{-u/2}\,dx.$$

To evaluate the integral, use the trigonometric substitutions

$$x = u\sin^2\theta, \quad u - x = u\cos^2\theta, \quad dx = 2u\sin\theta\cos\theta\,d\theta.$$

The limits of integration become 0 and $\pi/2$. Thus

$$(37.5) \qquad \phi(u) = ke^{-u/2}u^{m/2+n/2-1}\int_0^{\pi/2} \sin^{m-1}\theta \cos^{n-1}\theta \, d\theta.$$

We do not need to evaluate the final integral since it does not involve u and hence will reduce to a constant. Thus

$$(37.6) \qquad \phi(u) = k'u^{m/2+n/2-1}e^{-u/2}.$$

But this is the proper form for the density of $CS(m + n)$, as was to be proved.

By combining the result of Example 16.6 and (37.3) we now obtain

(37.7) THEOREM. *If* $X_1, \cdots, X_n$ *are independent values from* $N(0, 1)$, *the quantity* $X_1{}^2 + \cdots + X_n{}^2$ *is distributed according to* $CS(n)$.

Proof. By Example 24.4, $X_1{}^2 + X_2{}^2$ is distributed according to $CS(2)$; and, by Example 16.6, $X_3{}^2$ is from $CS(1)$. Applying (37.3) with the variables $X = X_1{}^2 + X_2{}^2$ and $Y = X_3{}^2$, we conclude that $X + Y = X_1{}^2 + X_2{}^2 + X_3{}^2$ is distributed according to $CS(3)$. Next we apply (37.3) with $X = X_1{}^2 + X_2{}^2 + X_3{}^2$ and $Y = X_4{}^2$ and conclude that $X + Y = X_1{}^2 + X_2{}^2 + X_3{}^2 + X_4{}^2$ is distributed according to $CS(4)$. By a series of steps of this kind we establish the theorem.

A slight generalization of (37.7) is the following:

(37.8) THEOREM. *If* $X_1, \cdots, X_n$ *are independent values drawn, respectively, from* $N(0, \sigma_1{}^2), \cdots, N(0, \sigma_n{}^2)$, *then the quantity* $X_1{}^2/\sigma_1{}^2 + \cdots + X_n{}^2/\sigma_n{}^2$ *is distributed according to* $CS(n)$.

The result follows immediately upon noting that $X_1/\sigma_1, \cdots, X_n/\sigma_n$ are independent values from $N(0, 1)$.

A geometrical application of the chi-square distribution, anticipating the results of the next section, is the following:

Example 37.1. Three independent values X, Y, and Z are drawn from $N(0, 5)$. What is the probability that the point (X, Y, Z) in three-dimensional rectangular coordinates, will be more than 2 units from the origin?

Solution. By (37.8) the quantity $\frac{1}{5}(X^2 + Y^2 + Z^2)$ is from $CS(3)$. We must therefore find $P(U > 2)$, where $U/5$ is from $CS(3)$. Writing $V = U/5$, we need to find $P(5V > 2) = P(V > .4)$, where V is from $CS(3)$. Interpolating in Table 3, we find $P(V > .4) = .896$.

In Section 39 it will be proved that, if s^2 is the variance of a sample of size n from $N(\mu, \sigma^2)$, then $(n - 1)s^2/\sigma^2$ has the distribution $CS(n - 1)$. This permits us to form confidence intervals for the population variance, as illustrated in the following example:

Example 37.2. The variance of a sample of size $n = 10$ from a normal population is $s^2 = 6.25$. Find a 95% confidence interval for σ^2.

Solution. The quantity $(n - 1)s^2/\sigma^2 = 9 \times 6.25/\sigma^2 = 56.25/\sigma^2$ has the distribution CS(9). The 2.5 and 97.5 percentiles (percentage points) of CS(9) are, according to Table 3, 2.70 and 19.02, respectively. Hence we can state, with 95% confidence, that $2.70 \leqq 56.25/\sigma^2 \leqq 19.02$, or $1/2.70 \geqq \sigma^2/56.25 \geqq 1/19.02$, or $20.8 \geqq \sigma^2 \geqq 3.0$. This is the required confidence interval.

The quantity $(n - 1)s^2/\sigma^2$ may be used as a critical statistic in order to test a hypothesis of the form $\sigma^2 = \sigma_0{}^2$, where the sample is assumed to be drawn from a normal population.

Example 37.3. The diameter of a mass-produced screw has shown, in the past, an approximately normal distribution with mean $\mu = .253$ inch, variance $\sigma^2 = .0020$. If a sample of size $n = 20$ has a variance $s^2 = .0050$, is there reason to believe the variance of the process has shifted significantly?

Solution. We make the hypothesis $H_0: \sigma^2 = .0020$, with the alternative $H_1: \sigma^2 > .0020$. The alternative is one sided because we are presumably unconcerned about a decrease in the variance. Let $\alpha = .01$. The 99th percentile of the chi-square distribution with 19 d.f. is 36.2, so H_0 will be rejected if $(n - 1)s^2/\sigma^2 > 36.2$. Using $\sigma^2 = .0020$, $s^2 = .0050$, $n = 20$, we find $(n - 1)s^2/\sigma^2 = 47.5$. Consequently we reject the null hypothesis and conclude that the variance has increased.

Example 37.4. Obtain 5 values from the distribution CS(5) by the method of (16.3).

Solution. Five four-figure random numbers, each prefixed by a decimal point, are .4599, .7666, .3901, .8123, .7644. To find the value from CS(5) corresponding to .4599, we need to obtain the 45.99 percentile of this distribution. By interpolation in Table 3 we find 4.08, approximately, for the required percentile. Repeating this process we find the following 5 values: 4.08, 6.86, 3.59, 7.41, 6.85.

EXERCISE 37

37.1. X, Y, and Z are independent random variables from $N(0, 2)$. Find the probability that the random point (X, Y, Z) will lie outside a sphere of radius 4.5.

37.2. X_1, X_2, X_3, X_4, X_5 are independent random values from the distributions $N(0, 2)$, $N(0, 3)$, $N(0, 4)$, $N(0, 6)$, and $N(0, 12)$, respectively. Find the probability that $Z = 6X_1{}^2 + 4X_2{}^2 + 3X_3{}^2 + 2X_4{}^2 + X_5{}^2$ will exceed 100.

37.3. X and Y are independent random values from $N(0, 2)$. Find the probability that the random point (X, Y) will fall in the circular strip bounded by the circles $x^2 + y^2 = 5$ and $x^2 + y^2 = 10$.

37.4. A sample of size $n = 5$ from a normal population has a variance of 42.8. Find a 90% confidence interval for the population variance.

37.5. A certain psychological test has been found to be nearly normally distributed when administered to a group of several thousand subjects, with a variance $\sigma^2 = 29.7$. The test, administered to a sample of 15 subjects, has a sample variance $s^2 = 52.1$. Does this indicate a significant change in variance, as compared with the national norm? Use a two-sided test, with $\alpha = .05$.

38. *n*-VARIATE NORMAL DISTRIBUTION

The chi-square distribution was derived in the preceding section by an *iterative* process; that is, CS(n) was built up step by step from CS(1). The method depended only on the use of bivariate distributions, so that in no case did we require the use of a sample space more complicated than a plane. In this section the general chi-square distribution CS(n) will be approached by considering first a multivariate distribution, namely, the joint distribution of n independent values from $N(0, 1)$. Since a single value from $N(0, 1)$ has the density $f_N(x) = (1/\sqrt{2\pi})e^{-x^2/2}$, it follows from (20.17) that the joint density of the independent values $x_1, \cdots, x_n$ is the product of the individual densities $(1/\sqrt{2\pi})e^{-x_1^2}, \cdots, (1/\sqrt{2\pi})e^{-x_n^2}$. Thus the joint density is

(38.1) $\qquad f(x_1, \cdots, x_n) = (2\pi)^{-n/2}e^{-(x_1^2+\cdots+x_n^2)/2}$.

This is an *n-variate* or *n-dimensional normal density*.

Actually (38.1) represents a specialized type of normal density. Although this special case is the one to which we must devote most of our attention, we shall give some indication of the form of the general multivariate normal density. Suppose, first, that the variables $X_1, \cdots, X_n$ are independently distributed and that X_i has the distribution $N(\mu_i, \sigma_i^2)$, $i = 1, \cdots, n$. The joint density of $X_1, \cdots, X_n$ then is

$$f(x_1, \cdots, x_n) = k \exp - \left(\frac{(x_1 - \mu_1)^2}{2\sigma_1^2} + \cdots + \frac{(x_n - \mu_n)^2}{2\sigma_n^2} \right).$$

We now observe that both of the densities thus far obtained are exponential functions in which the exponent is a quadratic function of $x_1, \cdots, x_n$. We may therefore generalize the distribution by considering a general quadratic function

$$Q = \sum_{i,j} a_{ij}x_i x_j + \sum_i b_i x_i + c.$$

There are certain mild restrictions on the coefficients a_{ij} which we shall not state. With these restrictions on Q the most general multivariate normal distribution has the density ke^{-Q}. In Exercise 27.9 the quadratic function Q has been explored for the bivariate case.

For $n = 2$ the density (38.1) assumes the form $f(x_1, x_2) = (1/2\pi)e^{-(x_1^2+x_2^2)/2}$. In Section 24 the distribution function of the random variable $U = X_1{}^2 + X_2{}^2$ was obtained by integrating this density over the interior of the circle $x_1{}^2 + x_2{}^2 = u$. In order to derive the corresponding result for $n = 3$, we must use the density

(38.2) $$f_N(x_1, x_2, x_3) = (2\pi)^{-3/2}e^{-(x_1{}^2+x_2{}^2+x_3{}^2)/2}.$$

We wish to find the distribution function of the random variable $U = X_1{}^2 + X_2{}^2 + X_3{}^2$, where X_1, X_2, X_3 possess the joint density (38.2). The required distribution function is

$$F(u) = P(U < u) = P(X_1{}^2 + X_2{}^2 + X_3{}^2 < u)$$

> = the probability that the random point (X_1, X_2, X_3) will lie inside a sphere of radius $\sqrt{u}$, with the origin as center.

We must therefore integrate the density (38.2) over the interior of the sphere. This may be accomplished by considering a spherical shell of radius r and thickness dr. Its surface area is kr^2, where k is a constant (it happens that $k = 4\pi$; our point here is that k need not be known). The probability density over a sphere of radius r is, from (38.2), uniformly equal to $(2\pi)^{-3/2}e^{-r^2/2}$. Hence the total probability associated with the thin shell is $k'r^2e^{-r^2/2}\,dr$, where k' is a constant. Thus

$$F(u) = k'\int_0^{\sqrt{u}} r^2 e^{-r^2/2}\,dr.$$

Let us make the change of variables $t = r^2$, $r = t$, $dr = \tfrac{1}{2}t^{-1/2}\,dt$. The integral then becomes

$$F(u) = k''\int_0^u t^{1/2}e^{-t/2}\,dt.$$

This is the distribution function of u. We obtain the density by differentiating with respect to u:

$$f(u) = k''u^{1/2}e^{-t^2/2}\,dt.$$

This is the proper form for the density of CS(3), as may be seen by comparing with (37.1). The conclusion is (obtained earlier by other methods) that, if X_1, X_2, X_3 are independent values, each from the distribution $N(0, 1)$, then $U = X_1{}^2 + X_2{}^2 + X_3{}^2$ has the distribution CS(3).

Consider now the n-dimensional case. We shall follow a procedure parallel to that for the two- and three-dimensional cases. However, since we do not wish to become involved in a detailed study of the geometry of n dimensions, the discussion must necessarily be incomplete at certain points.

We wish to investigate the distribution of the random variable $U = X_1^2 + \cdots + X_n^2$, given that $X_1, \cdots, X_n$ possess the joint density (38.1). As in the cases $n = 2$ and $n = 3$, we first obtain the distribution function of U and then differentiate to obtain the density. The distribution function of U will be given by

$$(38.3) \qquad F(u) = P(X_1^2 + \cdots + X_n^2 < u);$$

this is the probability we must evaluate.

In Section 20 we defined n-dimensional Euclidean space E_n as the totality of points $(x_1, \cdots, x_n)$, where each x_i, $i = 1, \cdots, n$, ranges over all the real numbers. The set of points in E_n satisfying the restriction $x_1^2 + \cdots + x_n^2 = u$, $u > 0$, is called a *hypersphere*, which we shall denote by S_u. The points for which $x_1^2 + \cdots + x_n^2 < u$ form the *interior* of S_u. We seek the probability that the random point $(X_1, \cdots, X_n)$ will fall in the interior of S_u; by (20.16) this probability is to be obtained by integrating the density (38.1) over the interior of S_u.

In order to perform the required integration, we consider a hypersphere S_{r^2}: $x_1^2 + \cdots + x_n^2 = r^2$. Over S_{r^2} the density (38.1) is constantly equal to $(2\pi)^{-n/2}e^{-r^2/2}$. By integration (too difficult to be carried out here) it may be shown that the set of points $x_1^2 + \cdots + x_n^2 = r^2$ possesses a "hypervolume" kr^{n-1}, where k is a constant; this is a generalization of the circumference of a circle or the surface area of a sphere. Let us form the n-dimensional analog of a spherical shell, with radius r and thickness dr, hence with hypervolume $kr^{n-1}\,dr$. Since the density is constant over the hypersphere, the probability associated with the shell will be obtained by multiplying the hypervolume by the density $(2\pi)^{-n/2}e^{-r^2/2}$ to obtain $k'r^{n-1}e^{-r^2/2}\,dr$, where k' is a constant. Hence the probability (38.3) is

$$F(u) = k' \int_0^{\sqrt{u}} r^{n-1}e^{-r^2/2}\,dr.$$

We now make the same substitution used in the two- and three-dimensional cases, namely, $r^2 = t$, obtaining

$$F(u) = k'' \int_0^u t^{n/2-1}e^{-t/2}\,dt.$$

Thus the density is

$$\frac{dF(u)}{du} = k''t^{n/2-1}e^{-t/2}, \quad t > 0.$$

This is the density for the distribution CS(n). We may therefore conclude that, if $X_1, \cdots, X_n$ are independent values, each with the distribution $N(0, 1)$, then $X_1^2 + \cdots + X_n^2$ has the distribution CS(n), a fact otherwise deduced in earlier sections.

In summary we remark that the essential fact about the density (38.1) is that it is constant over a hypersphere, just as the bivariate counterpart of (38.1), studied in Section 24, is constant over a circle about the origin and the density (38.2) is constant over a sphere about the origin. The matter may be somewhat differently expressed by saying that the density (38.1) is a function purely of the distance from the origin. By "distance from the origin" we here mean $\sqrt{x_1^2 + \cdots x_n^2}$, an obvious generalization of the familiar formula for distance in two dimensions.

EXERCISE 38

38.1. If X_1, X_2, and X_3 are independently distributed, X_1 according to $N(2, 4)$, X_2 according to $N(-3, 4)$, and X_3 according to $N(10, 16)$, find the joint density of (X_1, X_2, X_3).

38.2. If the independent random variables $X_1, \cdots, X_n$ have, respectively, the distributions $N(0, \sigma_1^2), \cdots, N(0, \sigma_n^2)$, find the joint density of $(X_1, \cdots, X_n)$.

38.3. If the independent random variables $X_1, \cdots, X_n$ have, respectively, the distributions $N(\mu_1, \sigma_1^2), \cdots, N(\mu_n, \sigma_n^2)$, find the joint density of $(X_1, \cdots, X_n)$.

38.4. If X_1, X_2, X_3, X_4, X_5 are independent values from $N(0, 25)$, find the probability that the point $(X_1, X_2, X_3, X_4, X_5)$ will fall inside the hypersphere $x_1^2 + x_2^2 + x_3^2 + x_4^2 + x_5^2 = 200$.

38.5. The parametric equations of a hypersphere in four dimensions may be written

$$x_1 = r \sin \phi_1$$

$$x_2 = r \cos \phi_1 \sin \phi_2$$

$$x_3 = r \cos \phi_1 \cos \phi_2 \sin \phi_3$$

$$x_4 = r \cos \phi_1 \cos \phi_2 \cos \phi_3.$$

Show that, for all values of ϕ_1, ϕ_2, ϕ_3, the coordinates (x_1, x_2, x_3, x_4) satisfy the equation $\Sigma x_i^2 = r^2$ of a hypersphere. Generalize this result, giving the parametric equations of a hypersphere in n dimensions and showing that the coordinates $(x_1, \cdots, x_n)$ satisfy the equation $\Sigma x_i^2 = r^2$.

*39. THE INDEPENDENCE OF LINEAR FUNCTIONS OF NORMAL VARIABLES

The concept of the *independence* of random variables is of crucial importance in connection with sampling distributions. In fact many of the theorems derived earlier are true only if the variables are independently distributed. In order to tell whether certain random variables are independently distributed, we need to know their joint distribution. Although the methods of Section 36, extended in an obvious way to n variables, will enable us to find the distribution of any function of several random variables, they do not give us any information about the joint distribution of several such functions. This section will, for an important special case, fill in that gap.

A general treatment of joint distributions of random variables requires the use of concepts from advanced calculus, particularly the properties of the Jacobian of a transformation. We shall not need to consider the general theory. The case of greatest usefulness, which is also the simplest, is that of a *linear transformation* from one set of random variables to another. We shall deal first with the two-dimensional case and then generalize to n dimensions.

If X_1 and X_2 are random variables with joint density $f(x_1, x_2)$ and if $g_1(x_1, x_2)$ and $g_2(x_1, x_2)$ are arbitrary functions, the quantities $U_1 = g_1(X_1, X_2)$ and $U_2 = g_2(X_1, X_2)$ are random variables whose joint density may be obtained by a process analogous to that used in Section 36. Let us immediately consider the special case in which g_1 and g_2 are homogeneous linear functions:

$$(39.1) \qquad \begin{aligned} U_1 &= a_{11}X_1 + a_{12}X_2, \\ U_2 &= a_{21}X_1 + a_{22}X_2. \end{aligned}$$

Given that the joint density of X_1 and X_2 is $f(x_1, x_2)$, we wish to find the joint density of U_1 and U_2. For this purpose we shall need the inverse of the transformation (39.1), obtained by solving Equations (39.1) for X_1 and X_2 in terms of U_1 and U_2. This can be done if the determinant of the transformation (39.1), namely, $a = a_{11}a_{22} - a_{12}a_{21}$, is non-zero. Assuming this to be the case, we write the inverse transformation as

$$(39.2) \qquad \begin{aligned} X_1 &= b_{11}U_1 + b_{12}U_2, & b_{11} &= a_{22}/a, & b_{12} &= -a_{12}/a, \\ X_2 &= b_{21}U_1 + b_{22}U_2, & b_{21} &= -a_{21}/a, & b_{22} &= a_{11}/a. \end{aligned}$$

If b denotes the determinant of (39.2), then

$$b = b_{11}b_{22} - b_{12}b_{21} = 1/a.$$

Let us consider the linear transformation (39.1) and its inverse (39.2) from the geometrical standpoint. We may regard (39.1) as mapping the random point (X_1, X_2) of the x-plane into the random point (U_1, U_2) of the u-plane (see Figure 39.1). Likewise the inverse transformation (39.2) maps (U_1, U_2) into (X_1, X_2). Now consider a rec-

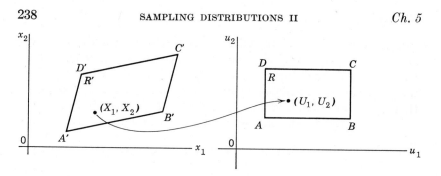

FIGURE 39.1

tangle R in the u-plane with sides parallel to the axes. Let its vertices be $A(u_1, u_2)$, $B(u_1 + \Delta u_1, u_2)$, $C(u_1 + \Delta u_1, u_2 + \Delta u_2)$, $D(u_1, u_2 + \Delta u_2)$. The images of these points under the transformation (39.2) will be

A': $(b_{11}u_1 + b_{12}u_2, b_{21}u_1 + b_{22}u_2)$,

B': $(b_{11}(u_1 + \Delta u_1) + b_{12}u_2, b_{21}(u_1 + \Delta u_1) + b_{22}u_2)$,

C': $(b_{11}(u_1 + \Delta u_1) + b_{12}(u_2 + \Delta u_2), b_{21}(u_1 + \Delta u_1) + b_{22}(u_2 + \Delta u_2))$,

D': $(b_{11}u_1 + b_{12}(u_2 + \Delta u_2), b_{21}u_1 + b_{22}(u_2 + \Delta u_2))$.

It may be readily shown (see Exercise 39.7) that the interior of the rectangle R is mapped into the interior of the quadrilateral R' joining the points A', B', C', and D', that this quadrilateral is actually a parallelogram, and that the area of R' is related to that of R by the equation

$$\text{Area } R' = |b| \text{ Area } R,$$

where $|b|$ is the absolute value of the determinant of the transformation (39.2). Furthermore, if (U_1, U_2) falls in R, its image (X_1, X_2) will fall in R' so that

$$P((U_1, U_2) \in R) = P((X_1, X_2) \in R').$$

Let $f(x_1, x_2)$ be the density of X_1 and X_2 at the point A', and let $\phi(u_1, u_2)$ be the density of U_1 and U_2 at the point A. Then

$$\phi(u_1, u_2) = \lim_{\substack{\Delta u_1 \to 0 \\ \Delta u_2 \to 0}} \frac{P((U_1, U_2) \in R)}{\text{Area } R} = \lim_{\substack{\Delta u_1 \to 0 \\ \Delta u_2 \to 0}} \frac{P((X_1, X_2) \in R')}{\text{Area } R'/|b|}$$

$$= |b| \lim_{\substack{\Delta u_1 \to 0 \\ \Delta u_2 \to 0}} \frac{P((X_1, X_2) \in R')}{\text{Area } R'}.$$

But, as Δu_1 and Δu_2 approach zero, the area of R' will approach zero, and the ratio $P((X_1, X_2) \in R')/(\text{Area } R')$ will approach the density $f(x_1, x_2) = f(b_{11}u_1 + b_{12}u_2, b_{21}u_1 + b_{22}u_2)$. Our conclusion now is that the density $\phi(u_1, u_2)$ is given by $|b| f(b_{11}u_1 + b_{12}u_2, b_{21}u_1 + b_{22}u_2)$. Hence we have the following theorem:

(39.3) THEOREM. *Let the random variables X_1, X_2 possess the density $f(x_1, x_2)$, and let the random variables U_1, U_2 be related to X_1, X_2 by the linear transformation (39.1) and its inverse (39.2). Then the joint density of U_1, U_2 is*

$$\phi(u_1, u_2) = |b| f(b_{11}u_1 + b_{12}u_2, b_{21}u_1 + b_{22}u_2),$$

where $|b|$ is the absolute value of the determinant of (39.2).

The feature of the above expression for $\phi(u_1, u_2)$ that deserves special notice is the factor $|b|$ on the right side of the equation. Theorem (39.3) should be compared with the corresponding one-dimensional result, as given in (16.1). The factor $|dh/dy|$ in (16.1) corresponds to the factor $|b|$ in (39.3).

The following example illustrates the use of Theorem (39.3).

Example 39.1. If X and Y are independently distributed according to CS(2) and $N(0, 1)$, respectively, find the joint density of the random variables $U = 3X - 5Y$ and $V = 4X + Y$.

Solution. The densities of X and Y are, respectively, $f(x) = \frac{1}{2}e^{-x/2}$ and $g(y) = (1/\sqrt{2\pi})e^{-y^2/2}$ so that their joint density is $f(x, y) = (8\pi)^{-1/2} e^{-(x+y^2)/2}$. The determinant of the given linear transformation is 23 so that the determinant of its inverse is $1/23$. Hence by (39.3) the joint density of U and V is

$$\phi(u, v) = \frac{1}{46\sqrt{2\pi}} e^{-(16u^2 - 24uv + 9v^2 + 23u + 115v)/1058}.$$

Suppose now that the variables X_1, X_2 are independently and normally distributed, with zero mean and variance σ^2. Their joint density then is

(39.4) $$f(x_1, x_2) = \frac{1}{2\pi\sigma^2} e^{-(x_1^2 + x_2^2)/2\sigma^2}.$$

We shall restrict our attention to a special kind of linear transformation known as an *orthogonal transformation*. The linear transformation (39.1) is said to be orthogonal if, when we make the substitutions (39.1) in the sum of squares $U_1^2 + U_2^2$, the result reduces algebraically to $X_1^2 + X_2^2$. That is,

(39.5) $$U_1^2 + U_2^2 = X_1^2 + X_2^2.$$

This implies that, identically in X_1 and X_2,

$$(a_{11}X_1 + a_{12}X_2)^2 + (a_{21}X_1 + a_{22}X_2)^2 = X_1^2 + X_2^2,$$

which in turn implies

$$(39.6) \quad a_{11}^2 + a_{21}^2 = 1, \quad a_{12}^2 + a_{22}^2 = 1, \quad a_{11}a_{12} + a_{21}a_{22} = 0.$$

These equations have the consequence that $|a| = 1$, as may be deduced from the algebraic identity

$$a^2 = (a_{11}a_{22} - a_{12}a_{21})^2$$

$$= (a_{11}^2 + a_{21}^2)(a_{12}^2 + a_{22}^2) - (a_{11}a_{12} + a_{21}a_{22})^2 = 1.$$

Since $|a| = 1$, Equations (39.2) take the form

$$X_1 = \pm(a_{22}U_1 - a_{12}U_2), \quad X_2 = \pm(-a_{21}U_1 + a_{11}U_2).$$

If the result of making these substitutions in $U_1^2 + U_2^2 = X_1^2 + X_2^2$ is to be an identity in U_1 and U_2, we must have

$$(39.7) \quad a_{11}^2 + a_{12}^2 = 1, \quad a_{21}^2 + a_{22}^2 = 1, \quad a_{11}a_{21} + a_{12}a_{22} = 0.$$

Equations (39.6) and (39.7) are referred to as *orthogonality conditions*.

Example 39.2. Consider the linear transformation

$$U_1 = X_1 \cos \theta - X_2 \sin \theta, \quad U_2 = X_1 \sin \theta + X_2 \cos \theta.$$

It may be readily verified that this transformation satisfies the orthogonality conditions (39.6) and (39.7) and that the determinant of the transformation is equal to 1. The inverse transformation is found to be

$$X_1 = U_1 \cos \theta + U_2 \sin \theta, \quad X_2 = -U_1 \sin \theta + U_2 \cos \theta.$$

These transformations are encountered in elementary analytic geometry, where X_1, X_2 and U_1, U_2 are interpreted as two rectangular coordinate systems in the same plane. In this case (X_1, X_2) and (U_1, U_2) are simply different names for the same point. The two coordinate systems have a common origin, and the angle θ is the positive angle through which the U_1, U_2 axes must be rotated in order to carry them into the X_1, X_2 axes

Let us now apply Theorem (39.3) to the random variables X_1, X_2 whose joint density is (39.4), making use of an orthogonal transformation, so that $x_1^2 + x_2^2 = u_1^2 + u_2^2$ and $|a| = |b| = 1$. We then find that the joint density of U_1 and U_2 is

$$\phi(u_1, u_2) = \frac{1}{2\pi\sigma^2} e^{-(u_1^2 + u_2^2)2\sigma^2}.$$

We now note that this density can be factored:

$$\phi(u_1, u_2) = \left[\frac{1}{\sigma\sqrt{2\pi}} e^{-u_1{}^2/2\sigma^2} \right] \left[\frac{1}{\sigma\sqrt{2\pi}} e^{-u_2{}^2/2\sigma^2} \right].$$

Theorem (20.14) now implies that U_1 and U_2 are independently distributed, each according to $N(0, \sigma^2)$. We have proved:

(39.8) THEOREM. *If X_1 and X_2 are independently distributed according to $N(0, \sigma^2)$, and U_1 and U_2 are random variables related to X_1 and X_2 by means of an orthogonal transformation, then U_1 and U_2 are independently distributed according to $N(0, \sigma^2)$.*

It is this result whose generalization to n dimensions constitutes the focal theorem of this section and has far-reaching consequences for applied statistics. Before proceeding with the generalization, we shall provide a simple illustration of the use of (39.8).

Example 39.3. Let X_1 and X_2 be independently distributed according to $N(0, \sigma^2)$, and let U_1 and U_2 be defined by $U_1 = (1/\sqrt{2})(X_1 + X_2)$, $U_2 = (1/\sqrt{2})(X_1 - X_2)$. It is readily verified that these equations satisfy the orthogonality conditions (39.6) and (39.7). Thus U_1 and U_2 are independently distributed according to $N(0, \sigma^2)$. Note that the normal reproductive law (25.4) would enable us to conclude that U_1 and U_2 each possess the distribution $N(0, \sigma^2)$ but would not permit us to conclude that they are independently distributed.

We now consider the generalization of the foregoing results to the case of n variables. Suppose that $X_1, \cdots, X_n$ are random variables with joint density $f(x_1, \cdots, x_n)$. If $U_1 = g_1(X_1, \cdots, X_n), \cdots, U_n = g_n(X_1, \cdots, X_n)$ are new random variables, we may inquire about the joint density of $U_1, \cdots, U_n$. We restrict our attention to the case of a linear transformation:

$$U_1 = a_{11}X_1 + \cdots + a_{1n}X_n$$

(39.9)

$$U_n = a_{n1}X_1 + \cdots + a_{nn}X_n$$

Let a be the determinant of the transformation:

$$a = \begin{vmatrix} a_{11} & \cdots & a_{1n} \\ \cdot & & \cdot \\ \cdot & & \cdot \\ \cdot & & \cdot \\ a_{n1} & \cdots & a_{nn} \end{vmatrix}.$$

If $a \neq 0$, Equations (39.9) may be solved for the X's in terms of the U's:

$$X_1 = b_{11}U_1 + \cdots + b_{1n}U_n$$

(39.10)

$$X_n = b_{n1}U_1 + \cdots + b_{nn}U_n$$

The transformation (39.10) is said to be the *inverse* of the transformation (39.9).

We may regard (39.9) as specifying a transformation or mapping from a point $(X_1, \cdots, X_n)$ of the n-dimensional space S_x to a point $(U_1, \cdots, U_n)$ of the n-dimensional space S_u, while (39.10) specifies the inverse mapping from S_u to S_x.

The set of points in S_n defined by the inequalities

$$u_i{}^* \leqq u_1 \leqq u_i{}^* + \Delta u_i, \quad i = 1, \cdots, n$$

is a *rectangular region R*. Suppose that $\phi(u_1, \cdots, u_n)$ is the joint density of $U_1, \cdots, U_n$. Then the probability that the random point $(U_1, \cdots, U_n)$ will fall in R may be found by integration:

(39.11) $P((U_1, \cdots, U_n) \in R)$

$$= \int_{u_n{}^*}^{u_n{}^*+\Delta u_n} \cdots \int_{u_1{}^*}^{u_1{}^*+\Delta u_1} \phi(u_1, \cdots, u_n) \, du_1 \cdots du_n.$$

Conversely, we may define the joint density of $U_1, \cdots, U_n$ as follows:

(39.12) $\phi(u_1, \cdots, u_n) = \lim_{\substack{\Delta u_i \to 0 \\ i=1,\ldots,n}} \dfrac{P((U_1, \cdots, U_n) \in R)}{\Delta u_1 \, \Delta u_2 \cdots \Delta u_n}.$

The expression in the denominator on the right of (39.12) is the *hypervolume* of the region R, denoted by V_R. If we call the fraction

$$\frac{P((U_1, \cdots, U_n) \in R)}{\Delta u_1 \, \Delta u_2 \cdots \Delta u_n}$$

the average probability per unit of hypervolume or the average density of probability over R, then the density $\phi(u_1, \cdots, u_n)$ is simply the limiting value of the average density as $V_R \to 0$.

Under the mapping (39.10) the region R of S_u is transformed into the region

$$R': \sum_{j=1}^{n} b_{ij}u_j{}^* \leqq x_i \leqq \sum_{j=1}^{n} b_{ij}(u_j{}^* + \Delta u_j), \quad i = 1, \cdots, n$$

of S_x. It may be shown that R' is an n-dimensional parallelepiped whose hypervolume $V_{R'}$ is related to V_R, the hypervolume of R, by the equation

$$(39.13) \qquad\qquad V_{R'} = |b|\, V_R,$$

where $|b|$ is the absolute value of the determinant of the transformation (39.10). The proof, which will not be given, involves the use of mathematical induction on n and can be considerably simplified by the use of matrix methods. At this point we shall drop the asterisk on the $u_1, \cdots, u_n$, which was useful only for the specification of the regions R and R' and for the limits of the integrals on the right side of (39.11).

We are now ready to prove the n-dimensional analog of Theorem (39.3); namely,

(39.14) THEOREM. *Let the random variables* $X_1, \cdots, X_n$ *possess the joint density* $f(x_1, \cdots, x_n)$, *and let the variables* $U_1, \cdots, U_n$ *be related to* $X_1, \cdots, X_n$ *by the linear transformation (39.10) and its inverse (39.11). Then the joint density of* $U_1, \cdots, U_n$ *is*

$$\phi(u_1, \cdots, u_n) = |b|\, f\left(\sum_{i=1}^{n} b_{1i}u_i, \cdots, \sum_{i=1}^{n} b_{ni}u_i\right),$$

where $|b|$ *is the absolute value of the determinant of* (39.11).

Proof. The density $\phi(u_1, \cdots, u_n)$ is given by

$$\phi(u_1, \cdots, u_n) = \lim_{\substack{\Delta u_i \to 0 \\ i=1,\ldots,n}} \frac{P((U_1, \cdots, U_n) \in R)}{V_R}$$

$$= \lim_{\substack{\Delta u_i \to 0 \\ i=1,\ldots,n}} \frac{P((X_1, \cdots, X_n) \in R')}{\dfrac{V_{R'}}{|b|}},$$

since $P((U_1, \cdots, U_n) \in R) = P((X_1, \cdots, X_n) \in R')$, and $V_R = V_{R'}/|b|$ by (39.13). Furthermore, as $\Delta u_1, \Delta u_2, \cdots, \Delta u_n$ simultaneously approach zero, the hypervolume $V_{R'}$ will approach zero, and the ratio $P((X_1, \cdots, X_n) \in R')/V_{R'}$ will approach the joint density $f(x_1, \cdots, x_n)$. This implies that

$$\phi(u_1, \cdots, u_n) = |b|\, f(x_1, \cdots, x_n).$$

When we eliminate $x_1, \cdots, x_n$ from the right side by the use of (39.10), we obtain the result stated in the theorem.

Paralleling the two-dimensional case, we now define an *orthogonal transformation*. The transformation (39.9) is said to be orthogonal if, when the substitutions (39.9) are made in the left side of the equation

$$(39.15) \qquad U_1^2 + \cdots + U_n^2 = X_1^2 + \cdots + X_n^2,$$

it reduces to an identity in $X_1, \cdots, X_n$. When we carry out the necessary algebra, we obtain the following orthogonality conditions, generalizing those given in (39.6):

$$(39.16) \qquad \begin{aligned} a_{1i}^2 + \cdots + a_{ni}^2 &= 1, \quad i = 1, \cdots, n, \\ a_{1i}a_{1j} + \cdots + a_{ni}a_{nj} &= 0, \quad i \neq j = 1, \cdots, n. \end{aligned}$$

Note that the first of these equations is a condition upon the coefficients of each equation of (39.9), whereas the second relates the coefficients of pairs of equations of (39.9). The following example gives an orthogonal transformation for the case $n = 4$.

Example 39.4.   Consider the transformation:

$$u_1 = \frac{1}{2}(x_1 + x_2 + x_3 + x_4)$$

$$u_2 = \frac{1}{\sqrt{2}}(x_1 - x_2)$$

$$u_3 = \frac{1}{\sqrt{6}}(x_1 + x_2 - 2x_3)$$

$$u_4 = \frac{1}{\sqrt{12}}(x_1 + x_2 + x_3 - 3x_4).$$

In checking the orthogonality of this transformation, it is convenient to write out the matrix of coefficients (see Appendix):

$$\begin{bmatrix} \dfrac{1}{2} & \dfrac{1}{2} & \dfrac{1}{2} & \dfrac{1}{2} \\[2mm] \dfrac{1}{\sqrt{2}} & -\dfrac{1}{\sqrt{2}} & 0 & 0 \\[2mm] \dfrac{1}{\sqrt{6}} & \dfrac{1}{\sqrt{6}} & -\dfrac{2}{\sqrt{6}} & 0 \\[2mm] \dfrac{1}{\sqrt{12}} & \dfrac{1}{\sqrt{12}} & \dfrac{1}{\sqrt{12}} & -\dfrac{3}{\sqrt{12}} \end{bmatrix}.$$

The orthogonality conditions (39.16) may be simply stated for such a matrix as this: (*a*) the sum of squares of elements in any column must be unity; (*b*) the sum of products of corresponding elements in any two columns must be zero. It is readily verified that these conditions are satisfied for the present example.

It may be shown that as a result of the orthogonality conditions (39.16) the absolute value of the determinant of the transformation (39.9) is equal to unity. As a consequence there is an inverse transformation (39.10). The coefficients of the inverse transformation have a simple relationship to the coefficients of the original transformation. In fact, if (39.9) is orthogonal, its inverse takes the form (see Appendix):

$$X_1 = a_{11}U_1 + \cdots + a_{n1}U_n,$$

$$\cdot \quad \cdot \quad \cdot \quad \cdot \quad \cdot \quad \cdot \quad \cdot \quad \cdot \quad \cdot \quad \cdot \quad \cdot$$

(39.17)

$$\cdot \quad \cdot \quad \cdot \quad \cdot \quad \cdot \quad \cdot \quad \cdot \quad \cdot \quad \cdot \quad \cdot \quad \cdot$$

$$\cdot \quad \cdot \quad \cdot \quad \cdot \quad \cdot \quad \cdot \quad \cdot \quad \cdot \quad \cdot \quad \cdot \quad \cdot$$

$$X_n = a_{1n}U_1 + \cdots + a_{nn}U_n.$$

Note carefully the way in which the coefficients of (39.17) are related to those of (39.9).

When the expressions (39.17) are substituted for $X_1, \cdots, X_n$ in the right side of (39.15), the result must be an identity in $U_1, \cdots, U_n$. This leads to the following additional orthogonality conditions, generalizing those of (39.7):

(39.18)
$$a_{i1}^2 + \cdots + a_{in}^2 = 1, \quad i = 1, \cdots, n,$$
$$a_{i1}a_{j1} + \cdots + a_{in}a_{jn} = 0, \quad i \neq j = 1, \cdots, n.$$

The orthogonality conditions (39.16) and (39.18) are readily stated in terms of the rows and columns of the coefficient matrix

$$\begin{bmatrix} a_{11} & \cdots & a_{1n} \\ \cdot & \cdots & \cdot \\ \cdot & \cdots & \cdot \\ \cdot & \cdots & \cdot \\ a_{n1} & \cdots & a_{nn} \end{bmatrix}$$

of the transformation (39.9). The first condition of (39.16) implies that the sum of the squares of the elements in any column must be unity; the second condition of (39.16) implies that the sum of products of corresponding elements in any pair of columns is zero. The orthogonality conditions (39.18) imply statements which may be obtained from the preceding sentence by replacing the word "column" by the word "row."

We shall be interested in the result of applying an orthogonal transformation to a set of random variables $X_1, \cdots, X_n$ which are independently distributed according to $N(0, \sigma^2)$. In this case the joint density becomes

$$f(x_1, \cdots, x_n) = (2\pi\sigma)^{-n/2} e^{-(x_1{}^2 + \cdots + x_n{}^2)/2\sigma^2}.$$

Let $U_1, \cdots, U_n$ be random variables related to $X_1, \cdots, X_n$ by an orthogonal transformation. Since the absolute value of the determinant of the inverse transformation is unity and $x_1{}^2 + \cdots + x_n{}^2 = u_1{}^2 + \cdots u_n{}^2$, Theorem (39.14) implies that the joint density of $U_1, \cdots, U_n$ is

$$\phi(u_1, \cdots, u_n) = (2\pi\sigma)^{-n/2} e^{-(u_1{}^2 + \cdots + u_n{}^2)/2\sigma^2}.$$

This density may be factored:

$$\phi(u_1, \cdots, u_n)$$

$$= \left[\frac{1}{\sqrt{2\pi}\sigma} e^{-u_1{}^2/2\sigma^2} \right] \left[\frac{1}{\sqrt{2\pi}\sigma} e^{-u_2{}^2/2\sigma^2} \right] \cdots \left[\frac{1}{\sqrt{2\pi}\sigma} e^{-u_n{}^2/2\sigma^2} \right].$$

Theorem (20.17) now permits us to conclude that $U_1, \cdots, U_n$ are independently distributed according to $N(0, \sigma^2)$. We have proved the following generalization of (39.8):

(39.19) THEOREM. *If $X_1, \cdots, X_n$ are random variables independently distributed according to $N(0, \sigma^2)$ and $U_1, \cdots, U_n$ are random variables related to $X_1, \cdots, X_n$ by means of an orthogonal transformation, then $U_1, \cdots, U_n$ are independently distributed according to $N(0, \sigma^2)$.*

This result is an important extension of the normal reproductive law (25.5). Whereas (25.5) declares that a *single* linear function of n independently and normally distributed variables is again normally distributed, (39.19) asserts that an *orthogonal set* of linear functions of n independently distributed variables, each with the distribution $N(0, \sigma^2)$, are themselves independently and normally distributed.

Our first application of Theorem (39.19) will be in proving that, if $(X_1, \cdots, X_n)$ is a random sample from $N(0, \sigma^2)$, the mean $\overline{X}$ and the variance s^2 of the sample are independently distributed. This fact, together with the properties of the t distribution to be derived in Section 41, is of vital importance for the applications of the t distribution already studied in Chapter 4. The proof will depend upon finding an orthogonal transformation of which the first equation is $U_1 = (1/\sqrt{n}) \times (X_1 + \cdots + X_n)$. Such a transformation can be found by an ingenious method known as the Gram-Schmidt orthogonalization process (Appendix). By this means the following orthogonal transformation was obtained:

$$U_1 = \frac{1}{\sqrt{n}} (X_1 + \cdots + X_n)$$

$$U_2 = \frac{1}{\sqrt{2}} (X_1 - X_2)$$

(39.20) $$U_3 = \frac{1}{\sqrt{6}} (X_1 + X_2 - 2X_3)$$

$$\vdots$$

$$U_n = \frac{1}{\sqrt{n(n-1)}} (X_1 + X_2 + \cdots + X_{n-1} - (n-1)X_n).$$

We have already considered this transformation for the case $n = 4$ in Example 39.4. The reader should verify that the orthogonality conditions (39.16) are indeed satisfied by the transformation (39.20).

Let us now assume that the variables $X_1, \cdots, X_n$ are independently distributed according to $N(0, \sigma^2)$. Then according to (39.19) the variables $U_1, \cdots, U_n$ defined by (39.20) are also independently distributed according to $N(0, \sigma^2)$. Thus the distribution of the random variable $\overline{X} = (1/\sqrt{n})U_1$ is independent of the distributions of $U_2, \cdots, U_n$. Since the transformation (39.20) is orthogonal,

$$U_2{}^2 + \cdots + U_n{}^2 = X_1{}^2 + \cdots + X_n{}^2 - U_1{}^2$$

$$= X_1{}^2 + \cdots + X_n{}^2 - n\overline{X}{}^2 = (n-1)s^2,$$

where s^2 is the sample variance. But according to (37.8) the quantity $(U_2{}^2 + \cdots + U_n{}^2)/\sigma^2$ possesses that chi-square distribution with $n - 1$ d.f. Hence we may conclude:

(39.21)   THEOREM.   *If $(X_1, \cdots, X_n)$ is a random sample from $N(0, \sigma^2)$, with mean $\overline{X}$ and variance s^2, then $\overline{X}$ and $(n - 1)s^2/\sigma^2$ are independently distributed, the first according to $N(0, \sigma^2/n)$, the second according to CS$(n - 1)$.*

A second consequence of (39.19), also essential for the applications considered in Chapter 4, is the following:

(39.22)   THEOREM.   *Let $(X_1, \cdots, X_m)$ and $(Y_1, \cdots, Y_n)$ be independent random samples from $N(0, \sigma^2)$. Let their means be $\overline{X}$ and $\overline{Y}$, and their variances $s_x{}^2$ and $s_y{}^2$. Let the pooled variance $s_p{}^2$ be defined by*

$$s_p{}^2 = \frac{(m-1)s_x{}^2 + (n-1)s_y{}^2}{m+n-2}.$$

Then $\bar{X} - \bar{Y}$ and $(m + n - 2)s_p{}^2/\sigma^2$ are independently distributed, the first according to $N(0, \sigma^2(1/m + 1/n))$, and the second according to $CS(m + n - 2)$.

Proof. The proof depends upon finding a suitable orthogonal transformation from the set of variables $X_1, \cdots, X_m, Y_1, \cdots, Y_n$ to a set $U_1, \cdots, U_{m+n}$. Such a transformation is the following:

$$U_1 = \frac{1}{\sqrt{m + n}} (X_1 + \cdots + X_m + Y_1 + \cdots + Y_n)$$

$$U_2 = \frac{1}{\sqrt{mn(m + n)}} (nX_1 + \cdots + nX_m - mY_1 - \cdots - mY_n)$$

$$U_3 = \frac{1}{\sqrt{2}} (X_1 - X_2)$$

$$\vdots$$

$$U_{m+1} = \frac{1}{\sqrt{m(m - 1)}} (X_1 + \cdots + X_{m-1} - (m - 1)X_m)$$

$$U_{m+2} = \frac{1}{\sqrt{2}} (Y_1 - Y_2)$$

$$\vdots$$

$$U_{m+n} = \frac{1}{\sqrt{n(n - 1)}} (Y_1 + \cdots + Y_{n-1} - (n - 1)Y_n).$$

The reader should verify that this transformation satisfies the criteria (39.16) of orthogonality. Since we are given that $X_1, \cdots, X_m, Y_1, \cdots, Y_n$ are independently distributed according to $N(0, \sigma^2)$, (39.19) permits us to conclude that the variables $U_1, \cdots, U_n$ are likewise independently distributed according to $N(0, \sigma^2)$ and thus that

$$\bar{X} - \bar{Y} = \sqrt{\frac{1}{m} + \frac{1}{n}}\, U_2 \quad \text{and} \quad S = \frac{(U_3{}^2 + \cdots + U_{m+n}{}^2)}{\sigma^2}$$

are independently distributed, the first according to $N(0, \sigma^2(1/m + 1/n))$, the second according to $CS(m + n - 2)$. But

$$\sigma^2 S = U_3{}^2 + \cdots + U_{m+n}{}^2$$

$$= X_1{}^2 + \cdots + X_m{}^2 + Y_1{}^2$$

$$+ \cdots + Y_n{}^2 - U_1{}^2 - U_2{}^2, \quad \text{(orthogonality)}$$

$$= \Sigma X^2 + \Sigma Y^2 - \frac{1}{m+n}(m\bar{X} + n\bar{Y})^2 - \frac{mn}{m+n}(\bar{X} - \bar{Y})^2$$

$$= \Sigma X^2 - m\bar{X}^2 + \Sigma Y^2 - n\bar{Y}^2$$

$$= (m-1)s_x{}^2 + (n-1)s_y{}^2 = (m+n-2)s_p{}^2.$$

The conclusion of (39.22) now follows immediately.

EXERCISE 39

39.1. Show that the linear transformation

$$u_1 = \frac{1}{\sqrt{10}}(x_1 - 3x_2)$$

$$u_2 = \frac{1}{\sqrt{10}}(3x_1 + x_2)$$

satisfies the conditions (39.6) and (39.7) of orthogonality. Find an angle θ such that the above transformation can be interpreted as a rotation of axes through the positive angle θ from the set of (u_1, u_2) axes to the set of (x_1, x_2) axes.

39.2. Show that the linear transformation

$$u_1 = \frac{1}{\sqrt{14}}(2x_1 - x_2 + 3x_3)$$

$$u_2 = \frac{1}{\sqrt{26}}(4x_1 - x_2 - 3x_3)$$

$$u_3 = \frac{1}{\sqrt{91}}(3x_1 + 9x_2 + x_1)$$

satisfies the conditions (39.16) and (39.18) of orthogonality.

39.3. By direct substitution and algebraic simplification, show that $u_1{}^2 + u_2{}^2 + u_3{}^2 = x_1{}^2 + x_2{}^2 + x_3{}^3$ for the linear transformation of Exercise 39.2.

39.4. Show that the linear transformation

$$u_1 = ax_1 + 2ax_2 + ax_3 + 2ax_4$$

$$u_2 = 9bx_1 - 2bx_2 - bx_3 - 2bx_4$$

$$u_3 = \qquad 5cx_2 - 2cx_3 - 4cx_4$$

$$u_4 = \qquad\qquad 2dx_3 - dx_4$$

satisfies the conditions $a_{i1}a_{j1} + \cdots + a_{in}a_{jn} = 0$, $i \neq j = 1, \cdots, n$ required for an orthogonal transformation. Show that a, b, c, and d may be chosen so that the remaining orthogonality conditions (39.18) are satisfied.

39.5. Show that the linear transformation given in the proof of (39.22) is orthogonal.

39.6. Let $(X_1, \cdots, X_n)$ be a random sample from $N(0, \sigma^2)$, and let $a_1, \cdots, a_n$ be a set of real numbers. Let $U = a_1 X_1 + \cdots + a_n U_n$, and let $V = (\Sigma X^2 - U^2/\Sigma a^2)/\sigma^2$. Show that U and V are independently distributed, the first according to $N(0, \sigma^2 \Sigma a^2)$, the second according to $CS(n-1)$. (Assume that an orthogonal transformation can be found with $U = a_1 X_1 + \cdots + a_n X_n$ as one of the equations.)

39.7. Under the mapping (39.2) the 4 vertices $A(u_1, u_2)$, $B(u_1 + \Delta u_1, u_2)$, $C(u_1 + \Delta u_1, u_2 + \Delta u_2)$, $D(u_1, u_2 + \Delta u_2)$ of the rectangle R are carried into the vertices A', B', C', D' of the quadrilateral R', whose coordinates are given in the text. (a) Using slopes, show that R' is a parallelogram. (b) From analytic geometry it is known that the area of a parallelogram is given by the absolute value of the determinant

$$\begin{vmatrix} x_1 & y_1 & 1 \\ x_2 & y_2 & 1 \\ x_3 & y_3 & 1 \end{vmatrix},$$

where (x_1, y_1), (x_2, y_2), (x_3, y_3) are any three vertices of the parallelogram. Use this fact in order to prove that the areas of R and R' are related by Area $R' = |b|$ Area R, where $|b|$ is the absolute value of the determinant of the transformation (39.2). (c) Let $P(u_1^*, u_2^*)$ be a point interior to R, so that $u_1 < u_1^* < u_1 + \Delta u_1$, $u_2 < u_2^* < u_2 + \Delta u_2$. Show that these inequalities imply that $b_{11}u_1^* + b_{12}u_2^*$ lies between $b_{11}u_1 + b_{12}u_2$ and $b_{11}(u_1 + \Delta u_1) + b_{12}(u_2 + \Delta u_2)$ and that $b_{21}u_1^* + b_{22}u_2^*$ lies between $b_{21}u_1 + b_{22}u_2$ and $b_{21}(u_1 + \Delta u_1) + b_{22}(u_2 + \Delta u_2)$. Hence conclude that, if P is interior to R, then P' is interior to R'.

39.8. If the variables u_1 and u_2 are related to the variables x_1 and x_2 by the transformation $u_1 = u_1(x_1, x_2)$, $u_2 = u_2(x_1, x_2)$, then the Jacobian of u_1 and u_2 with respect to x_1 and x_2 is defined to be

$$\frac{\partial(u_1, u_2)}{\partial(x_1, x_2)} = \begin{vmatrix} \dfrac{\partial u_1}{\partial x_1} & \dfrac{\partial u_1}{\partial x_2} \\ \dfrac{\partial u_2}{\partial x_1} & \dfrac{\partial u_2}{\partial x_2} \end{vmatrix}.$$

Show that the Jacobian of the linear transformation $u_1 = a_{11}x_1 + a_{12}x_2$, $u_2 = a_{21}x_1 + a_{22}x_2$ is the determinant

$$\begin{vmatrix} a_{11} & a_{12} \\ a_{21} & a_{22} \end{vmatrix}$$

and that this determinant is ± 1 if the transformation is orthogonal.

39.9. If the variables $u_1, \cdots, u_n$ are related to the variables $x_1, \cdots, x_n$ by the transformation $u_1 = u_1(x_1, \cdots, x_n)$, $u_2 = u_2(x_1, \cdots, x_n)$, $\cdots$, $u_n = u_n(x_1, \cdots, x_n)$, then the Jacobian of $u_1, \cdots, u_n$ with respect to $x_1, \cdots, x_n$ is

$$\frac{\partial(u_1, \cdots, u_n)}{\partial(x_1, \cdots, x_n)} = \begin{vmatrix} \dfrac{\partial u_1}{\partial x_1} & \cdots & \dfrac{\partial u_1}{\partial x_n} \\ \cdot & & \cdot \\ \cdot & & \cdot \\ \cdot & & \cdot \\ \dfrac{\partial u_n}{\partial x_1} & \cdots & \dfrac{\partial u_n}{\partial x_n} \end{vmatrix}.$$

Show that the Jacobian of the transformation of Example 39.4 is

$$\begin{vmatrix} 1/2 & 1/2 & 1/2 & 1/2 \\ 1/\sqrt{2} & -1/\sqrt{2} & 0 & 0 \\ 1/\sqrt{6} & 1/\sqrt{6} & -2/\sqrt{6} & 0 \\ 1/\sqrt{12} & 1/\sqrt{12} & 1/\sqrt{12} & -3/\sqrt{12} \end{vmatrix}.$$

39.10. We may regard the 4 equations in Exercise 38.5 as a transformation between the variables x_1, x_2, x_3, x_4 and the variables r, ϕ_1, ϕ_2, ϕ_3. Show that the Jacobian $\dfrac{\partial(x_1, x_2, x_3, x_4)}{\partial(r, \phi_1, \phi_2, \phi_3)}$ reduces to $-r^3 \cos^2 \phi_1 \cos \phi_2$.

39.11. Prove the following generalization of (39.21): If $(Y_1, \cdots, Y_n)$ is a random sample from $N(\mu, \sigma^2)$, with mean $\bar{X}$ and variance s^2, then $\bar{X}$ and $(n - 1)s^2/\sigma^2$ are independently distributed, the first according to $N(\mu, \sigma^2/n)$, the second according to $CS(n - 1)$. [Use (39.21), noting the relationship between the quantities $Y_1, \cdots, Y_n$ and the quantities $X_1, \cdots, X_n$ of (39.21).]

39.12. Prove the following generalization of (39.22): Let $(U_1, \cdots, U_m)$ and $(V_1, \cdots, V_n)$ be independent random samples from $N(\mu, \sigma^2)$. Let their means be $\bar{U}$ and $\bar{V}$, and their variances s_u^2 and s_v^2. Let the pooled variance s_q^2 be defined by $s_q^2 = [(m - 1)s_u^2 + (n - 1)s_v^2]/(m + n - 2)$. Then $\bar{U} - \bar{V}$ and $(m + n - 2)s_q^2/\sigma^2$ are independently distributed, the first according to $N(o, \sigma^2(1/m + 1/n))$ and the second according to $CS(m + n - 2)$.

*40. PEARSON'S CHI-SQUARE TEST

Karl Pearson, about 1900, suggested a very direct attack upon the problem of statistical inference, beginning with the following question: given, on the one hand, a set of empirical data and, on the other hand, a particular frequency function which presumably describes the population from which the data are drawn, how may we test the hypothesis that the given data actually come from a population with the proposed distribution? Since we are interested in testing how well the observed data conform to, or fit, the hypothetical distribution, Pearson's test is often referred to as a test of *goodness of fit*. For purposes of illustration let us return to the experiment of throwing a dime-store die 100 times. The frequency distribution was given in Table 5.1, and is shown in the following table:

Value	1	2	3	4	5	6
Frequency	18	18	17	13	18	16

Our question is: are such results as these consistent with the hypothesis that the die is well-constructed, with probability 1/6 for each face? Karl Pearson proposed the statistic

$$(40.1) \qquad \chi^2 = \sum \frac{(x_o - x_e)^2}{x_e}$$

as a means of testing the hypothesis that the sample is drawn from the specified population. The quantity defined by (40.1) is called *chi square* and the test Pearson devised is the *chi-square test*. We shall see that its sampling distribution is, approximately, the familiar chi-square distribution.

The data are assumed to fall into a series of classes $C_1, \cdots, C_k$ for which estimated frequencies can in some way be formed. In (40.1), x_e denotes the expected frequency, and x_o the corresponding observed frequency. For the dice data of Example 40.1, the values of x_o are the frequencies given in the table. The expected frequencies are the values $np = 100/6 = 50/3$. Hence chi square is

$$\chi^2 = \frac{3}{50} \left[\left(18 - \frac{50}{3}\right)^2 + \left(18 - \frac{50}{3}\right)^2 \right.$$

$$\left. + \left(17 - \frac{50}{3}\right)^2 + \left(13 - \frac{50}{3}\right)^2 + \left(18 - \frac{50}{3}\right)^2 + \left(16 - \frac{50}{3}\right)^2 \right]$$

$$= \frac{3}{50} \times \frac{174}{9} = 1.16.$$

Note that chi square is so constructed that a large discrepancy between the sample frequency distribution and the expected frequency distribution leads to a large value of chi square. We are therefore led to ask whether the value $\chi^2 = 1.16$ is large enough to be significant. We have already remarked that the quantity defined by (40.1) possesses, approximately, the chi-square distribution. The number of degrees of freedom is the number of observations, minus the number of conditions to which the x_o must submit. In the present example there is one such condition, namely, $\Sigma x_o = 100$, so there are $6 - 1 = 5$ d.f. For 5 d.f. the 95th percentage point of the chi-square distribution is 11.070. That is, χ^2 would have to be greater than 11.070 in order to reject, at the 5% level, the hypothesis that the die is true. We accordingly accept the hypothesis.

We shall now outline the proof that the quantity defined by (40.1) actually possesses, approximately, the chi-square distribution. The proof is adapted from that given in Fry (7),* and this in turn is based on Pearson's original treatment, given in Pearson (14). We shall alter the notation somewhat. The data are assumed to fall into classes C_1, $\cdots$, C_k; let p_1, $\cdots$, p_k represent the probabilities associated with these classes, and let x_1, $\cdots$, x_k be the frequencies corresponding to these classes, where $x_1 + \cdots + x_k = n$. Then according to (7.13) the frequencies x_1, $\cdots$, x_k will possess the multinomial distribution:

$$(40.2) \qquad f(x_1, \cdots, x_k) = \frac{n!}{x_1! \cdots x_k!} p_1^{x_1} \cdots p_k^{x_k}.$$

This distribution could actually be used to test the hypothesis that the obtained sample comes from the specified population. But the calculations involved would, in most cases, be prohibitive. What we require is an approximation to (40.2) analogous to the approximation to the binomial distribution provided by the normal distribution.

If we proceed as we did in Section 34 and use Stirling's approximation (17.6) for each of the factorials in (40.2), we find, after some rearranging, that $f(x_1, \cdots, x_k)$ is approximately equal to

$$(40.3) \quad (2\pi n)^{-(k-1)/2}(p_1 \cdots p_k)^{-1/2} \left(\frac{np_1}{x_1}\right)^{x_1+1/2} \cdots \left(\frac{np_k}{x_k}\right)^{x_k+1/2}.$$

We wish to simplify the factors $(np_i/x_i)^{x_i+1/2}$, $i = 1, \cdots, k$, occurring in (40.3). To do this, we note that there is a dichotomy associated with each class C_i since each observation either does or does not fall in the class C_i. Thus the mean and standard deviation of the variable x_i are np_i and $\sigma_i = \sqrt{np_i(1 - p_i)}$. These expressions permit us to introduce new variables y_1, $\cdots$, y_k which are obtained by expressing the x_i in standard units, so that

$$y_i = \frac{x_i - np_i}{\sigma_i} = \frac{x_i - np_i}{\sqrt{np_i(1 - p_i)}}, \quad x_i = np_i + \sigma_i y_i$$

* See pp. 280–289 in Fry (7).

By using this substitution, the factors in (40.3) assume the form

$$(40.4) \quad \left(\frac{np_i}{x_i}\right)^{x_i+1/2} = \left(\frac{x_i}{np_i}\right)^{-x_i-1/2} = \left(1 + \frac{\sigma_i y_i}{np_i}\right)^{-np_i-\sigma_i y_i-1/2}.$$

We wish to find the form taken by the expression (40.3) as n becomes large. Our procedure parallels that used in Section 34. We take the logarithm of (40.3), using the substitution (40.4) and the notation

$$A = \log_e (2\pi n)^{-(k-1)/2}(p_1 \cdots p_k)^{-1/2},$$

and we obtain an expression which reduces to

$$(40.5) \quad A - \sum_i \left(\sigma_i y_i + \frac{\sigma_i^2 y_i^2}{2np_i} + \text{terms involving } n^{-2}, n^{-3}, \cdots \right).$$

But the fact that $\Sigma x_i = n$ implies that $\Sigma \sigma_i y_i = 0$. Furthermore $\sigma_i^2/np_i = 1 - p_i$ so that (40.5) reduces to

$$A - \frac{1}{2} \Sigma y_i^2 (1 - p_i) + \text{terms involving } n^{-2}, n^{-3}, \cdots.$$

Thus, if n is sufficiently large,

$$(40.6) \quad \begin{aligned} f(x_1, \cdots, x_k) &\doteq (2\pi n)^{-(k-1)/2}(p_1 \cdots p_k)^{-1/2} e^{-(1/2)\Sigma y_i^2(1-p_i)} \\ &= (2\pi n)^{-(k-1)/2}(p_1 \cdots p_k)^{-1/2} e^{-(1/2)\Sigma z_i^2}, \end{aligned}$$

where

$$(40.7) \quad z_i = y_i \sqrt{1 - p_i} = \frac{x_i - np_i}{\sqrt{np_i}}.$$

The reason for introducing the new variables z_i is that with their use the frequency function has assumed the form $Ke^{-(1/2)\Sigma z^2}$, reminiscent of the multivariate normal distribution. In fact we may say that for large n the frequency function $f(x_1, \cdots, x_k)$ bears the same relation to the multivariate normal distribution that the binomial distribution does to the univariate normal distribution.

Let us recall that our objective is to find the probability that the random quantity χ^2, defined by (40.1), will exceed an arbitrarily assigned positive number, say u. We first note that, from (40.1) and (40.7), $\chi^2 = \Sigma z_i^2$. Thus the sample points for which $\chi^2 > u$ will be those lying outside the hypersphere $z_1^2 + \cdots + z_k^2 = u$. For convenience, let us find the total probability of all points lying *inside* this hypersphere; this will give us the distribution function of χ^2. In order to do this, we replace the discrete distribution with which we have been dealing by the continuous distribution whose density is

$$(40.8) \qquad f(z_1, \cdots, z_k) = Ke^{-(1/2)\Sigma z^2},$$

where K is the appropriate constant. Since the integral over the whole sample space must be unity, K must, in fact, be $(2\pi)^{-k/2}$. Then the summation of probability over all points interior to the hypersphere may be replaced by an integration over the interior of the hypersphere. The justification for this procedure is essentially the same as the justification for using the normal distribution in order to approximate binomial probabilities. It turns out that in a complete discussion of this matter it is essential to show that each sample point in the z-space is associated with the same sized portion of the sample space; this can be done without difficulty, using (40.7).

Let us leave to one side, for the moment, the important fact that the x-values are subject to the restriction $x_1 + \cdots + x_k = n$. Neglecting this condition, we are led to conclude that the distribution function of χ^2 is obtained by integrating the density (40.8) over the interior of the hypersphere $\Sigma z_i{}^2 = u$. But in Section 38 we found that this integral is the distribution function for the chi-square distribution. Thus, ignoring the condition $\Sigma x_i = n$, we would conclude that the quantity χ^2 defined by (40.1) has, approximately, the chi-square distribution with k d.f. Alternatively one may argue that since the density (40.8) is factorable into

$$(2\pi)^{-1/2}e^{-z_1{}^2/2} \cdots (2\pi)^{-1/2}e^{-z_k{}^2/2},$$

it follows that the quantities $z_1, \cdots, z_k$ are independently distributed according to $N(0, 1)$ and hence that $\chi^2 = \Sigma z_i{}^2$ has the stated chi-square distribution. We must now outline the argument by which one concludes that the restriction $\Sigma x_i = n$ reduces the degrees of freedom to $k - 1$.

When the restriction $\Sigma x_i = n$ is expressed in terms of the z's, using (40.7), it assumes the form $\Sigma \sqrt{p_i}\, z_i = 0$. We wish, then, to find the integral of the density (40.8) over the portion of the sample space specified by

$$\Sigma z_i{}^2 < u, \quad \Sigma \sqrt{p_i}\, z_i = 0.$$

To accomplish this, we use an orthogonal transformation of the kind employed in Section 39. The Gram-Schmidt process (see Appendix) enables us to find an orthogonal transformation of the form

$$
\begin{aligned}
u_1 &= \sqrt{p_i}\, z_1 + \cdots + \sqrt{p_k}\, z_k \\
u_2 &= a_{21} z_1 + \cdots + a_{2k} z_k
\end{aligned}
$$

(40.9)

$$\vdots \qquad \vdots$$

$$u_k = a_{k1} z_1 + \cdots + a_{kk} z_k.$$

We are not interested in the actual values of the coefficients, except those in the first equation; we need only know that they can be obtained.

We have already remarked that the form of the density (40.8) enables us to conclude that $z_1, \cdots, z_k$ are independently distributed according to $N(0, 1)$. Thus, using (39.19), we conclude that the quantities $u_1, \cdots, u_k$, defined by (40.9), are also independently distributed according to $N(0, 1)$. The restriction $\Sigma \sqrt{p_i}\, z_i = 0$ now merely implies that we are confining our attention to the portion of the sample space for which $u_1 = 0$. For this region

$$\chi^2 = z_1{}^2 + \cdots + z_k{}^2 = u_2{}^2 + \cdots + u_k{}^2.$$

Since the $k - 1$ quantities $u_2, \cdots, u_k$ are independently distributed according to $N(0, 1)$, (37.7) permits us to conclude that χ^2 has the chi-square distribution with $k - 1$ d.f.

The chi-square test is applicable in many situations similar to that of the example with which we began this section, where an empirical distribution is being compared with a theoretical distribution. How this may be accomplished when the theoretical distribution is continuous is exhibited in the following example:

Example 40.1. Let us test whether the distribution of lengths of lima beans, as given in Table 13.2, can reasonably be regarded as that of a sample from a normal population. That is, we shall test the hypothesis H_0 that the parent population is normally distributed. To do this, we consider a normal distribution whose mean and standard deviation are those of the sample of lima beans. For this distribution we may compute the probabilities associated with each of the intervals of Table 13.2 by the methods of Section 15. We then obtain theoretical frequencies for each of these intervals by multiplying the probabilities by $n = 157$. The necessary computations are shown in Table 40.1, with additional columns for the computation of χ^2.

Column 3 gives the values of z obtained from $z = (x - 20.4)/1.727$, where x is any one of the boundary values. Column 4 gives the corresponding values of $F_N(z)$. Column (5), obtained by differencing column 4, gives the theoretical normal probabilities for each of the given intervals. Column 6 is obtained by multiplying each value in column 5 by $n = 157$. Note that when a very small value of x_e occurs in column 6, the corresponding term that will enter into the

TABLE 40.1

(1) Boundaries	(2) Observed Frequency x_o	(3) z	(4) $F_N(z)$	(5) Probability	(6) Expected Frequency x_e	(7) $x_o - x_e$	(8) $\dfrac{(x_o - x_e)^2}{x_e}$
14.95		−3.16	.0008	.0008	.1		
	1			.0033	.5		
15.85		−2.64	.0041			8.5 → 2.5	.74
	4			.0129	2.0		
16.75		−2.12	.0170				
	6			.0378	5.9		
17.65		−1.60	.0548				
	10			.0853	13.4	−3.4	.86
18.55		−1.08	.1401				
	23			.1476	23.1	−.9	.04
19.45		−.56	.2877				
	22			.2003	31.4	−9.4	2.81
20.35		−.03	.4880				
	42			.1999	31.4	10.6	3.59
21.25		.49	.6879				
	28			.1559	24.5	3.5	.50
22.15		1.01	.8438				
	13			.0932	14.6	−1.6	.18
23.05		1.53	.9370				
	7			.0428	6.7		
23.95		2.05	.9798			9.9 → −1.9	.36
	0			.0151	2.4		
24.85		2.57	.9949				
	1			.0041	.6		
25.75		3.09	.9990	.0010	.2		
	157				**156.8**		**9.08**

computed value of χ^2 will tend to be large, since x_e enters into the denominator of the fractions that make up χ^2. It is customary to group the values of x_e that are smaller than 5 so as to make up a series of estimated frequencies, each of which is larger than 5. Thus in column 6 the first 4 and the last 4 values of x_e have been combined, and the combined values have been used in the computation of χ^2. It can be shown that the degrees of freedom for chi-square in such an example as this is 2 less than the number of terms being added in column 8, the number 2 arising from the fact that 2 parameters μ and σ are being estimated from the sample and used in the calculation of chi square. The value of chi square obtained from our data is 9.08. If we use the 1% level of significance, we should compare the obtained value of chi square with the 99th percentile of chi square, for $8 - 2 = 6$ d.f., namely 16.812. Thus we can accept the null hypothesis and conclude that the empirical data with which we started may reasonably be regarded as normally distributed.

Example 40.2. *Contingency Table.* Suppose we have two independent random experiments. Then we can set up a two-way probability table, such as Table 6.2 or Table 20.2, for which the entries in the body of the table will be the products of marginal probabilities, by (20.8). Now suppose that we have a sample of observations which may be cross-classified under sets of categories $\{A_1, \cdots, A_h\}$ and $\{B_1, \cdots, B_k\}$ and that the frequency associated with the pair of categories (A_i, B_j) is x_{ij}. Then the data may be displayed as a two-way frequency table, or *contingency table.*

	B_1	$\cdots$	B_k	
A_1	x_{11}	$\cdots$	x_{1k}	$x_{1.}$
.	.	$\cdots$	,	.
.	.	$\cdots$	.	.
.	.	$\cdots$	.	.
A_h	x_{h1}	$\cdots$	x_{hk}	$x_{h.}$
	$x_{.1}$		$x_{.k}$	$x_{..}$

We may be interested in testing the hypothesis that the two systems of classification $\{A_i\}$ and $\{B_j\}$ are *independent.* It may be shown that under this hypothesis the maximum likelihood estimates of the parameters corresponding to the frequencies x_{ij}, based on the marginal frequencies, are $\hat{x}_{ij} = x_{i.}x_{.j}/n$. As a consequence we may set up the quantity

$$\chi^2 = \sum \frac{(x_{ij} - \hat{x}_{ij})^2}{\hat{x}_{ij}},$$

which will possess the chi-square distribution with $(h-1)(k-1)$ d.f. The following example illustrates the procedure. A study of the New York City Youth Board classifies 918 boys as delinquent and nondelinquent and also classifies the disciplinary attitude of the father in 4 categories, as shown in Table 40.2. The numbers in parentheses in each cell are the expected frequencies as calculated from $\hat{x}_{ij} = x_{i.}x_{.j}/n$. We may now calculate chi square and use it as a test of the hypothesis that the behavior of the boy is independent of the disciplinary attitude of the father. We find that $\chi^2 = 278.0$. At the 1% level, this should

TABLE 40.2

Disciplinary Attitude of Father	Behavior of Boy	
	Delinquent	Non-delinquent
Lax	122 (102.0)	82 (102.0)	204
Overstrict	120 (80.0)	40 (80.0)	160
Erratic	191 (136.5)	82 (136.5)	273
Firm but kindly	26 (140.5)	255 (140.5)	281
	459	459	918

be compared with a chi-square value, for 3 d.f., of 11.34. Thus the null hypothesis is rejected, leading to the conclusion that the behavior of the boy and the attitude of the father are most probably related.

EXERCISE 40

40.1. Among Gregor Mendel's many experiments with sweet peas was one involving 580 plants. Of these, 428 bore peas in green pods, 152 in yellow pods. Test the hypothesis, proposed by Mendel, that the probabilities for green pods and for yellow pods are, respectively, 3/4 and 1/4.

40.2. According to an Associated Press dispatch, an experiment was performed to test the effectiveness of a combination of streptomycin and bone marrow cells as protection against exposure to large doses of neutron radiation. Approximately 15% of neutron-irradiated mice receiving the treatment died within 30 days, while 95% of untreated mice died. Assume 100 mice are in each of the 2 experimental groups, and test the hypothesis that treatment and mortality are unrelated (i.e., independent).

40.3. In Exercise 4.3 a relative frequency distribution was constructed for the data of Table 4.2, and in Exercise 8.15 the mean of this distribution was found to be 4.68. In Exercise 35.10 a Poisson distribution was constructed with $k = 4.68$. Use chi square to test the hypothesis that the sample in Table 4.2 is from a Poisson-distributed population, considering the expected frequencies to be given by the distribution of Exercise 35.10. The degrees of freedom for chi square will be one less than the number of classes, since the sample mean has been used in computing the expected frequencies.

40.4. In Table 5.2 frequency distributions are given for the first 100, the first 200, the first 500 and the whole set of 1000 throws of a cardboard icosahedral die. Use chi square to test, in each of the 4 cases, the hypothesis that the sample came from a population in which $f(x) = .1$, $x = 0, 1, \cdots, 9$.

40.5. Using the distribution prepared in Exercise 4.2 and the method of Exercise 40.3, test the hypothesis that the data are Poisson distributed.

40.6. Let a contingency table possess the frequencies shown. Let $P(A_1) = p_A$, $P(B_1) = p_B$. Assuming that the four events A_1B_1, A_1B_2, A_2B_1, and A_2B_2

	A_1	A_2
B_1	x_{11}	x_{12}
B_2	x_{21}	x_{22}

are independent, show that the joint likelihood of $x_{11}, x_{12}, x_{21}, x_{22}$ is

$$L = (p_A p_B)^{x_{11}}[p_B(1 - p_A)]^{x_{12}}[p_A(1 - p_B)]^{x_{21}}[(1 - p_A)(1 - p_B)]^{x_{22}}.$$

Hence show that maximum likelihood estimates of p_A and p_B are

$$\hat{p}_A = \frac{x_{11} + x_{21}}{n}, \quad \hat{p}_B = \frac{x_{11} + x_{12}}{n},$$

where $n = x_{11} + x_{12} + x_{21} + x_{22}$.

40.7. Suppose that the 4 frequencies in a 2 by 2 contingency table are a, b, c,

and d, as shown. Show that chi square for such a table reduces algebraically to

$$\frac{n(ad - bc)^2}{(a + b)(a + c)(b + d)(c + d)},$$

where $n = a + b + c + d$.

41. THE CAUCHY DISTRIBUTION, THE t DISTRIBUTION, AND THE F DISTRIBUTION

The three distributions with which we shall deal in this section have this in common: each of the three arises as the distribution of the *ratio* of quantities with known distributions. The Cauchy distribution, as has been mentioned in Section 18 (Example 18.5), is peculiar in that it possesses no moments of any order and is important in that it "defies" the central limit theorem. The t distribution and the F distribution are of central importance in modern statistical methods because of their remarkable versatility in evaluating the results of experiments in many fields. We have mentioned, in Section 26, that the t distribution was first investigated by W. S. Gosset, writing under the pseudonym of "Student." The first rigorous derivation of the distribution was given by Fisher in 1923. The F distribution, which in a sense generalizes the t distribution, was so named by G. W. Snedecor, who published the first table of F, in recognition of the work of R. A. Fisher. Fisher had previously given the distribution of the quantity $z = \frac{1}{2} \log_e F$, and Snedecor recognized the computational simplification in using F rather than Fisher's z. In Europe the quantity F is generally known as the *variance ratio*, for reasons that will be apparent from the definition below.

We first show the relationship between the Cauchy distribution and the normal distribution, as stated in:

(41.1) THEOREM. *If X and Y are independent values from $N(0, 1)$, then the ratio $U = Y/X$ possesses the Cauchy distribution, with density* $(\pi(1 + u^2))^{-1}$.

Proof. We use (36.2) with $u = g(x, y) = y/x$ so that $y = h(x, u) = ux$, and $\partial h/\partial u = x$. The joint density of X and Y is $f(x, y) = (1/2\pi)e^{-(x^2+y^2)/2}$.

Hence

$$\phi(u) = \frac{1}{2\pi} \int e^{-(x + u \cdot x \cdot)/2} x \, dx.$$

For $u = $ const., x may range from $-\infty$ to ∞. We make the change of variable $z = x^2(1 + u^2)/2$, $dz = (1 + u^2)x \, dx$, in which u is a constant. Thus z goes from 0 to ∞ twice as x goes from $-\infty$ to ∞, and we have

$$\phi(u) = \frac{2}{2\pi} \int_0^\infty e^{-z} \frac{dz}{1 + u^2} = \frac{1}{\pi(1 + u^2)}.$$

In connection with Example 18.5 it was pointed out that a spinner with scale of Example 2.9 will yield a random variable with the Cauchy distribution.

The t distribution, whose density is

(41.2) $$f(t) = \frac{\Gamma\left(\dfrac{n + 1}{2}\right)}{\sqrt{n\pi}\, \Gamma\left(\dfrac{n}{2}\right)} (1 + t^2/n)^{-(n+1)/2},$$

has been used in Chapter 4 for various purposes of statistical inference. The basic theorem upon which the applications of the t distribution depend is the following:

(41.3) THEOREM. *If X and Y are independently distributed, the first according to $N(\mu, \sigma^2)$, the second according to $\mathrm{CS}(n)$, then the quantity*

$$U = \frac{(X - \mu)}{\sigma} \sqrt{\frac{n}{Y}}$$

has the t distribution with n d.f.

Proof. In order to eliminate μ and σ at the outset, let $Z = (X - \mu)/\sigma$. Then Z is from $N(0, 1)$, and $U = Z\sqrt{n/Y}$. The joint density of Y and Z is

$$f(y, z) = ke^{-z^2/2} y^{n/2-1} e^{-y/2},$$

where k denotes the combined constants of the densities of Y and Z. From this point on we shall ignore the value of k and other multiplied constants, denoting them by the letters k', k'', etc., without being concerned about their values. The multiplied constant will necessarily turn out to be the factor required to make the total area or volume equal to unity.

In order to apply (36.2), we have $u = g(y, z) = z\sqrt{n/y}$, and the

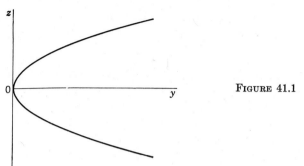

FIGURE 41.1

inverse function is $z = h(y, u) = u\sqrt{y/n}$ so that $\partial z/\partial u = \sqrt{y/n}$. Hence, using (36.2), we have

$$\phi(u) = k\int e^{-u^2 y/2n} y^{n/2-1} e^{-y/2} \sqrt{y/n}\, dy$$

$$= k\int y^{(n-1)/2} e^{-(u^2(y/n)+y)/2}\, dy.$$

Now y must run from 0 to ∞. The curves $u = z\sqrt{n/y} = \text{const.}$ are parabolas, as shown in Figure 41.1. We make the substitution

$$v = \frac{y}{2}\left(\frac{u^2}{n} + 1\right).$$

Then

$$dv = \frac{dy}{2}\left(\frac{u^2}{n} + 1\right), \quad dy = \frac{2\,dv}{1 + \dfrac{u^2}{n}},$$

and v goes from 0 to ∞ as y goes from 0 to ∞. By making this substitution,

$$\phi(u) = k'\int_0^\infty \left(\frac{2v}{1 + \dfrac{u^2}{n}}\right)^{(n-1)/2} e^{-v}\, \frac{2\,dv}{1 + \dfrac{u^2}{n}}$$

$$= k''\left(1 + \frac{u^2}{n}\right)^{-(n+1)/2} \int_0^\infty v^{(n-1)/2} e^{-v}\, dv$$

$$= k'''\left(1 + \frac{u^2}{n}\right)^{-(n+1)/2}.$$

This completes the proof.

We are now in a position to prove the following theorem, quoted in Sections 26 and 29.

(41.4) **THEOREM.** *If $\overline{X}$ and S are the mean and standard deviation of a sample of size n from a normal distribution with mean μ, then*

$$t = \frac{\overline{X} - \mu}{s/\sqrt{n}}$$

has the t distribution with $n - 1$ d.f.

Proof. Since X has mean μ, it follows that the quantity $Y = X - \mu$ has mean zero. Let the variance of X be σ^2. Then the values $Y_1 = X_1 - \mu, \cdots, Y_n = X_n - \mu$ constitute a random sample from $N(0, \sigma^2)$. Hence, according to (39.21), $\overline{Y}$ and $(n - 1)s^2/\sigma^2$ are independently distributed, the first according to $N(0, \sigma^2/n)$, the second according to $CS(n - 1)$. This implies that $\overline{X} = \overline{Y} + \mu$ and $(n - 1)s^2/\sigma^2$ are independently distributed according to $N(\mu, \sigma^2/n)$ and $CS(n - 1)$. We now use (41.3) in order to conclude that

$$t = \frac{\overline{X} - \mu}{\sigma/\sqrt{n}} \sqrt{\frac{\sigma^2}{s^2}} = \frac{\overline{X} - \mu}{s/\sqrt{n}}$$

has the t distribution with $n - 1$ d.f.

In Section 29 use was made of the following application of the t distribution:

(41.5) **THEOREM.** *If $\overline{X}_1$ and $s_1{}^2$ are the mean and variance of a sample of size m from $N(\mu_1, \sigma^2)$ and if $\overline{X}_2$ and $s_2{}^2$ are the mean and variance of a sample of size n from $N(\mu_2, \sigma^2)$, then the quantity*

$$t = \frac{\overline{X}_1 - \overline{X}_2 - (\mu_1 - \mu_2)}{s_p \sqrt{\dfrac{1}{m} + \dfrac{1}{n}}}$$

possesses the t distribution with $m + n - 2$ d.f., where $s_p{}^2$ is the pooled variance defined by

$$s_p{}^2 = \frac{(m - 1)s_1{}^2 + (n - 1)s_2{}^2}{m + n - 2}$$

Proof. Let the samples be $(X_1, \cdots, X_m)$ and $(X_1', \cdots, X_n')$. Then the quantities $Y_1 = X_1 - \mu_1, \cdots, Y_m = X_m - \mu_1$ and $Y_1' = X_1' - \mu_2, \cdots, Y_n' = X_n' - \mu_2$ constitute 2 random samples from $N(0, \sigma^2)$, with means $\overline{Y} = \overline{X}_1 - \mu_1$ and $\overline{Y}_2 = \overline{X}_2 - \mu_2$ and with variances $s_1{}^2$

and $s_2{}^2$. Hence, according to (39.22), $\overline{Y}_1 - \overline{Y}_2 = \overline{X}_1 - \overline{X}_2 - (\mu_1 - \mu_2)$ and $(m + n - 1)s_p{}^2/\sigma^2$ are independently distributed, the first according to $N(0, \sigma^2(1/m + 1/n))$, the second according to $\text{CS}(m + n - 2)$. Using (41.3), we immediately reach the stated conclusion.

One of the most versatile tools at the disposal of the experimenter, for the purposes of analyzing the results of complex experiments, is the analysis of variance. In making tests of significance in an analysis of variance, the basic distribution is the F distribution, defined by

$$(41.6) \quad f_{F(m,n)}(F) = \frac{\Gamma\dfrac{(m+n)}{2}}{\Gamma\left(\dfrac{m}{2}\right)\Gamma\left(\dfrac{n}{2}\right)} \left(\frac{m}{n}\right)^{m/2} F^{m/2-1} \left(1 + \frac{m}{n}F\right)^{-(m+n)/2}.$$

The F distribution possesses two parameters m and n, whose order must always be carefully considered. As will be proved in (41.7), the F distribution with m and n d.f. arises as the distribution of a quantity $U = nY/(mX)$, in whose numerator and denominator are independently distributed variables Y and X, possessing chi-square distributions with m and n d.f., respectively. When we speak of an F distribution with m and n d.f., we always mention *first* the parameter m, which is the degrees of freedom of the quantity Y appearing in the *numerator* of the fraction.

(41.7) THEOREM. *Let X and Y be independently distributed random variables, whose distributions are, respectively, $\text{CS}(n)$ and $\text{CS}(m)$. Then the ratio $U = nY/(mX)$ possesses the F distribution with m and n d.f.*

Proof. As in the proof of (41.3) we shall denote the multiplied constant in the various density functions appearing in the proof by k, k', k'', etc., ignoring the values of these constants, which must always be such as to make the area under the density curve equal to unity. The joint density of X and Y is

$$f(x, y) = kx^{n/2-1}y^{m/2-1}e^{-(x+y)/2}.$$

On the other hand, $u = g(x, y) = ny/(mx)$, so that $y = h(x, u) = mux/n$ and $\partial h/\partial u = mx/n$. Thus from (36.2) we have

$$\phi(u) = k \int x^{n/2-1}(mux/n)^{m/2-1}e^{-(x+mux/n)/2}(mx/n)\,dx.$$

Since the chi-square distribution runs from 0 to ∞, the joint density covers the first quadrant of the xy-plane. The curve $u = ny/(mx)$ is a

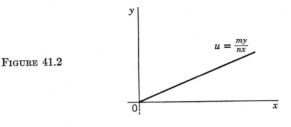

FIGURE 41.2

straight line through the origin (Figure 41.2). Thus, for a fixed value of u, x runs from 0 to ∞. Hence

$$\phi(u) = k' \int_0^\infty x^{n/2+m/2-1} u^{m/2-1} e^{-x(1+mu/n)/2} \, dx.$$

We now make the change of variable $z = x(1 + mu/n)$, so that $dx = dz/(1 + mu/n)$ and z runs from 0 to ∞ as x runs from 0 to ∞. Thus

$$\phi(u) = k' \int_0^\infty \left(\frac{z}{1+mu/n}\right)^{m/2+n/2-1} u^{m/2-1} e^{-z/2} \frac{dz}{1+mu/n}$$

$$= k' u^{m/2-1}(1 + mu/n)^{-(m+n)/2} \int_0^\infty z^{m/2+n/2-1} e^{-z/2} \, dz$$

$$= k'' u^{m/2-1}(1 + mu/n)^{-(m+n)/2},$$

so that U possesses the F distribution with m and n d.f., as stated.

In the consideration of tests of significance in Chapter 4, the only systematic method of selecting a suitable critical statistic was the likelihood ratio method of Section 33. We close this section by showing the close relationship that exists between the quantity t defined in (41.4) and the likelihood ratio statistic λ of Section 33, as applied in Exercise 33.1 to an n-variate normal distribution. For this purpose we replace μ by μ_0 in the expression for t in (41.4), obtaining

$$t = \frac{\bar{X} - \mu_0}{s/\sqrt{n}}, \quad t^2 = \frac{n(\bar{X} - \mu_0)^2}{s^2}.$$

Let us rewrite the quantity λ of Exercise 33.1 by replacing x by X and $\bar{x}$ by $\bar{X}$:

$$\lambda = \left(\frac{\Sigma(X - \bar{X})^2}{\Sigma(X - \mu_0)^2}\right)^{n/2}.$$

We now use the identity (see Exercise 8.4)

$$\Sigma(X - \mu_0)^2 = \Sigma(X - \bar{X})^2 + n(\bar{X} - \mu_0)^2,$$

and write

$$\lambda^{-2/n} = \frac{\Sigma(X - \mu_0)^2}{\Sigma(X - \bar{X})^2} = \frac{\Sigma(X - \bar{X})^2 + n(\bar{X} - \mu_0)^2}{\Sigma(X - \bar{X})^2} = 1 + \frac{n(\bar{X} - \mu_0)^2}{\Sigma(X - X)^2}$$

$$= 1 + \frac{n(\bar{X} - \mu_0)^2}{(n - 1)s^2} = 1 + \frac{t^2}{n - 1}.$$

Thus

$$\lambda = \left(1 + \frac{t^2}{n - 1}\right)^{-n/2}.$$

EXERCISE 41

41.1. X and Y are independent values from $N(0, 1)$. Find $P(Y/X > 3)$ and also $P(Y > 3X)$.

41.2. X and Y are independent values, X from the distribution $N(0, 5)$, Y from the distribution $N(0, 10)$. Find $P(Y/X > 2)$ and also $P(Y > 2X)$.

41.3. Show that, if X is a random variable with the Cauchy distribution, then $Z = 1/X$ also has the Cauchy distribution. [Use (16.1).]

41.4. Show that, if X is a random variable possessing the F distribution with m and n d.f., then $Z = 1/X$ has the F distribution with n and m d.f.

41.5. Use the result of Exercise 41.4 to show that, if $F_{m,n,.95}$ is the 95th percentile of the F distribution with m and n d.f., then $1/F_{m,n,.95}$ is the 5th percentile of the F distribution with n and m d.f. Hence find, from Table 5, the 5th percentile of the F distribution with 5 and 10 d.f.

41.6. Let s_1^2 be the variance of a random sample of size n_1 from a population with distribution $N(\mu_1, \sigma_1^2)$. Let s_2^2 be the variance of a random sample of size n_2 from a population with distribution $N(\mu_2, \sigma_2^2)$. Show that $(s_1^2\sigma_2^2)/(s_2^2\sigma_1^2)$ has the F distribution with $n_1 - 1$ and $n_2 - 1$ d.f. [Use (39.21).]

41.7. A chemist made, on each of two successive days, 10 determinations of the calcium in a certain substance. The variance of the 10 values obtained on the first day was 32.15; the variance of the 10 values obtained on the second day was 21.06. Set up a complete test of the null hypothesis that $\sigma_1^2 = \sigma_2^2$, where σ_1^2 and σ_2^2 are the variances of the populations consisting of all possible determinations on the first day and all possible determinations on the second day. Both populations are assumed to be normal.

41.8. From Table 5, using the method of Exercise 41.5, find the 1st and 99th percentiles of the F distribution with 9 and 9 d.f. Call these $F_{.01}$ and $F_{.99}$. Let σ_1^2 and σ_2^2 be defined as in Exercise 41.7. Let $s_1^2 = 32.15$ and $s_2^2 = 21.06$ be the variances of the two sets of 10 determinations of Exercise 41.7. Then we can state with 98% confidence that

$$F_{.01} \leqq \frac{s_1^2\sigma_2^2}{s_2^2\sigma_1^2} \leqq F_{.99},$$

or

$$F_{.01} \leq \frac{32.15\sigma_2^2}{21.06\sigma_1^2} \leq F_{.99}.$$

Hence find a 98% confidence interval for the ratio σ_2^2/σ_1^2.

41.9. Show that, if t is a random variable possessing the t distribution with n d.f., then t^2 has the F distribution with 1 and n d.f.

41.10. X and Y are independently distributed, X with the distribution $N(5, 15)$ and Y with the distribution CS(5). Find $P(X - 5 > 3\sqrt{Y})$.

*41.11. Let random samples of sizes $m + 1$ and $n + 1$, and with variances $\hat{v}$ and $\hat{w}$ respectively, be drawn from independent normal populations with variances v and w, respectively. Show that the joint density of $\hat{v}$ and $\hat{w}$ is

$$k \left(\frac{\hat{v}}{v} \right)^{m/2-1} \left(\frac{\hat{w}}{w} \right)^{n/2-1} e^{-(m\hat{v}/v + n\hat{w}/w)/2}.$$

*41.12. Use the joint density obtained in Exercise 41.12 to show that the likelihood ratio statistic, λ, for the hypothesis $v = w$ can be expressed

$$\lambda = K \left(1 + \frac{nF}{m} \right)^{-(m+n-4)/2} F^{n/2-1},$$

where K is a constant, and $F = \hat{w}/\hat{v}$.

42. DISTRIBUTIONS OF ORDER STATISTICS

Many of the methods of inference thus far described rest directly on the properties of the normal distribution and depend for their validity on the normality of the underlying population. The exceptions are those methods of inference based on the broad family of distributions which includes the binomial and multinomial distributions, such as, for example, Pearson's chi-square test. The term *non-parametric* is sometimes used for such methods of inference because the familiar parameters (mean, variance) do not enter in directly. The term is better used for the methods of the present section, which avoid any assumptions concerning either the parameters or the form of the distribution of the underlying population.

In the broad sense the term "order statistics" is understood to include such quantities as the median, the quartiles, the percentiles, and in general any quantity that divides the elements of either population or sample, conceived as arrayed in order of magnitude, into two groups with a specified proportion in each group. In a narrower sense the term is used for the actual values of a sample $X_1, \cdots, X_n$ when the values have been arranged in order of magnitude. In this sense, for example, X_1 denotes the smallest value in the sample, and X_n the largest. We shall find in this section that, when order statistics are used for purposes of statistical inference, no knowledge of the form of the population distribution need be assumed. Thus the use of order statistics leads to what may be called *distribution-free* methods.

The basic idea underlying the use of order statistics for statistical inference is very simple. Let Y be a continuous random variable whose 75th percentile is .62, i.e., $P(Y < .62) = .75$. Now suppose that a random sample of size $n = 10$ is drawn from the population. If X is the number of values in the sample which are less than .62, then X will possess the binomial distribution with parameters $n = 10$, $p = .75$, whose frequency function is $f(x) = \binom{10}{x}(.75)^x(.25)^{n-x}$. Note that we are choosing to ignore all information about the original observations except their relation to the value .62. Thus we are in effect converting the given distribution into a dichotomy whose two classes are $Y < .62$ and $Y > .62$. By this means we have shifted our attention from the continuous random variable Y to the discrete random variable X, whose sample space is the set $\{0, 1, \cdots, 10\}$. The fact that the sample space is discrete will alter somewhat our approach to critical regions and levels of significance.

In order to set up a test of significance based on the preceding ideas, we shall denote the 75th population percentile by $\mu_{.75}$ and consider the hypothesis $H_0: \mu_{.75} = .62$, with alternative $H_1: \mu_{.75} < .62$. The one-sided alternative H_1 implies that if the sample contains too few values $< .62$ we shall reject H_0 and conclude that $\mu_{.75} < .62$. Thus a suitable critical statistic is X, the number of sample values falling below .62. In the figure below we represent the sample space by means of 11 dots,

$X=0$	$X=1$	$X=2$	$X=3$	$X=4$	$X=5$	$X=6$	$X=7$	$X=8$	$X=9$	$X=10$
.0000	.0000	.0004	.0031	.0162	.0584	.1460	.2503	.2816	.1877	.0563

whose probabilities are given below them. Suppose we decide on a critical region $X < 3$, as indicated by the 3 black dots at the left of the figure. The probability that X shall fall in this region is .0004, which is the level of significance, α, for the test.

Two important features of this type of test of significance are now evident: first, there are only a finite number of choices for the critical region, since it must be some subset of the sample space; second, there are only a finite number of possible values for α. We note also that these possible values of the level of significance must always be obtained as sums of terms of the binomial distribution.

Example 42.1. Consider again the data of Table 29.1. The 12 values arranged in order of magnitude are: $-4.3, -1.5, -1.4, -1.4, -1.3, -1.2, -1.1,$ $-1.1, -.4, -.3, -.1, .4$. We shall test the hypothesis H_0: $\mu_{.5} = 0$ against the alternative H_1: $\mu_{.5} < 0$. Here $\mu_{.5}$ is the population median. Our critical statistic is X, the number of negative values in the sample. The table below gives possible critical regions R with the corresponding values of α:

R	$X > 12$	$X > 11$	$X > 10$	$X > 9$	$X > 8$	$X > 7$
α	0	.0002	.0032	.0193	.0730	.1938

Each value of α is a sum of terms of the binomial distribution; for example, the last value on the right is $\alpha = P(X > 7) = \sum_{x=8}^{12} \binom{12}{x} (.5)^{12}$. Let us select as critical region $X > 10$ with $\alpha = .0032$. Now, in our example there are $X = 11$ negative values. Hence H_0 is rejected at the .0032 level of significance, and we conclude, as in Example 29.6, that the meal is having an effect on the activity of the heart.

The test that has just been performed is called the *sign test*. It is an extremely simple test to apply, since all that is required is a count of the number of values in the sample on either side of the hypothetical value of the median. It will generally be appropriate to take the hypothetical value as zero, in which case we need only count the number of $+$ and $-$ signs; hence the name of the test. Tables for use with the sign test may be found in Dixon and Massey (4).

We shall next show that instead of using as critical statistic the number of values in the sample which are less than the hypothetical value of the median we may equivalently use the rth order statistic, X_r. The probability that X_r is less than the median is identical with the probability that r or more sample values are less than the median, and this in turn is given by the sum

$$P(X_r < \mu_{.5}) = \sum_{x=r}^{12} \binom{12}{x} (.5)^{12}.$$

The values of this probability are tabulated below; compare with the table in Example 42.1. For a test of significance of the hypothesis H_0: $\mu_{.5} = 0$ we shall be able to select any one of the order statistics

r	1	2	3	4	5	6
$P(X_r < \mu_{.5})$	.9998	.9968	.9807	.9270	.8062	.6128
r	7	8	9	10	11	12
$P(X_r < \mu_{.5})$	.3872	.1938	.0730	.0193	.0032	.0002

$X_1, \cdots, X_{12}$, but we shall not be able to select the critical region, which in every case is simply $X_r < 0$. If we use $\alpha = .0032$, as we did earlier, the appropriate critical statistic will be X_{11}. We shall, in fact, reject H_0 if X_{11} is negative, with a significance of $\alpha = .0032$. This is merely an alternative way of formulating the sign test.

Consider now the problem of testing a hypothesis concerning the $100p$th percentile, which we shall denote by μ_p. Let the hypothesis be $\mu_p = \eta$. Under this hypothesis the number of values exceeding η in a sample of n will possess the binomial distribution. Let $X_1, \cdots, X_n$ be the order statistics of the sample, that is, the values of the sample numbered in order of magnitude. Then

$$P(X_r > \eta) = \sum_{i=0}^{r-1} \binom{n}{i} p^i (1 - p)^{n-i},$$

(42.1)
$$= \text{Probability that, at most, } r - 1 \text{ values are } < \eta.$$

$$P(X_r < \eta) = \sum_{i=r}^{n} \binom{n}{i} p^i (1 - p)^{n-i},$$

$$= \text{Probability that, at least, } r \text{ values are } < \eta.$$

We evidently have here the basis for a test of significance concerning any percentile of the population.

Confidence intervals for population percentiles can readily be constructed on the basis of the binomial distribution. We shall evaluate the probability that μ_p, the $100p$th population percentile, will lie between X_r and X_s, where $r < s$. We know that X_r will be less than μ_p if at least r values lie to the left of μ_p. On the other hand X_s will be greater than μ_p if at least $n - s + 1$ values lie to the right of μ_p, that is, if at most $s - 1$ values fall to the left of μ_p. Thus both these conditions will obtain, namely, $X_r < \mu_p < X_s$, if the number of observations falling to the left of μ_p is any number from r to $s - 1$. Since the probability of a single observation falling to the left of μ_p is p, we have

(42.2) $$P(X_r < \mu_p < X_s) = \sum_{i=r}^{s-1} \binom{n}{i} p^i (1 - p)^{n-i},$$

or more correctly (see Section 31) we may say that X_r and X_s are $100P$ per cent confidence limits for the $100p$th percentile, where

$$P = \sum_{i=r}^{s-1} \binom{n}{i} p^i (1 - p)^{n-i}.$$

Example 42.2. For the data of Table 29.1, test the hypothesis that the 75th percentile of the population of d-values is (a) zero, (b) $-.5$.

Solution. We need all terms of the binomial distribution with $p = .75$, $n = 12$. They are:

x	0	1	2	3	4	5	6	7	8	9	10	11	12
$f(x)$	0	0	0	.0004	.0024	.0115	.0401	.1032	.1936	.2581	.2323	.1267	.0317

Then the probability that the rth order statistic will exceed η, where η is the hypothetical value of the 75th percentile, is

$$P(X_r > \eta) = \sum_{x=0}^{r-1} f(x).$$

From the values tabulated above we find the following values for $P(X_r > \eta)$:

r	1	2	3	4	5	6	7	8	9	10	11	12
$P(X_r > \eta)$	0	0	0	.0004	.0028	.0143	.0544	.1576	.3512	.6093	.8416	.9683

(a) Choose as critical statistic the number T of values in the sample exceeding zero. For our sample $T = 1$. But $P(X_{12} > 0) = .9683$. Hence with $\alpha = .9683$ the null hypothesis is accepted.

(b) Choose as critical statistic the number t of values exceeding $-.5$. For the sample $t = 4$. Actually $X_9 > -.5$. But $P(X_9 > -.5)$ under the null hypothesis is .3512, and so we accept the null hypothesis. If we want to work with a value of α smaller than .05, we choose $\alpha = .0143$, and from the second table above we find $P(X_6 > \eta) = .0143$. But for our sample $X_6 = -1.2$. Hence the hypothesis H_0: $\eta = \mu_{.75} = -1.25$ would be rejected. This sample is unlikely to have come from a population in which $\mu_{.75} = -1.25$.

Example 42.3. Returning to the data of Example 29.6, which were arranged as order statistics at the beginning of this section, let us form a confidence interval for the 75th population percentile $\mu_{.75}$, using as confidence limits the first and final order statistics, $X_1 = -4.3$ and $X_{12} = .4$. In order to obtain the confidence coefficient for this interval, we must, from (42.2), evaluate

the sum $\sum_{i=1}^{11} \binom{12}{i} (.75)^i (.25)^{12-i}$. Since only the first and last terms of the

complete binomial expansion are missing from this sum, the result is easily found to be .968, using the table in Example 42.1. Thus the confidence coefficient is 96.8%.

In Exercises 42.4 and 42.5, a method is outlined for evaluating such sums of binomial probabilities as are involved in (42.1) and (42.2) by means of the *incomplete beta function*, namely, the integral

$$(42.3) \qquad I_p(\alpha, \beta) = \frac{1}{B(\alpha, \beta)} \int_0^p x^{\alpha-1}(1 - x)^{\beta-1} \, dx.$$

The name arises from the evident relation of this integral to the beta function (17.7). Tables of the incomplete beta function are provided, for example, in E. S. Pearson and H. O. Hartley, *Biometrika Tables for Statisticians*, Vol. I (Cambridge University Press, 1956).

EXERCISE 42

42.1. The following are the first 10 observations of background radiation in the table of Exercise 4.2: 7, 8, 14, 9, 4, 8, 12, 10, 6, 8. Order the sample, and thus determine the following order statistics: X_1, X_3, X_5, X_9, X_{10}.

42.2. The table below gives the complete binomial distribution for $n = 10$, $p = .5$:

X	0	1	2	3	4	5	6	7	8	9	10
Prob.	.0010	.0098	.0439	.1172	.2051	.2461	.2051	.1172	.0439	.0098	.0010

(a) Test the hypothesis that the median of the population from which the sample in Exercise 42.1 was drawn is actually $\mu_{.5} = 10$, against the alternative $\mu_{.5} < 10$.

(b) Find the confidence coefficient associated with a confidence interval whose limits are the second- and ninth-order statistics, $X_2 = 6$ and $X_9 = 12$.

42.3. The following table gives the complete binomial distribution for $n = 10$ and $p = .6$:

X	0	1	2	3	4	5	6	7	8	9	10
Prob.	.0001	.0016	.0106	.0425	.1115	.2007	.2508	.2150	.1209	.0403	.0060

(a) Test the hypothesis that the 60th percentile of the population from which the sample in Exercise 42.1 is drawn is actually $\mu_{.6} = 6$, against the alternative $\mu_{.6} > 6$.

(b) Use the third- and eighth-order statistics to form a confidence interval for the 60th percentile, and find the confidence coefficient.

42.4. Prove the identity

$$\sum_{i=\alpha}^{n} \binom{n}{i} p^i (1 - p)^{n-i} = I_p(\alpha, n - \alpha + 1).$$

Use repeated integration by parts on the integral which represents the right-hand side. The first such integration is

$$\int_0^p x^{a-1}(1 - x)^{n-\alpha}\, dx = \frac{1}{\alpha} p^\alpha (1 - p)^{n-\alpha} + \frac{n - \alpha}{\alpha} \int_0^p x^\alpha (1 - x)^{n-\alpha-1}\, dx.$$

42.5. Prove the identity

$$\sum_{i=r}^{s-1} \binom{n}{i} p^i (1 - p)^{n-i} = I_p(r, n - r + 1) - I_p(s, n - s + 1).$$

*43. HIGHER MOMENTS OF A SUM

In Section 27 we saw that the mean of a sum of independent random variables was given by the sum of the means, and the variance by the sum of the variances. No such simple rule obtains for the higher moments. We shall obtain the necessary formulas in this section and show how they may be simplified in the case for which all the variables possess the same distribution. This will be a preliminary to the proof, in the next section, of the important central limit theorem.

As a preliminary example, consider the third moment of the sum of 4 random variables $E(X_1 + X_2 + X_3 + X_4)^3$. In an expression such as this one, it will always be understood that the expression is to be cubed before its expectation is evaluated. We may use the multinomial theorem (7.13) in order to evaluate the cube. We find

$$
\begin{aligned}
(X_1 + X_2 + X_3 + X_4)^3 = {} & X_1{}^3 + X_2{}^3 + X_3{}^3 + X_4{}^3 + 3X_1X_2{}^2 \\
& + 3X_1{}^2X_2 + 3X_1X_3{}^2 + 3X_1{}^2X_3 \\
& + 3X_1X_4{}^2 + 3X_1{}^2X_4 + 3X_2X_3{}^2 \\
& + 3X_2{}^2X_3 + 3X_2X_4{}^2 + 3X_2{}^2X_4 \\
& + 3X_3X_4{}^2 + 3X_3{}^2X_4 + 6X_1X_2X_3 \\
& + 6X_1X_2X_4 + 6X_1X_3X_4 \\
& + 6X_2X_3X_4.
\end{aligned}
$$

We are primarily interested in the case in which all 4 X's possess the same distribution. In this case the expectations of the first 4 terms in the above expansion will each equal μ_3', the third moment of the distribution. Similarly the expectations of the next 12 terms will each equal $3\mu\mu_2'$; and finally the expectations of the last 4 terms will each equal $6\mu^3$. Thus, combining these identical terms, we obtain

$$
E(X_1 + \cdots + X_4)^3 = 4\mu_3' + 36\mu\mu_2' + 24\mu^3.
$$

Let us proceed immediately to the general case. Here we must evaluate $E(X_1 + \cdots + X_n)^k$. According to the multinomial theorem

$$
(X_1 + \cdots + X_n)^k = \sum \frac{k!}{e_1! \cdots e_n!} X_1{}^{e_1} \cdots X_n{}^{e_n},
$$

where the summation is over all possible partitions of k as a sum of n positive integers $e_1 + \cdots + e_n = k$. Under the assumption that the X's are independently distributed,

(43.1)

$$E(X_1 + \cdots + X_n)^k = \sum \frac{k!}{e_1! \cdots e_n!} E(X_1)^{e_1} E(X_e)^{e_2} \cdots E(X_n)^{e_n}.$$

Assuming that all the X's possess the same distribution, we may combine into a single term all the terms on the right of (43.1) which possess the same set of exponents $e_1, \cdots, e_n$ permuted in different orders. This is precisely what happened in the particular example considered earlier in this section. In order to determine the number of such combinable terms, let a_0 be the number of zeros in the sequence $e_1, \cdots, e_n$, let a_1 be the number of 1's, a_2 the number of 2's, $\cdots$, a_k the number of k's. We need to know the number of ways of permuting n things (the exponents $e_1, \cdots, e_n$) of which a_0 are alike of one kind, a_1 are alike of another, $\cdots$, a_k alike of another. According to (7.6) this is $n!/a_0!a_1! \cdots a_k!$. Using this result and assuming that all the X's possess the same distribution,

$$(43.2) \quad E(X_1 + \cdots + X_n)^k = \sum \frac{k!}{e_1! \cdots e_n!} \frac{n!}{a_0! \cdots a_k!} \mu_1^{a_1} \cdots \mu_k^{a_k},$$

where now the summation is over all sets of e's and a's such that

$$(43.3) \qquad e_1 + \cdots + e_n = a_1 + 2a_2 + \cdots + ka_k = k,$$

$$a_0 + \cdots + a_k = n.$$

Example 43.1. Use (43.2) and (43.3) to obtain $E(X_1 + \cdots + X_4)^3$.
Solution. We make up a table which shows each possible set of exponents $e_1, \cdots, e_4$ and the associated set of values $a_0, \cdots, a_3$. From them the coefficients are immediately computed by means of (43.2). Note that, as a check, the sum of all the exponents should equal $n^k = 4^3 = 64$.

e_1	e_2	e_3	e_4	a_0	a_1	a_2	a_3	First Factor	Second Factor	Coefficient
3	0	0	0	3	0	0	1	1	4	4
2	1	0	0	2	1	1	0	3	12	36
1	1	1	0	1	3	0	0	6	4	24
										—
										64

In the above table, "first factor" stands for $k!/e_1! \cdots e_n!$, and "second factor" stands for $n!/a_0! \cdots a_k!$. The answer is the same as obtained above.

Example 43.2. Find $E(X_1 + \cdots + X_6)^5$.
Solution. We make a table similar to that in Example 43.1. Zeros have been omitted.

e_1	e_2	e_3	e_4	e_5	e_6	a_0	a_1	a_2	a_3	a_4	a_5	First Factor	Second Factor	Coefficient
5						5					1	1	6	6
4	1					4	1			1		5	30	150
3	2					4		1	1			10	30	300
3	1	1				3	2		1			20	60	1200
2	2	1				3	1	2				30	60	1800
2	1	1	1			2	3	1				60	60	3600
1	1	1	1	1		1	5					120	6	720
														7776

We check that $n^k = 6^5 = 7776$. Thus we have found

$$E(X_1 + \cdots + X_6)^5 = 6\mu_5' + 150\mu\mu_4' + 300\mu_3'\mu_2' + 1200\mu^2\mu_3' + 1800\mu\mu_2'^2$$
$$+ 3600\,\mu^3\mu_2' + 720\mu^5.$$

EXERCISE 43

43.1. Find the following moments of sums in terms of the moments $\mu = \mu_1'$, μ_2', μ_3', μ_4', $\cdots$, where X_1, X_2, and X_3 possess the same distribution:

(a) $E(X_1 + X_2)^3$ (b) $E(X_1 + X_2)^4$ (c) $E(X_1 + X_2)^5$
(d) $E(X_1 + X_2 + X_3)^3$ (e) $E(X_1 + X_2 + X_3)^4$

43.2. The moment generating function may be used to find $E(X_1 + X_2)^3$ in the following way. The m.g.f. of $X_1 + X_2$ is M^2 [by (27.24)], where M is the m.g.f. of X. According to (12.4) we need to find the third derivative of M^2; let us use the operator D to designate differentiation:

$$D(M^2) = 2MDM, \quad D^2(M^2) = 2MD^2M + 2(DM)^2,$$
$$D^3(M^2) = 2MD^3M + 6DMD^2M.$$

Evaluated for $t = 0$,

$$M = 1, \quad DM = \mu, \quad D^2M = \mu_2', \quad D^3M = \mu_3'.$$

Hence
$$E(X_1 + X_2)^3 = D^3(M^2)\,|_{t=0} = 2\mu_3' + 6\mu\mu_2'.$$

Apply this method to Exercise 43.1*b*, *c*, *d*, and *e*.

*44. THE CENTRAL LIMIT THEOREM

The central limit theorem is one of the most intriguing results in all mathematics, one which for 200 years has commanded the ingenuity of able mathematicians the world over for its analysis. Actually there are many forms of the theorem, and we shall deal only with one of the simpler forms, which is all that we require for the kinds of statistical inference discussed in this book. We shall first describe the result intuitively, in terms of an urn model, before proceeding toward its proof. Assume that we have a number of identical urns, let us say a dozen, each containing the same number of balls. We may number the balls in the first of these urns in any manner we please, so that the distribution of values in the urn has quite a wild-looking histogram, far from normal. Then we number the balls in each of the other urns in exactly the same way as those in the first so that we have a dozen repetitions of the same urn. We then perform the following experiment: Draw a ball at random from each urn, add the values and write down the result, then return each ball to the urn from which it came. If this experiment is performed a great many times, of course mixing the balls between drawings, we shall find that the distribution of the sums we have obtained will approximate the normal distribution quite closely. Furthermore, by increasing the number of urns we can make the distribution conform even more closely to the normal distribution; we can make it come as close as we please to a true normal distribution by taking a sufficient number of urns. Thus the normal distribution wins out, no matter how much we try to frustrate it by the form of distribution we put in the urns, if only we use a sufficient number of urns. It will be recognized that this result is a generalization of the similar result proved in Section 34 for the binomial distribution. In that special case, each of our urns would contain balls with just 2 numbers, 0 and 1.

In this section we shall give a combinatorial (i.e., algebraic) proof of the central limit theorem, for the case in which all moments of the parent distribution exist. This is the only case with which we really need be concerned, for it includes virtually all the distributions we have dealt with; the only exception is the Cauchy distribution. The proof will be based on the formula (43.2) developed in the last section for the kth moment of a sum of n independent random values from the same population. It should be noted that (43.2) is primarily a general theorem on moments, which holds whether the variables involved are discrete or continuous. Proofs of the central limit theorem based on moment generating functions are given in Mood (12), Hoel (9), and Wilks (15); a proof based on the characteristic function is given in Cramér (3) and is sketched in Wilks. The proof based on moment generating functions requires all the moments of the parent distribution to exist, while that based on characteristic functions requires only that the second moment exists. (See Exercises 44.1–44.3.)

We shall make the simplifying assumption that the original population has zero mean and unit variance. This can always be brought about by means of a linear transformation (Section 8). The first and second moments of a sum of n independent values from the population will be

$$E(X_1 + \cdots + X_n) = 0, \quad E(X_1^2 + \cdots + X_n^2) = n.$$

Thus, although the mean of the sum is stable with increase of n, the variance is not. Consequently there can be no possibility of the distribution of this sum tending toward a limit as $n \to \infty$. In order to correct this condition, we shall deal with the quantity $Z_n = (1/\sqrt{n}) \times (X_1 + \cdots + X_n)$. We immediately verify that $E(Z_n) = 0$ and $E(Z_n)^2 = 1$. The result which we must prove is the following:

(44.1) THEOREM. CENTRAL LIMIT THEOREM. *Let $X_1, \cdots, X_n$ be independent values from a distribution all of whose moments exist and for which $E(X) = 0$, $E(X^2) = 1$. Let $Z_n = (1/\sqrt{n})(X_1 + \cdots + X_n)$. Then the limiting distribution of Z_n, as $n \to \infty$, is $N(0, 1)$.*

The proof will depend on showing that the moments of Z_n approach those of the distribution $N(0, 1)$ as $n \to \infty$. From Exercise 19.9 we note that for $N(0, 1)$

$$(44.2) \quad \mu'_{2n+1} = 0, \quad \mu'_{2n} = 1 \cdot 3 \cdot 5 \cdot \cdots \cdot (2n - 1), \quad n = 0, 1, 2, \cdots.$$

It will be assumed that, if we have a density $f_n(x)$ whose moments approach those of the density $f(x)$ as $n \to \infty$, then $f_n(x) \to f(x)$ as $n \to \infty$.

Let us first work with the general even moment,

$$(44.3) \quad E(Z_n)^{2k} = E\left[\frac{X_1 + \cdots + X_n}{\sqrt{n}}\right]^{2k} = n^{-k} E(X_1 + \cdots + X_n)^{2k}.$$

We shall assume that $n > k$; this involves no restriction since n will approach ∞. According to (43.2) the expression in (44.3) possesses an expansion involving the moments of the original distribution. We propose to show that all terms of this expansion, *except one*, will approach zero as $n \to \infty$. The exceptional term is that for which the non-zero exponents consist solely of 2's:

$$e_1 = e_2 = \cdots = e_k = 2, \quad e_{k+1} = e_{k+2} = \cdots = e_n = 0$$

so that

$$a_0 = n - k, \quad a_2 = k, \quad a_1 = a_3 = a_4 = \cdots = a_{2k} = 0.$$

Note that a_1 must be zero for a non-zero term to result since we have assumed $E(X) = 0$. Writing this particular term first, we have, remembering that $\mu_2 = 1$,

(44.4) $E(Z_n)^{2k} = n^{-k} \dfrac{(2k)!}{2!2! \cdots 2! \, k!(n-k)!} \dfrac{n!}{} + $ other terms.

Let T designate the term shown on the right of (44.4), which may be written

$$T = \frac{(2k)!}{2^k k!} \frac{n(n-1) \cdots (n-k+1)}{n^k}$$

$$= \frac{(2k)!}{2^k k!} \frac{n}{n} \cdot \frac{n-1}{n} \cdot \frac{n-2}{n} \cdot \cdots \cdot \frac{n-k+1}{n}$$

$$= \frac{(2k)!}{2^k k!} 1 \left(1 - \frac{1}{n}\right)\left(1 - \frac{2}{n}\right) \cdots \left(1 - \frac{k-1}{n}\right).$$

It is evident that, as $n \to \infty$,

$$T \to \frac{(2k)!}{2^k k!} = \frac{1 \cdot 2 \cdot 3 \cdot 4 \cdot \, \cdots \, \cdot (2k-1)2k}{2 \cdot 4 \cdot 6 \cdot \, \cdots \, \cdot 2k} = 1 \cdot 3 \cdot 5 \cdot \, \cdots \, \cdot (2k-1).$$

According to (44.2), this is the $2k$th moment, μ_{2k}, of $N(0, 1)$. Thus our proof for the even moments will be complete if we can show that the "other terms" on the right of (44.4) all vanish as $n \to \infty$.

We have already noted that a_1, the exponent of μ, must be zero since we have assumed $E(X) = 0$. Thus (43.3) becomes

$$a_0 + a_2 + a_3 + \cdots + a_{2k} = n$$

$$2a_2 + 3a_3 + \cdots + 2ka_{2k} = 2k$$

Eliminating a_2 from these equations and solving for a_0, we obtain

(44.5) $a_0 = n - k + \frac{1}{2}(a_3 + 2a_4 + \cdots + 2(k-1)a_{2k}).$

The term T which we have been considering is the one for which all the e's are either 0 or 2. Any other term must therefore involve e's whose values are other than 0 or 2 and furthermore cannot be 1. Hence for such terms some of the numbers $a_3, a_4, \cdots, a_{2k}$ must be not equal to 0, and by (44.5) it follows that $a_0 > n - k$. This will increase the power of n in the denominator of the term as compared with the power of n in the denominator of T, and as a result terms other than T must vanish as $n \to \infty$. The reader may verify, for example, that the term for which $e_1 = e_2 = 3$, $e_3 = e_4 = \cdots = e_{k-2} = 2$, the remainder of the e's being zero, reduces to an expression in which the part dependent on n is

$$\frac{n(n-1) \cdots (n-k+3)}{n^k}.$$

The highest power of n in the numerator is n^{k-2}, while that in the denominator is n^k.

The argument that all odd moments vanish as $n \to \infty$ is similar to that in the preceding paragraph. Consider, in fact, the term in the expansion of $E(Z_n)^{2k+1}$ for which $e_1 = 3$, $e_2 = e_3 = \cdots = e_k = 2$, the other e's being zero. It may be verified without difficulty that the portion of this term which is dependent on n reduces to

$$\frac{n(n-1) \cdots (n-k+1)}{n^k \sqrt{n}}.$$

Since the highest power of n in the numerator is n^k, while that in the denominator is $n^{k+1/2}$, the term must vanish as $n \to \infty$. Furthermore all other terms in the expansion of $E(Z_n)^{2k+1}$ will involve still higher powers of n in the denominator and will likewise vanish in the limit as $n \to \infty$. This completes the proof.

EXERCISE 44

44.1. Show that, if Z_n is defined as in (44.1), $M_{Z_n}(t) = [M_x(t/\sqrt{n})]^n$.

44.2. Let us assume that the random variable X has zero mean and unit variance so that $\mu = 0, \mu_2' = 1$. Thus the expansion of $M_x(t)$ given in Exercise 19.12 assumes the form

$$M_x(t) = 1 + \frac{t^2}{2} + \text{higher powers of } t.$$

Thus $M_x(t/\sqrt{n})$ may be expanded

$$M_x\left(\frac{t}{\sqrt{n}}\right) = 1 + \frac{t^2}{2n} + \text{terms involving } n^{-2}, n^{-3}, \cdots.$$

Show, using the expansion $\log_e(1 + x) = x - x^2/2 + x^3/3 - \cdots$ and assuming that $|t|$ is sufficiently small for the operations involved to be valid, that

$$\log M_x\left(\frac{t}{\sqrt{n}}\right) = \frac{t^2}{2n} + \text{terms involving } n^{-2}, n^{-3}, \cdots.$$

44.3. Defining Z_n as in (44.1) and using the results of Exercises 44.1 and 44.2, show that

$$\log M_{Z_n}(t) = \frac{t^2}{2} + \text{terms involving } n^{-2}, n^{-3}, \cdots.$$

Hence conclude that $\lim_{n\to\infty} \log M_{Z_n}(t) = t^2/2$ and thus that $\lim_{n\to\infty} M_{Z_n} = e^{t^2/2}$, which is the m.g.f. of the unit normal density. If we now assume that (*a*) a distribution is uniquely determined by its m.g.f. and that (*b*), if a distribution approaches a limiting form as $n \to \infty$, the limit of the m.g.f. of the distribution is equal to the m.g.f. of the limiting distribution, we have proved Theorem

44.1. The assumptions (a) and (b) may be proved to be true at a more advanced level of mathematical statistics.

44.4. Let a discrete random variable Y possess the distribution

$$\begin{Bmatrix} y_1, & \cdots, & y_k \\ x_1, & \cdots, & x_k \end{Bmatrix},$$

where $\Sigma x_i = n$. Use the results of Section 40 to show that the sample mean $\overline{Y} = \frac{1}{n} \Sigma x_i y_i$ is approximately normally distributed. In fact, show that $\Sigma x_i z_i$ is approximately normally distributed, where $z_1, \cdots, z_k$ are arbitrary constants. Use the normal reproductive law (25.5).

CHAPTER 6

Regression and Correlation

45. TYPES OF BIVARIATE DATA

A set of ordered pairs (X_1, X_1), $\cdots$, (X_n, Y_n) will be called a set of bivariate data. Such data may be a sample from a bivariate distribution; this will be the case when X and Y are a pair of measurements made on each member of a random sample from some population. For example, a chemist may make two different kinds of chemical determination, X and Y, on 50 samples of ore taken from a conveyor belt. Both X and Y are subject to random fluctuations; the chemist is not attempting to control either of them in his process of selection. This type of experiment will be called a *correlation experiment*.

In many experiments, however, one of the variables being measured may be controlled by the experimenter with considerable precision. A biologist who studies the growth of an organism *selects* the times at which the measurements are to be made; a physicist *selects* the voltage to be applied to a circuit; an agronomist *selects* the quantity of fertilizer to be applied to a plot. The controlled variable is not reasonably regarded as random, although there undoubtedly remains a small element of randomness due to the imprecision of instruments and human error. This type of experiment will be called a *regression experiment*.

The two examples below provide illustrations of the two types of sets of bivariate data discussed above. Example 45.1 concerns a sample from a bivariate distribution, and in Example 45.2 one variable (in this case, time) is subject to the control of the experimenter.

Example 45.1. Table 45.1 gives the lengths (X) in millimeters and weights (Y) in grams of a sample of 157 lima beans. In Figure 45.1 these pairs of values are graphed. The predominant feature of the graph is the tendency of the points to lie in a rather narrow region sloping from lower left to upper right. When this tendency is present, we say that the graph exhibits *regression*, that is, it exhibits some tendency for high values of X to be associated with high values of Y. This use of the term regression is due to Sir Francis Galton, who

281

TABLE 45.1

LENGTHS IN MM. (X) AND WEIGHTS IN GM. (Y) OF A SAMPLE OF 157 LIMA BEANS

X	Y	X	Y	X	Y	X	Y	X	Y
20.6	1.00	21.7	1.11	23.3	1.47	19.4	.87	18.1	.80
20.6	1.01	22.0	1.30	22.0	1.08	22.5	1.22	20.9	1.11
22.5	1.17	20.6	1.01	19.0	.82	20.5	1.09	20.1	.84
20.1	1.15	22.8	1.58	21.1	.99	22.1	1.23	18.9	.82
19.5	.99	21.5	1.21	20.1	1.01	20.1	.91	23.7	1.45
18.7	.77	22.3	1.25	18.2	.68	19.3	.88	19.0	.94
20.7	1.07	20.3	.93	21.4	1.07	20.0	1.01	22.7	1.10
16.7	.61	21.2	1.00	19.4	.65	18.4	1.01	18.7	.99
19.0	.81	18.5	.77	20.7	1.04	17.8	.75	20.7	1.08
22.1	1.27	21.1	1.10	19.1	.93	18.6	.85	21.8	1.11
19.4	.88	21.3	1.10	20.6	1.01	20.8	.97	23.1	1.35
21.5	1.30	19.6	.86	22.0	1.22	20.6	.91	20.7	1.01
21.2	1.12	21.5	1.18	16.6	.71	20.0	.87	20.5	1.08
17.0	.72	18.7	.74	20.8	1.13	22.5	1.50	23.1	1.36
22.3	1.35	19.8	.92	15.8	.50	19.7	.86	20.7	1.03
22.2	1.18	22.5	1.22	18.9	.96	20.1	.94	19.8	.98
18.6	.74	21.7	1.05	21.1	.95	17.1	.48	19.3	.81
20.8	1.22	23.1	1.28	22.0	1.30	21.3	1.10	21.6	1.06
20.5	1.04	21.4	1.20	20.3	1.09	17.0	.56	21.6	1.12
23.2	1.27	22.2	1.22	20.1	1.00	20.5	1.05	20.6	.95
20.7	1.10	20.7	1.04	21.9	1.17	17.5	.80	18.1	.91
20.9	1.01	22.0	1.31	20.5	1.08	22.0	1.28	20.8	1.24
19.8	.88	21.6	1.19	18.2	.80	20.6	1.08	16.4	.72
19.4	1.00	20.4	.97	18.1	.60	19.7	.88	19.1	.95
20.6	1.11	17.5	.57	21.0	1.05	19.9	.92	16.8	.66
18.7	.99	20.7	1.04	18.7	.81	18.3	.75	20.0	.90
22.3	1.15	19.8	.99	20.2	.91	20.4	1.00	18.0	.59
21.6	1.24	21.1	.92	19.7	.92	20.5	1.10	16.7	.65
20.5	.96	25.1	1.72	21.0	1.10	21.5	.96	21.6	1.11
19.0	.82	21.2	1.17	22.1	1.22	22.6	1.28	23.7	1.62
21.8	1.12	21.8	1.25	20.7	1.05	22.4	1.34	19.4	.88
21.1	.76	19.2	.87						

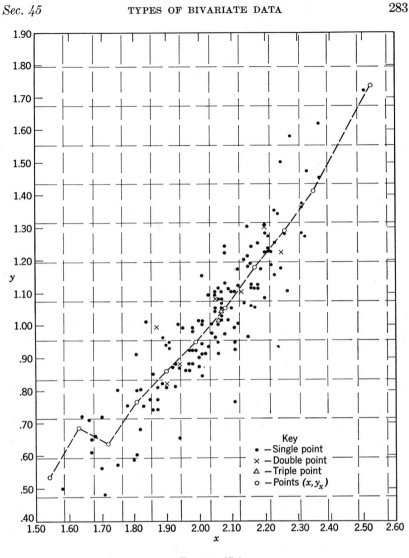

FIGURE 45.1

studied it in connection with the relationship between height of father and height of son.

In Figure 45.1 a grid of horizontal and vertical lines is shown, dividing the plane into rectangular cells. In Figure 45.2 a *solid histogram* is shown, constructed by erecting above each cell of Figure 45.1 a rectangular prism whose height is proportional to the frequency of the cell.

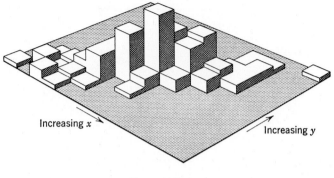

FIGURE 45.2

The solid histogram may be viewed as approximating the probability surface $z = f(x, y)$, which has the same relation to the population as the solid histogram has to the sample.

Example 45.2.   In an experiment to measure the effect of deprivation of thiamin, a subject was maintained on a diet deficient in thiamin while a series of tests of reaction speed was administered.   Table 45.2 shows the result of the experiment.   The units are .02 sec. reaction time, so that a higher score represents poorer performance.

TABLE 45.2

SPEED OF REACTION OF THIAMIN-DEFICIENT SUBJECT

Date	11/18	11/25	12/2	12/7
Time, x	-10	-3	4	9
Score, Y	57.5	67.0	67.0	75.5

The second line of the table gives the time in days from the midpoint of the experiment, denoted by x.   A lower case letter x is used here

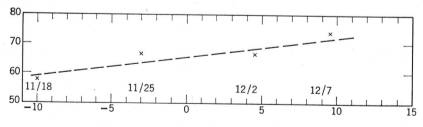

FIGURE 45.3

since the time values are not random but selected by the experimenter. These x-values may be termed the *deviations from mean time*, given by $x = t - \bar{t}$, where t represents the time measured from an arbitrary origin. The use of these time values considerably simplifies later calculations. Figure 45.3 is a graph of the data of Table 45.2. The significance of the straight line which has been inserted will be discussed later.

EXERCISE 45

Classify each of the following experiments as a correlation or a regression experiment.

45.1. The Gross National Product (Y) in the United States is tabulated for the years 1930–1959. X is "years since 1930."

45.2. 100 normal individuals aged 50 are randomly selected and divided into 10 groups, each of which is fed for one week a diet containing a prearranged amount of salt (X). Y is the difference $B_1 - B_2$, where B_1 is the blood pressure at the beginning of the week, B_2 the blood pressure at the end of the week.

45.3. 50 farmers are selected at random and a rain gauge is placed in an alfalfa field of each farm. X = rain in inches during growing season, Y = yield of alfalfa in tons per acre.

45.4. For each of the ages 7, 8, 9, 10, 11, 12, 13, 14, 15, 16 a random sample of 20 children is given a psychological test (Y). X = age.

45.5. Alfalfa is grown on 50 experimental plots. X is "inches of water during growing season," including both rainfall and water applied by means of sprinklers to make a specified total for each plot. Y is yield of alfalfa in tons per acre.

45.6. A random sample of 500 children is given 2 tests, X and Y.

45.7. 1000 individuals aged 50 in a certain city are selected randomly, and the following variables are recorded: X = total amount of salt in weekly diet; Y = systolic blood pressure.

45.8. For 500 factories, selected at random, the number of employees (X) and the gross annual receipts (Y) are recorded.

46. REGRESSION CURVE

We now define, for both types of experiment mentioned in the preceding section, the important concept of the *regression curve*. Consider first a correlation experiment. The pair of random values (X, Y) possess a joint density $f(x, y)$, from which we may find the conditional densities (Section 20):

$$f_1(x|y) = \frac{f(x, y)}{f_2(y)}, \quad f_2(y|x) = \frac{f(x, y)}{f_1(x)}.$$

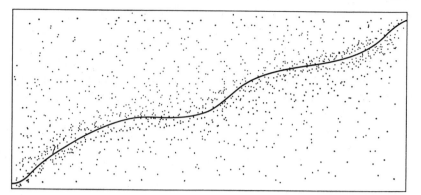

FIGURE 46.1

Let us consider the second of these, the conditional density of y, given x. It gives us the probability distribution of points in the x, y plane along a line parallel to the y-axis. Let $\mu_{y.x}$ and $\sigma_{y.x}^2$ denote the mean and variance of this one-dimensional distribution. When we graph $\mu_{y.x}$ as ordinate against x as abscissa, we obtain a curve such as is shown in Figure 46.1. This curve is known as the *regression of y on x*. In the figure the dots surrounding the curve suggest many repetitions of the random experiment; the dots will, typically, tend to be most dense in the neighborhood of the curve. In a similar way, in order to define the regression of x on y, we define $\mu_{x.y}$ and $\sigma_{x.y}^2$ as the mean and variance of the conditional density of x given y. The regression of x on y is then the curve obtained by graphing $\mu_{x.y}$ as abscissa against y as ordinate.

In Figure 45.1 an estimate of the regression of y on x, known as a *regression polygon*, has been formed by finding, for each interval of X, the mean value of Y for all points whose abscissae fall in the X-interval, which we may denote by $\overline{Y}_{x.}$. If x denotes the midvalue of the X-interval, then the point $(x, \overline{Y}_{x.})$ will approximate the point $(x, \mu_{y.x})$. Thus the polygon obtained by joining a series of such points, one in each interval, will approximate the regression of y on x; this polygon is shown in Figure 45.1 by means of a dashed line.

The regression of y on x may also be defined for a regression experiment, such as that of Example 45.2, in which the time values are selected by the experimenter. Corresponding to each value of x, we conceive of a population of repetitions of the experiment, each yielding a value of Y. The mean and variance of this population of Y-values, $\mu_{y.x}$ and $\sigma_{y.x}^2$, may thus be regarded as functions of x. The graph of

$\mu_{y.x}$ as ordinate against x as abscissa will be called, as before, the regression of y on x. Notice, however, that in this case there is no regression curve of x on y, because variation in the x direction is not random.

A regression polygon, approximating the regression of y on x, may be constructed for an experiment such as that of Example 45.2, provided the number of observations is sufficiently large. More frequently, however, we estimate the regression curve by assuming some analytic form for the equation of the curve. Two approaches are open to us:

(a) The preferred approach is to deduce the analytic form of the curve from known physical, chemical, biological, or other facts about the phenomena under investigation. In the case of the lima bean example, if we assume that larger beans tend to preserve the same proportions as smaller beans and that the density of the beans tends to be independent of size, it follows from simple geometrical considerations that the relation between weight and length will be of the form

$$y = kx^3.$$

Similarly, a scientist with considerable experience in the biochemistry and physiology of thiamin deprivation might be able to suggest a theoretical equation for an "ideal" regression curve for an experiment such as that of Example 45.2.

(b) In the absence of a theoretical basis for the choice of a particular type of curve, we may choose as simple a type of curve as seems to fit the assembly of points. A great deal of the time we shall be content with a straight line as an estimate of the regression curve. In some instances we may use a parabola or an algebraic curve of higher degree; in still others there may be reason for utilizing a logarithmic or exponential type of function. In dealing with data which appear to fluctuate periodically, a trigonometric function might be the appropriate choice.

The process of determining the curve of a specific type which conforms most closely to the data is known as *curve fitting*. At this point we shall confine our attention to the simplest case, namely, that in which we are interested in fitting a straight line to empirical data.

47. THE METHOD OF LEAST SQUARES— MAXIMUM LIKELIHOOD

One of the most widely used methods of curve fitting, and one of the oldest, is the *method of least squares*. At this point we shall consider only the case in which the regression curve is assumed to be a straight line; this is the case of *linear regression*. We shall first concern ourselves with the computational aspects of the method. Then we shall show that when suitable assumptions are made concerning the underlying distribution, the method of least squares will yield the same estimate of the regression coefficients as the method of maximum likelihood.

Suppose that the observational data consist of the n pairs (X_1, Y_1), $\cdots$, (X_n, Y_n). The X-values may be either random or fixed; the Y-values are considered to be random. We are seeking a linear relationship of the form

$$(47.1) \qquad Y' = a + bX$$

which will "best fit" the observed data in some reasonable sense. From (47.1) we obtain, corresponding to the values $X_1, \cdots, X_n$, the following values of Y': $a + bX_1, \cdots, a + bX_n$; these may be termed the estimated values of Y. The difference

$$(47.2) \qquad Y - Y' = Y - a - bX$$

is called the *deviation* of the observed value of Y from the estimated value. Geometrically, if the pairs (X, Y) are represented as points and the equation (47.1) is represented as a line, the deviations (47.2) will be the vertical distances from the points to the line. It is reasonable that we should try to make the deviations, collectively, as small as possible. Suppose we put their sum equal to zero. Then

$$\Sigma(Y - a - bX) = \Sigma Y - na - b\Sigma X = 0.$$

Dividing by n, we obtain

$$(47.3) \qquad \bar{Y} - a - b\bar{X} = 0.$$

This is equivalent to requiring that the line (47.1) go through the point $(\bar{X}, \bar{Y})$, so that the line is incompletely specified. The *principle of least squares* says that a desirable approach is to *minimize the sum of the squares of the deviations* (47.2). Thus we shall minimize

$$(47.4) \quad S = \Sigma(Y - a - bX)^2$$
$$= \Sigma(Y^2 + a^2 + b^2X^2 - 2aY - 2bXY + 2abX)$$
$$= \Sigma Y^2 + na^2 + b^2 \Sigma X^2 - 2a \Sigma Y - 2b \Sigma XY + 2ab \Sigma X.$$

This is a quadratic function of a and b which we may minimize by setting simultaneously equal to zero the partial derivatives of S with regard to a and b. They yield, after division by 2:

(47.5)
$$na + b\,\Sigma X - \Sigma Y = 0$$
$$a\,\Sigma X + b\,\Sigma X^2 - \Sigma XY = 0$$

Note that the first of these equations is equivalent to (47.3) and thus requires the line (47.1) to go through the point $(\overline{X}, \overline{Y})$.

The equations (47.5) are called the *normal equations*. They may be readily solved for a and b, yielding

(47.6) $$a = \frac{\Sigma Y\,\Sigma X^2 - \Sigma X\,\Sigma XY}{n\,\Sigma X^2 - (\Sigma X)^2},\qquad b = \frac{n\,\Sigma XY - \Sigma X\,\Sigma Y}{n\,\Sigma X^2 - (\Sigma X)^2}$$

These values of a and b, substituted in (47.1), yield the *least squares straight line*, or the *regression line*.

Example 47.1.   A simple illustration is provided by the data of Table 45.2, for which $n = 4$. We find the following sums:

$$\Sigma x = 0,\quad \Sigma x^2 = 206,\quad \Sigma Y = 267.0,\quad \Sigma xY = 171.5.$$

The normal equations reduce to:

$$4a - 267.0 = 0,\quad 206b = 171.5,$$

so that

$$a = \frac{267}{4} = 66.75,\quad b = \frac{171.5}{206} = .832.$$

Thus the least square straight line has the equation $Y' = 66.75 + .832x$. This line has been shown as a dashed line in Figure 45.3.

Note that in Example 47.1 the use of the deviation from mean time, for which $\Sigma x = 0$, has resulted in a material simplification of the normal equations, which reduce to

(47.7) $$na - \Sigma Y = 0,\quad b\,\Sigma X^2 - \Sigma XY = 0.$$

In many applications of the method of least squares, it will be found convenient to subtract $\overline{X}$ from each of the values of X in order that $\Sigma X = 0$, with resulting simplification of the normal equations.

Consider now the case in which the $x_1, \cdots, x_n$ are fixed values (for this reason we use small letters) and the values $Y_1, \cdots, Y_n$ have a distribution specified as follows: (a) the regression of y on x is linear, say of the form $\mu_{y.x} = \alpha + \beta x$; (b) the variance of Y for fixed x, $\sigma^2_{y.x}$, is independent of x (let us denote it simply by σ^2); (c) the distribution of Y for fixed x is normal. These assumptions have the consequence that Y_i has the distribution $N(\alpha + \beta x_i, \sigma^2)$, and thus the density

$$\frac{1}{\sqrt{2\pi}\sigma}\,e^{-(y_i - \alpha - \beta x_i)^2/2\sigma^2}.$$

Thus the joint density of $Y_1, \cdots, Y_n$ is

$$(47.8) \qquad L = (2\pi\sigma)^{-n/2} e^{-\Sigma(y_i - \alpha - \beta x_i)^2/2\sigma^2}.$$

In order to form maximum likelihood estimates $\hat{\alpha}$ and $\hat{\beta}$ of α and β, we first note that $\log_e L$ is a quadratic function of α and β:

$$\log_e L = \frac{-n}{2}\log_e (2\pi\sigma) - \sum \frac{(y_i - \alpha - \beta x_i)^2}{2\sigma^2}.$$

We maximize $\log L$ by setting the partial derivatives with respect to α and β equal to zero. Note the algebraic similarity between these operations and those involved in maximizing (47.4). We obtain the two equations for $\hat{\alpha}$ and $\hat{\beta}$:

$$n\hat{\alpha} + \hat{\beta}\,\Sigma x - \Sigma Y = 0$$

$$\hat{\alpha}\,\Sigma x + \hat{\beta}\,\Sigma x^2 - \Sigma x Y = 0.$$

These are seen to be identical with the normal equations (47.5), thus substantiating the statement that for the normal regression model specified at the beginning of this paragraph, the method of least squares leads to the same result as the method of maximum likelihood.

EXERCISE 47

47.1. The following table gives the length Y of a steel bar in millimeters at various centigrade temperatures x:

Temperature, x	20	40	50	60
Length, Y	1000.22	1000.65	1000.90	1001.65

Find the least square relationship $Y' = a + bx$ between Y and x.

47.2. Show that the equation of the least square straight line may be written $Y' - \bar{Y} = b(x - \bar{x})$, where $\bar{x}$ and $\bar{Y}$ are the means of x and Y and where b is given by (47.6).

47.3. Show that $\partial S/\partial a = 0$ and $\partial S/\partial b = 0$ actually produce a minimum of the quadratic function (47.4).

47.4. Making use of the normal equations (47.5), show that the sum of the squares of the deviations S, as given by (47.4), may be expressed in the form $S = \Sigma Y^2 - a\,\Sigma Y - b\,\Sigma X Y$.

47.5. In order to fit the parabola $Y' = a + bx + cx^2$ to a set of points $(x_1, Y_1), \cdots, (x_n, Y_n)$ by the method of least squares, we minimize the sum of squares $S = \Sigma(Y - a - bx - cx^2)^2$, in which the Y's and the x's are fixed and the coefficients a, b, and c are to be chosen so as to minimize S. Show that this leads to the 3 normal equations:

$$\Sigma Y - na - b\,\Sigma x - c\,\Sigma x^2 = 0$$

$$\Sigma x Y - a\,\Sigma x - b\,\Sigma x^2 - c\,\Sigma x^3 = 0$$

$$\Sigma x^2 Y - a\,\Sigma x^2 - b\,\Sigma x^3 - c\,\Sigma x^4 = 0.$$

Investigate the simplification which results when $\Sigma x = 0$.

47.6. The work involved in obtaining a least square relationship may sometimes be reduced by subtracting a suitable constant from the x-values, and another constant from the Y-values. Let $u = x - p$, $V = Y - q$. Show that if $V = d + eu + fu^2$ is a least square relationship between u and V, then $Y - q = d + e(x - p) + f(x - p)^2$ is a least square relationship between x and Y.

47.7. The data shown in the table are from "Report on the Physics and Hydraulics of the Mississippi River," by Humphreys and Abbott. Find a least squares relation of the form $Y' = a + bx + cx^2$ to fit the data.

Fractional Depth x	Velocity, in ft/sec Y
0	3.195
.1	3.230
.2	3.253
.3	3.261
.4	3.252
.5	3.228
.6	3.181
.7	3.127
.8	3.059
.9	2.976

Hint: Use the transformed variables

$$u = x - .45, \quad V = Y - 3.$$

47.8. Generalize the result of Exercise 47.5 for the case in which we are fitting a polynomial of degree k, $Y' = a_0 + a_1 x + \cdots + a_k x^k$ to the data $(x_1, Y_1), \cdots, (x_n, Y_n)$. Obtain the k normal equations.

47.9. Let $u_1, \cdots, u_k$ be controllable variables, whose values are selected by the experimenter, and let Y be the observed variable. Suppose we have n sets of observations: $(Y_1, u_{11}, \cdots, u_{k1}), \cdots (Y_n, u_{1n}, \cdots, u_{kn})$, and wish to find a relation of the form $Y' = a_0 + a_1 u_1 + \cdots + a_k u_k$ by choosing $a_0, a_1, \cdots, a_n$ so as to minimize $S = \Sigma(Y - a_0 - a_1 u_1 - \cdots - a_k u_k)^2$. Find the normal equations.

47.10. In order to treat the situation of Exercise 47.9 by the method of maximum likelihood, assume that Y_i is normally distributed with mean $\alpha_0 + \alpha_1 u_{1i} + \cdots + \alpha_k u_{ki}$ and variance σ^2. Thus the density of Y_i is

$$\frac{1}{\sqrt{2\pi}\sigma} e^{-(y_i - \alpha_0 - \alpha_1 u_{1i} - \cdots - \alpha_k u_{ki})^2/2\sigma}.$$

Form the joint density of $Y_1, \cdots, Y_n$, and regard it as a likelihood function in order to find equations leading to maximum likelihood estimates of α_0, $\alpha_1, \cdots, \alpha_k$. Compare these equations with the normal equations of Exercise 47.9.

48. PARTITION OF THE SUM OF SQUARES

In Section 27 a parameter of a bivariate population known as the correlation coefficient was defined. In this section and the next we shall show how the corresponding statistic emerges naturally for a sample of bivariate data, and we shall also prepare the way for methods of inference from a sample correlation coefficient to a population correlation coefficient. The results in this section will also lead to the sampling distributions of regression coefficients, and thus to methods of inference concerning these coefficients.

The germinal idea is contained in the observation (due primarily to Fisher) that the numerator of the variance of a sample may frequently be subdivided into two or more portions, each portion being related to a particular factor influencing the experiment. Out of this observation grows, as we shall see in Chapter 7, the powerful method known as analysis of variance. We shall first show that $\Sigma(Y - \overline{Y})^2$, the numerator of the variance of Y, can be subdivided into two portions, each of which has a useful interpretation. The quantity $\Sigma(Y - \overline{Y})^2$ with which we shall be working is called a "sum of squares"; hence the heading of this section.

Let us square both members of the algebraic identity

$$(48.1) \qquad Y - \overline{Y} = (Y - Y') + (Y' - \overline{Y}),$$

where Y' is the predicted or estimated value of Y. We obtain

$$(Y - \overline{Y})^2 = (Y - Y')^2 + 2(Y - Y')(Y' - \overline{Y}) + (Y' - \overline{Y})^2.$$

We now sum over all values of Y in the sample. It may be shown (see Exercise 48.2) that, in view of the normal equations, $\Sigma(Y - Y') \times (Y' - \overline{Y}) = 0$. Thus we have

$$(48.2) \qquad \Sigma(Y - \overline{Y})^2 = \Sigma(Y - Y')^2 + \Sigma(Y' - \overline{Y})^2.$$

We now consider separately each of the terms in (48.2). The quantity $\Sigma(Y - \overline{Y})^2$ we shall call the *total sum of squares*. Since $Y - Y'$ is the deviation of the point (X, Y) from the least squares straight line, or regression line, we shall call $\Sigma(Y - Y')^2$ the *sum of squares due to deviation from regression*. The final term, $\Sigma(Y' - \overline{Y})^2$, is readily found to be equal to $b^2 \Sigma(X - \overline{X})^2$. For if we divide the first equation of (47.5) by n we obtain $\overline{Y} = a + b\overline{X}$. Hence $Y' - \overline{Y} = a + bX - (a + b\overline{X}) = b(X - \overline{X})$, so that

$$(48.3) \qquad \Sigma(Y' - \overline{Y})^2 = b^2 \Sigma(X - \overline{X})^2.$$

Because of (48.3) we shall call $\Sigma(Y' - \overline{Y})^2$ the *sum of squares due to regression*. Thus we may verbalize (48.2) as follows:

Total sum of squares = Sum of squares due to deviation from regression + Sum of squares due to regression.

We have already pointed out that the method of least squares is applicable whether we are dealing with data from a correlation experiment or from a regression experiment. Thus (48.2) is valid in either of these cases. We shall, however, make quite different use of (48.2) in the two cases. In the next section we shall see how the correlation coefficient may be defined in terms of the ratio of the "sum of squares due to regression" to the "total sum of squares." In Section 51, on the other hand, we shall test the significance of the regression coefficient by a comparison of the "sum of squares due to regression" and the "sum of squares due to deviation from regression."

Example 48.1. The table below reproduces, in the first two lines, the data of Example 45.2. The values of Y' are calculated from the regression equation

x	-10	-3	4	9
Y	57.5	67.0	67.0	75.5
Y'	58.43	64.25	70.08	74.24
$Y - Y'$	$-.93$	2.75	-3.08	1.26
$Y' - \overline{Y}$	-8.32	-2.50	3.33	7.49
$Y - \overline{Y}$	-9.25	.25	.25	8.75

$Y' = 66.75 + .832x$, as obtained in Example 47.1. The final 3 lines of the table are formed from the values of Y, Y', and $\overline{Y} = 66.75$. From these values we obtain

$$\Sigma(Y - \overline{Y})^2 = 162.25, \quad \Sigma(Y - Y')^2 = 19.50, \quad \Sigma(Y' - \overline{Y})^2 = 142.66.$$

These three sums of squares do not quite fulfill (48.2), due to the accumulation of rounding errors.

EXERCISE 48

48.1. For the (artificial) data in the table, find the least squares relation $Y' = a + bx$. From this equation, obtain the values of Y' in the final line of the table. Calculate, independently, the three sums of squares $\Sigma(Y - \bar{Y})^2$, $\Sigma(Y - Y')^2$, and $\Sigma(Y' - \bar{Y})^2$, and verify that they satisfy (48.2).

x	-2	-1	0	1	2
Y	3	7	8	12	15
Y'					

48.2. Use the equations $Y - Y' = Y - a - bx$ and $Y' - Y = b(X - X)$ and the normal equations to show that $\Sigma(Y - Y')(Y' - \bar{Y}) = 0$.

48.3. Show that, if we square both sides of the equation $Y = (Y - Y') + (Y' - \bar{Y}) + \bar{Y}$ and add, we obtain the identity

$$\Sigma Y^2 = \Sigma(Y - Y')^2 + \Sigma(Y' - \bar{Y})^2 + n\bar{Y}^2.$$

(Note that one must show that several sums of products vanish.) This identity may also be obtained using (48.2) and the identity in Exercise 8.3.

48.4. Assume that the following table gives the 10 pairs of values (x, y) resulting from a correlation experiment:

x	6	9	10	7	7	6	8	10	7	6
y	10	15	15	12	11	9	10	16	13	10

Find the least square relation $Y' = a + bX$, and thus obtain the values of Y' corresponding to the given values of X. Calculate, independently, the sums of squares $\Sigma(Y - \bar{Y})^2$, $\Sigma(Y - Y')^2$, and $\Sigma(Y' - \bar{Y})^2$, and verify that they satisfy (48.2).

48.5. For the case in which $\Sigma x = 0$, show that the "sum of squares due to regression" may be obtained from the formula:

$$\Sigma(Y' - \bar{Y})^2 = \frac{(\Sigma x Y)^2}{\Sigma x^2}.$$

48.6. In the general case, show that the "sum of squares due to regression" may be obtained from the formula:

$$\Sigma(Y' - \bar{Y})^2 = \frac{(n \Sigma XY - \Sigma X \Sigma Y)^2}{n(n \Sigma X^2 - (\Sigma X)^2)}$$

49. COEFFICIENT OF CORRELATION

In Section 27 a parameter, known as the correlation, ρ, was defined for the joint distribution of random variables X and Y. The vanishing of ρ was found to be a necessary, but not a sufficient, condition for the independence of X and Y. In this section we shall consider the corresponding statistic, denoted by r, and called the *coefficient of correlation*.

Consider again equation (48.2). We have already observed that of the two terms on the right, the first depends on the deviations from the regression line, the second on the slope of the regression line. It is reasonable to assume that neither $\Sigma(X - \overline{X})^2$ nor $\Sigma(Y - \overline{Y})^2$ vanishes for the set of data with which we are concerned. The second of these assumptions implies that the terms on the right of (48.2) are not simultaneously zero. If all of the given points were collinear, the first of the terms on the right of (48.2) would vanish; if the slope were zero the second term would vanish. Thus the ratio

$$(49.1) \qquad r^2 = \frac{\Sigma(Y' - \overline{Y})^2}{\Sigma(Y - \overline{Y})^2} = b^2 \frac{\Sigma(X - \overline{X})^2}{\Sigma(Y - \overline{Y})^2}$$

varies from zero, when $b = 0$, to 1, when the points are collinear. The statistic r^2 may therefore be regarded as a measure of the collinearity of the given set of points (X, Y). The coefficient of correlation, r, may now be defined by taking the square root of each member of (49.1):

$$(49.2) \qquad r = b \sqrt{\frac{\Sigma(X - \overline{X})^2}{\Sigma(Y - \overline{Y})^2}} = b \frac{s_x}{s_y}.$$

Thus, by definition, r has the same sign as b.

Note that r may be looked upon as a measure of the "goodness of fit" of the given points to the least squares straight line, since it is equal to ± 1 only when the points are collinear.

Example 49.1. Let us find the coefficient of correlation between X and Y for the first 20 pairs (X, Y) of Table 45.1, that is, the pairs $(20.6, 1.00)$, $(20.6, 1.01)$, $\cdots$, $(23.2, 1.27)$. We find the following sums: $\Sigma X = 407.2$, $\Sigma Y = 20.67$, $\Sigma X^2 = 8349.98$, $\Sigma Y^2 = 22.2531$, $\Sigma XY = 427.574$. From these, we readily obtain in succession: $s_x = 1.768$, $s_y = .2165$, $b = .1134$, $r = .9257$.

The usefulness of the coefficient of correlation is severely limited by the difficulty of interpreting it. What can we conclude from the fact that the correlation coefficient is .9257 in Example 49.1? We can test the hypothesis that the data are drawn from a bivariate population for which $\rho = 0$. We use the fact that if $\rho = 0$ (and thus $\beta = 0$), then

$$F = \frac{(n - 2)r^2}{1 - r^2}$$

has the F distribution with 1 and $n - 2$ d.f. (see Exercise 51.4). Suppose we decide to test the hypothesis $\rho = 0$ at the 1% level of significance. We find that, with 1 and 18 d.f., $F_{.99} = 8.29$. On the other hand, the sample value of F is $F = 18(.857)/.143 = 107.9$. So we decisively reject the null hypothesis. But this fact is of little use to someone who wishes an interpretation of the significance of the statement $r = .9257$.

EXERCISE 49

49.1. Show that, if the *sample covariance* cov(x, y) of X and Y is defined analogously to Definition (27.12)

$$\text{cov}(X, Y) = \frac{1}{n}\Sigma XY - X \cdot Y = \frac{1}{n^2}(n\,\Sigma XY - (\Sigma X)(\Sigma Y)),$$

the correlation between X and Y is given by $r = \text{cov}(X, Y)/(D(X) \cdot D(Y))$.

49.2. Show that the coefficient of correlation is given by

$$r = \frac{n\,\Sigma XY - (\Sigma X)(\Sigma Y)}{\sqrt{(n\,\Sigma X^2 - (\Sigma X)^2)(n\,\Sigma Y^2 - (\Sigma Y)^2)}}.$$

49.3. Show that, if the variables X and Y are subjected to linear transformations $X = aU + b$, $Y = cV + d$, the covariances cov(X, Y) and cov(U, V) bear the following relation to each other: cov(X, Y) = ac cov(U, V). Use this result together with (8.9) to show that the coefficient of correlation is unaffected by a linear transformation of both variables.

49.4. Let the variables U and V be defined by

$$U = \frac{X - X}{D(X)}, \quad V = \frac{Y - Y}{D(Y)}.$$

Show that the correlation between X and Y is given by

$$r_{XY} = \frac{1}{n}\Sigma UV.$$

49.5. Two standard mathematics tests, X and Y, were administered to 19 members of a freshman mathematics class, with the following results:

X	55	62	59	40	43	56	58	52	34	64
Y	58	58	59	63	70	67	70	61	51	70

X	43	54	40	50	50	56	55	43	26
Y	67	67	56	68	56	71	67	74	52

(a) Graph the 19 pairs of values.
(b) Find the least square regression relation $Y' = a + bx$.
(c) Find the coefficient of correlation.

49.6. For a set of pairs (X_1, Y_1), $\cdots$, (X_n, Y_n), let $Y' = a + bX$ be the least square straight line obtained as in Section 47, and let $X' = c + dY$ be the least square straight line obtained by minimizing the sum of squares of deviations in the X-direction. The first of these lines is often called the *regression of Y on X*, the second the *regression of X on Y*. Show that r, the coefficient of correlation, is given by $r = \pm\sqrt{bd}$, where the sign, $+$ or $-$, is that possessed by both b and d.

50. GROUPED DATA

In Chapter 2 the method of grouping data was found convenient where the number of observations was sufficiently large (say $n > 50$). Similarly with bivariate data, where the number of pairs is fairly large, we may profitably set up systems of intervals for both X and Y.

Consider Example 45.1, with $n = 157$. The X-values for this example were dealt with in Chapter 2; we use here the same set of intervals for X. Since the range of Y is from .48 to 1.72, that is, 1.24 gm., we shall use an interval size of $\Delta Y = .12$ gm., and the following set of 11 intervals: .48 − .59, .60 − .71, $\cdots$, 1.68 − 1.79. In Figure 45.1, a *grid*, or system of rectangles (cells), has been superimposed on the graph at the boundaries of the X- and Y-intervals. Thus the 157 points are distributed among the cells, and the numbers, or *cell frequencies*, are recorded in Table 50.1 in the upper left of each cell. In the bottom margin of the table are the totals for each column. This series of numbers, here denoted by f_x, is identical with the set of frequencies in Table 13.2. Similarly, in the right margin of the table are the row totals, f_y, which are the grouped frequencies for the weights Y of the lima beans. These two sets of values are, because of their position, called the *marginal frequencies* of the table. From them we can calculate the mean and variance of X and Y by the methods of Chapter 2. This requires a code to be set up for both X and Y. Let u denote the code for X, v the code for Y. The base value for X is $X_0 = 2.08$, as before; that for Y is $Y_0 = 1.015$. These are simply the mid-values of the intervals to which the zero code values are assigned. The calculation of the mean and variance of X has already been carried out in Table 13.3; the corresponding calculation of the mean, variance, and standard deviation of Y is as follows:

$$n = 157, \quad \Sigma f_y v = 10, \quad \Sigma f_y v^2 = 532, \quad \bar{v} = \frac{10}{157} = .06369,$$

$$D^2(v) = \frac{(157 \times 532 - 10^2)}{157^2} = 3.385, \quad D(v) = 1.840,$$

$$\bar{Y} = \bar{v} \cdot \Delta Y + Y_0 = .12 \times .06369 + 1.015 = 1.0226,$$

$$D(Y) = D(v) \cdot \Delta Y = 1.840 \times .12 = .2208.$$

In Section 13 it was seen that the procedure of coding constitutes a case of linear transformation, as considered in Section 8. In Exercise 49.3 it is asserted that the coefficient of correlation is unaffected by a

TABLE 50.1

CALCULATION OF CORRELATION COEFFICIENT

Each body cell is shown as *product* / *frequency*.

X → Y ↓	1.50–1.58	1.59–1.67	1.68–1.76	1.77–1.85	1.86–1.94	1.95–2.03	2.04–2.12	2.13–2.21	2.22–2.30	2.31–2.39	2.40–2.48	2.49–2.57	f_y	v	vf_y	v^2f_y	Σuv
1.68–1.79												30 / 1	1	6	6	36	30
1.56–1.67									10 / 1	15 / 1			2	5	10	50	25
1.44–1.55									8 / 1	24 / 2			3	4	12	48	32
1.32–1.43									12 / 2	18 / 2			4	3	12	36	30
1.20–1.31							0 / 2	26 / 13	20 / 5	12 / 2			22	2	44	88	58
1.08–1.19						−2 / 2	0 / 14	11 / 11	8 / 4				31	1	31	31	17
.96–1.07				0 / 1	0 / 4	0 / 6	0 / 21	0 / 4					36	0			
.84–.95				3 / 1	18 / 9	14 / 14	0 / 4						28	−1	−28	28	35
.72–.83		10 / 1	16 / 2	30 / 5	36 / 9		0 / 1						18	−2	−36	72	92
.60–.71		45 / 3	12 / 1	18 / 2	6 / 1								7	−3	−21	63	81
.48–.59	24 / 1		48 / 3	12 / 1									5	−4	−20	80	84
f_x	1	4	6	10	23	22	42	28	13	7		1	157		10	532	484
u	−6	−5	−4	−3	−2	−1	0	1	2	3	4	5					
uf_x	−6	−20	−24	−30	−46	−22	0	28	26	21		5	−68				
u^2f_x	36	100	96	90	92	22	0	28	52	63		25	604				
Σuv	24	55	76	63	60	12		37	58	69		30	484				

linear transformation. Using this result, we obtain the correlation between X and Y simply by computing the correlation between the code
values u and v. For this we require the sums Σu, Σv, Σu^2, Σv^2, Σuv.
The first 4 of them have already been obtained:

$$\Sigma u = -68, \quad \Sigma u^2 = 604, \quad \Sigma v = 10, \quad \Sigma v^2 = 532.$$

Note that in all these expressions we have suppressed the frequencies
that must enter into the computations. In order to calculate Σuv, we
have inserted in the lower right of each cell of Table 50.1 the product
fuv for that cell. The total of these values, Σfuv, or simply Σuv, is 484;
the summation has been checked by obtaining both row totals and
column totals in the table and adding them. Hence

$$r_{XY} = r_{uv} = \frac{\dfrac{1}{n}\Sigma uv - \bar{u}\cdot\bar{v}}{D(u)\cdot D(v)} = \frac{\dfrac{484}{157} + .4331 \times .06369}{1.913 \times 1.840} = .884.$$

This coding method for the calculation of r is used principally in dealing
with rather large sets of data. The availability of modern computers
tends to make these methods relatively less attractive.

EXERCISE 50

50.1. Suppose that for a set of data the X-values are grouped in just 2
classes, and likewise the Y-values are classified in 2 categories. Suppose that
the frequencies for the 4 cells of the correlation table are a, b, c, and d, as

a	b
c	d

shown in the table. Prove that the square of the coefficient of correlation
reduces to

$$\frac{(ad - bc)^2}{(a + b)(a + c)(b + d)(c + d)}.$$

Compare with Exercise 40.7.

*51. DISTRIBUTIONS OF REGRESSION COEFFICIENTS

We now obtain the distributions of the regression coefficients a and
b, defined by (47.6), and show how hypotheses concerning them may
be set up and tested.

We shall limit ourselves to the case in which the controlled variable x obeys the simplifying relation $\Sigma x = 0$. This may always be brought about by a simple shift of the origin of x.

We are considering the case in which $x_1, \cdots, x_n$ are regarded as fixed quantities. The quantities $Y_1, \cdots, Y_n$ are independently distributed according to $N(\alpha + \beta x_1, \sigma^2), \cdots, N(\alpha + \beta x_n, \sigma^2)$.* Thus, for each $i = 1, \cdots, n$, the quantity $Z_i = Y_i - \alpha - \beta x_i$ has the distribution $N(0, \sigma^2)$. We shall prove that with these assumptions as to the distribution of the $Y_1, \cdots, Y_n$ the 3 quantities a, b, and $\Sigma(Y - a - bx)^2/\sigma^2$ are independently distributed, a according to $N(\alpha, \sigma^2/n)$, b according to $N(\beta, \sigma^2/\Sigma x^2)$, and $\Sigma(Y - a - bx)^2/\sigma^2$ according to $CS(n - 2)$. Using these distributions, we can readily set up t distributions suitable for tests concerning α and β.

The essential element in the proof is the use of an orthogonal transformation:

$$u_1 = \frac{1}{\sqrt{n}}(Z_1 + \cdots + Z_n)$$

$$= \frac{1}{\sqrt{n}}(Y_1 + \cdots + Y_n - n\alpha) = \sqrt{n}(a - \alpha)$$

$$(51.1) \quad u_2 = \frac{1}{\sqrt{\Sigma x^2}}(x_1 Z_1 + \cdots + x_n Z_n)$$

$$= \frac{1}{\sqrt{\Sigma x^2}}(x_1 Y_1 + \cdots + x_n Y_n - \Sigma x^2 \beta) = \sqrt{\Sigma x^2}(b - \beta)$$

$$u_3 = a_{31} Z_1 + \cdots + a_{3n} Z_n$$
$$\vdots \qquad \vdots$$
$$u_n = a_{n1} Z_1 + \cdots + a_{nn} Z_n.$$

It is readily verified that u_1 and u_2 are orthogonal, because of $\Sigma x = 0$. The fact that the coefficients in the remaining equations can be so selected as to give an orthogonal transformation will be assumed.

Since $Z_1, \cdots, Z_n$ are independently distributed according to $N(0, \sigma^2)$, Theorem (39.19) permits us to conclude that $u_1, \cdots, u_n$ are likewise independently distributed according to $N(0, \sigma^2)$. But from the first 2 equations of (51.1) we may conclude

$$a = \frac{u_1}{\sqrt{n}} + \alpha, \quad b = \frac{u_2}{\sqrt{\Sigma x^2}} + \beta.$$

* The α and β used in this section are not related to the α and β used in Section 28 for the probabilities of errors I and II.

Thus a and b are independently distributed, according to $N(\alpha, \sigma^2/n)$ and $N(\beta, \sigma^2/\Sigma x^2)$. Furthermore, these quantities are distributed independently of the distribution of $(u_3{}^2 + \cdots + u_n{}^2)/\sigma^2$ which, according to (37.8), possesses the chi-square distribution with $n - 2$ d.f. Now, by (39.15),

$$u_3{}^2 + \cdots + u_n{}^2 = Z_1{}^2 + \cdots + Z_n{}^2 - u_1{}^2 - u_2{}^2$$

(51.2)

$$= \Sigma(Y - \alpha - \beta x)^2 - n(a - \alpha)^2 - \Sigma x^2(b - \beta)^2.$$

By the use of the relations

$$\Sigma x = 0, \quad \Sigma xY = b\, \Sigma x^2, \quad \Sigma Y = na$$

we may show that the final expression in (51.2) is equivalent to $\Sigma(Y - a - bx)^2 = \Sigma Y^2 - na^2 - b^2\, \Sigma x^2$.

The quantity

$$s_{y \cdot x}^2 = \frac{1}{n - 2} \Sigma(Y - a - bx)^2$$

is called the *standard error of estimate*. Thus we have found that a, b, and $(n - 2)s_{y \cdot x}^2/\sigma^2$ are independently distributed, with distributions $N(\alpha, \sigma^2/n)$, $N(\beta, \sigma^2/\Sigma x^2)$, and $CS(n - 2)$. Using Theorem (41.4) we are now in a position to draw the conclusions stated in the following theorem:

(51.3) THEOREM. *Let $x_1, \cdots, x_n$ be fixed values such that $\Sigma x = 0$, and let $Y_1, \cdots, Y_n$ possess the independent distributions $N(\alpha + \beta x_1, \sigma^2), \cdots$, $N(\alpha + \beta x_n, \sigma^2)$, respectively. Let $a = \overline{Y}$, $b = \Sigma xY/\Sigma x^2$, and $s_{y \cdot x}^2 = \Sigma(Y - a - bx)^2/(n - 2)$. Then the quantities*

$$t_a = \frac{\sqrt{n}(a - \alpha)}{s_{y \cdot x}} \quad \text{and} \quad t_b = \frac{\sqrt{\Sigma x^2}(b - \beta)}{s_{y \cdot x}}$$

each possess the t distribution with $n - 2$ d.f.

Example 51.2. In the analysis of Example 45.2 we are interested in whether there is a significant relationship between the period of thiamin deprivation x and the score on the speed of reaction test Y. A suitable hypothesis is $\beta = 0$, i.e., the regression line has zero slope. Under this hypothesis, according to (51.3), the quantity $t = b\sqrt{\Sigma x^2}/s_{y \cdot x}$ has the t distribution with $n - 2$ d.f. We shall use a one-sided test (since there is prior evidence that thiamin deprivation may adversely affect speed of reaction). With a level of significance of .05, and with 2 d.f., the critical value of t is 2.920. On the other hand, for the data of Example 45.2 we have

$$b = .832, \quad \Sigma x^2 = 206, \quad s_{y \cdot x} = 3.063,$$

from which we find $t = 3.90$. Thus the hypothesis is rejected, and we conclude that thiamin depreciation has adversely affected the speed of reaction.

EXERCISE 51

51.1. In the table, the Y-values are actually random values from $N(0, 1)$. Thus the model implies that $\beta = 0$. Find the regression coefficient b for the tabulated values, and use it to test the hypothesis $\beta = 0$.

x	-3	-2	-1	0	1	2	3
Y	.90	.97	-1.15	-1.46	1.42	.48	-1.89

51.2. Show that, if $\Sigma x = 0$, the square of the standard error of estimate can be evaluated by means of the formula

$$s_{y \cdot 2}^2 = \frac{1}{n-1} \left[\Sigma Y^2 - \frac{(\Sigma Y)^2}{n} - \frac{(\Sigma x Y)^2}{\Sigma x^2} \right].$$

How must this formula be modified for the case in which $\Sigma x \neq 0$?

51.3. Suppose that the random quantities $Y_1, \cdots, Y_n$ are distributed as in this section. The likelihood function L for α, β, and σ is given by (47.8). Show that the maximum likelihood estimate of σ^2 is

$$\frac{1}{n} \left[\Sigma Y^2 - \frac{(\Sigma Y)^2}{n} - \frac{(\Sigma x Y)^2}{\Sigma x^2} \right].$$

51.4. Let $x_1, \cdots, x_n$ be fixed, and let $Y_1, \cdots, Y_n$ have the distributions specified in this section. Show that if $\beta = 0$, then the quantity

$$F = \frac{(n-2)r^2}{1-r^2}$$

has the F distribution with 1 and $n - 2$ d.f. Hence find the density of $u = r^2$.

CHAPTER 7

Analysis of Variance

52. EXPERIMENTAL DESIGNS

It is always the aim of an experimenter, whether tacit or explicit, to reach certain scientific conclusions with a maximum of assurance and a minimum of cost. It is clear, however, that he can always get more assurance by increasing the size and therefore the cost of the experiment. One way of resolving this dilemma is to estimate the costs of errors of Type I and Type II and the cost of experimentation and to minimize the total cost. In theory this will help to determine the proper size of the experiment and the level of significance; but in actual situations the cost estimates are so difficult to obtain that this principle turns out to be useful only in the simplest types of experiment, for example, certain types of industrial quality control.

The experimenter has at his disposal a large number of possible experimental designs, about which much is known as to their effectiveness in various types of investigation. His first task is to select an appropriate design and to decide how to allocate his experimental material to the design. His completed design will be a plan for the whole experiment, showing exactly how many observations are to be performed under each experimental condition or treatment. The careful experimenter will have specified in advance most (ideally all) of the hypotheses he will wish to investigate, and he will have a clear idea of the capability of the design he has chosen to test these hypotheses. We have already considered the following 6 important designs and have discussed in some detail the tests of significance associated with them:

A. Comparison of 2 Groups

There are 2 groups of experimental units (animals, plots of ground, etc.), each group subject to the same experimental conditions. The first group is the control group. It is assumed to be a random sample of the control population, whose mean is μ_c. Similarly the second group, called the experimental group, is assumed to be a sample of the experimental population, whose mean is μ_e. We may test the hypothesis $\mu_c = \mu_e$ in the manner outlined in Section 29.

B. Paired Comparisons

The control and experimental groups are chosen in such a way that to each member of the control group there corresponds a paired member of the experimental group. For example, in an experiment with animals the paired animals might come from the same litter. Let X_{ci} and X_{ei} be the observed values for the ith pair. Then we form the difference $d_i = X_{ci} - X_{ei}$ and test the hypothesis that μ_d, the mean of the hypothetical population from which the observed sample of d values was drawn, is zero.

C. Evaluating a Proportion

Using the methods of Sections 28 and 29, we may test the hypothesis that a population proportion is a specified value or that the proportions of 2 populations are equal or differ by a specified amount.

D. Linear Regression

A series of values of a control variable x are selected by the experimenter, and one or more values of an experimental variable Y are observed corresponding to each value of x. We may then test hypotheses concerning a linear relationship between Y and x. If Y_i is the observed value corresponding to the control value x_i, $i = 1, \cdots,$ n, we assume a model of the form $Y_i = \alpha + \beta x_i$ and test the hypothesis $\beta = 0$ or the hypothesis $\alpha = 0$. (See Section 51.)

E. Multiple Regression

In this design there are several control variables $u_1, \cdots, u_k$. The model takes the form $Y_i = \alpha_0 + \alpha_1 u_{1i} + \cdots + \alpha_k u_{ki}, i = 1, \cdots, n,$ and hypotheses may be tested concerning the parameters $\alpha_0, \alpha_1, \cdots, \alpha_k.$ (See Exercises 47.9, 47.10.)

F. Testing Goodness of Fit

Under this design we include the two basic types considered in Section 40: the comparison of an empirical distribution with a theoretical distribution (Example 40.1), and the contingency table (Example 40.2).

Actually many other minor variations on the above main types are possible, and some have been discussed in passing. Those listed above are the principal designs that have already been treated. In this chapter we shall discuss several additional designs which are of constant use in experimentation. They will serve to introduce the powerful method known as analysis of variance, an analytical device useful in evaluating many types of elaborate experiments.

G. One-Way Classification

This type of experiment is a generalization of type A above, in which there are more than 2 groups being compared. Suppose, for example, that an agricultural experimenter wishes to compare 4 types of hog feed. He has 20 hogs of the same age and breed and assigns 5 randomly chosen hogs to each feed; he then observes their weight gain over a period of a month. The resulting observations (weight gains) may be tabulated in the form shown in Table 52.1.

TABLE 52.1

Replicates

	1	x	x	x	x	x
	2	x	x	x	x	x
Rations	3	x	x	x	x	x
	4	x	x	x	x	x

Each column of the table is regarded as a *replicate*, that is, essentially a repetition of the same experimental pattern. Replication is a device that enables us to determine what "error" or residual variation is present when we perform an experiment repeatedly under conditions as nearly identical as possible. The analysis of variance will enable us to determine whether this residual variation is sufficiently large to account for other identifiable types of variation present in the data. Corresponding to each type of hog feed we conceive of a hypothetical population, namely, the population of weight gains when an indefinitely large group of hogs of this particular age and breed are fed the ration in question. Let μ_1, μ_2, μ_3, μ_4 be the means of the 4 hypothetical populations, corresponding to rations 1, 2, 3, and 4. The hypothesis usually tested in an experiment of this type is that the means of the 4 hypothetical populations are equal: $\mu_1 = \mu_2 = \mu_3 = \mu_4$. That is, the null hypothesis is that there is no difference between the feeds, as far as such a difference is reflected in weight gains.

Two important subtypes of this experimental design may be distinguished:

G1. *Fixed Model.* Here the 4 hog feeds are of quite different types, and we are interested in these particular feeds and no others.

G2. *Random Model.* Here the 4 hog feeds are a random selection from many brands of the same type of feed. The experiment will aid us in determining whether the brands in general are significantly different.

H. Two-Way Classification

Table 52.1 cannot be regarded as a two-way table because the elements of any particular column have nothing in common that distinguishes them from the elements of another column. A slight modification and improvement of the experiment will make the columns meaningful so that the results may be presented in a two-way table. We now suppose that the experimenter has, at the beginning of his experiment, 5 litters of healthy hogs. From the first litter he randomly selects 4 hogs and assigns them (randomly) to the 4 positions of the first column of Table 52.1; the remaining litters are similarly treated. The table would now assume the form shown in Table 52.2.

TABLE 52.2

	Litters				
	1	2	3	4	5
1	x	x	x	x	x
2	x	x	x	x	x
Rations 3	x	x	x	x	x
4	x	x	x	x	x

In addition to the hypothesis that there is no difference between the rations, discussed under Type G, we may also test the hypothesis that there is no difference between litters. Thus with Type H we obtain more information than with Type G, although the number of observations is the same in both cases. This design is sometimes known as the randomized block design. We note several modifications and subtypes of this design:

H1. *Fixed Model.* Only 4 rations and 5 litters are under consideration, and we have no interest in extending the conclusions to a population—perhaps because no population is conceivable.

H2. *Random Model.* The 4 rations are a random sample of a population of products from different manufacturers of hog feed, and the 5 litters are a random sample from a population of litters. The hypotheses to be tested are then hypotheses concerning these populations.

H3. *Mixed Model.* Either the rations or the litters are a random sample from some population.

H4. *Replication.* Replication may be included with any of the preceding designs by assigning 2 or more animals to each combination of ration with litter. The replication has the advantage that we may test for *interaction* between feed and litter, that is, a tendency for certain litters to respond especially well to certain feeds.

EXERCISE 52

Classify the following experiments according to the types discussed in this section.

52.1. In order to test fertilizers A and B, 25 experimental plots are used, all of the same size but with a variety of soil, drainage, and tillage conditions. The plots are seeded with wheat, and one-half of each plot (randomly selected) is treated with fertilizer A, the other half with fertilizer B. The data will consist of records of wheat yield for all 50 half-plots.

52.2. Three fertilizers A, B, and C are to be tested using 30 experimental plots. Ten varieties of wheat w_1, w_2, $\cdots$, w_{10} are used. Each of the 30 combinations (A, w_1), (A, w_2), $\cdots$, (C, w_{10}) is randomly assigned to one of the 30 plots. The data will consist of the grain yields of the 30 plots.

52.3. Fertilizer of a particular kind is applied to 10 experimental plots in the amounts $.1k$, $.2k$, $.3k$, $\cdots$, k, where k is a suitably chosen maximum value. The allocation of a particular amount of fertilizer to a particular plot is by means of random numbers. Wheat is planted (the same variety on all plots), and the yields are recorded.

52.4. A standard fertilizer made by many manufacturers is being tested. Five manufacturers A, B, C, D, E are selected at random, and a supply of fertilizer is procured from each. The same variety of wheat is planted on 50 experimental plots, and 10 of the plots, selected at random, are treated with fertilizer A, 10 with fertilizer B, $\cdots$, 10 with fertilizer E. The yields from all 50 plots are recorded.

52.5. Two fertilizers A and B are to be compared by treating 25 randomly selected plots with A and 25 randomly selected plots with B. All 50 plots are then planted with the same variety of wheat. The yields from all 50 plots are recorded.

52.6. From many manufacturers of fertilizer three are randomly selected; call their products A, B, and C. From many varieties of wheat 4 are randomly selected, say w_1, w_2, w_3, and w_4. Of 60 plots 5 are randomly assigned to each of the 12 combinations of fertilizer and wheat variety (A, w_1), (A, w_2), $\cdots$, (C, w_4). The yields of all 60 plots are recorded.

52.7. Five manufacturers of fertilizer are randomly selected from many available manufacturers. Their products are A, B, C, D, E. We wish to compare three selected varieties of wheat w_1, w_2, w_3. Each of the 15 combinations (A, w_1), (A, w_2), $\cdots$, (E, w_3) is applied to one of 15 experimental plots, randomly selected. The yields of all 15 plots are recorded.

53. MODELS AND HYPOTHESES

In the remainder of this chapter our discussion will be confined to experiments of types G and H. In this section we shall briefly discuss the models and hypotheses that are appropriate to these designs. In Section 54 we shall deal with the various tests of significance that may be carried out and with the computations involved in these tests. Finally in Section 55 we develop the distribution theory associated with the tests of significance.

Our basic assumption is that the observations conform to a *linear* (or *additive*) *model;* that is, we assume that each observed value can be expressed as a sum of components, each of which is associated with one factor affecting the experiment. In the case of the one-way classification (G) we shall use the model

$$(53.1) \quad X_{ij} = \mu + r_i + e_{ij} = \mu_i + e_{ij}, \quad i = 1, \cdots, 4, j = 1, \cdots, 5,$$

where the means for the 4 treatments (rations) are $\mu_1 = \mu + r_1$, $\cdots$, $\mu_4 = \mu + r_4$. For the fixed model (G1), μ is the mean of the 4 values μ_1, $\cdots$, μ_4. This implies that $r_1 + \cdots + r_4 = 0$. The quantity e_{ij} is the deviation of the observation X_{ij} from the mean of the ith treatment: $e_{ij} = X_{ij} - \mu_i = X_{ij} - \mu - r_i$.

For the fixed model (G1), the quantities r_i are fixed. For the random model (G2), on the other hand, the quantities r_i are assumed to be normally and independently distributed with mean zero and variance σ_r^2. For both of these models the quantities e_{ij} are normally and independently distributed with mean zero and variance σ^2. The distributions of the r_i are assumed independent of the distributions of the e_{ij}. The quantity σ^2 will be called the *error variance* associated with the experiment. All the assumptions up to this point constitute the model. The hypotheses are

For (G1): $r_1 = r_2 = r_3 = r_4 = 0.$

For (G2): $\sigma_r^2 = 0.$

They are simply two different ways of stating that the rations are not different in their effect on weight gain.

With the two-way classification, we require another term in the linear model:

$$(53.2) \qquad X_{ij} = \mu + r_i + c_j + e_{ij}.$$

For the fixed model (H1) the quantity $\mu + r_i + c_j$ is the mean of the values of X_{ij} for all possible repetitions of the experiment. That is, it is the mean of the population of repetitions associated with the cell in the ith row and the jth column. It is assumed that $r_1 + \cdots + r_4 = 0$ and $c_1 + \cdots + c_5 = 0$. Thus μ is the grand mean, summed over i and j and over all possible repetitions of the experiment. For the random model (H2) we assume that the r_i possess the distribution $N(0, \sigma_r^2)$ and that the c_j possess the distribution $N(0, \sigma_c^2)$. For both models we assume that the e_{ij} have the distribution $N(0, \sigma^2)$, where σ^2 is again described as the error variance. All these distributions are assumed independent of each other. For the mixed model (H3) one set of treatment parameters (either the r_i or the c_j) is assumed to be fixed, and the other to possess the appropriate normal distribution.

For each of the models (H1), (H2), and (H3) there are two possible hypotheses which may be tested and which we shall denote by H_1 and H_2 in each case:

(H1) *Fixed model* H_1: $r_1 = \cdots = r_4$

                           H_2: $c_1 = \cdots = c_5$

(H2) *Random model* H_1: $\sigma_r^2 = 0$

                           H_2: $\sigma_c^2 = 0$

(H3) *Mixed model* H_1: $r_1 = \cdots = r_4$ H_1: $\sigma_r^2 = 0$

                                      or

                        H_2: $\sigma_c^2 = 0$ H_2: $c_1 = \cdots = c_5$

Fortunately, as far as tests of significance are concerned, models (H1), (H2), and (H3) are treated in the same way; that is, the test of the hypothesis H_1 in all the cases listed above is numerically the same. This is also true of the hypothesis H_2. The models differ in that it is possible for (H2) to estimate σ_r^2 and σ_c^2 and in the case of (H3) to estimate either σ_r^2 or σ_c^2. We shall not consider the methods of obtaining such estimates, which are to be found in many books on statistical methods or mathematical statistics.

EXERCISE 53

*53.1. For each of the Exercises 52.1 through 52.7, specify the underlying model, and state the hypothesis or hypotheses that may be tested.

54. TESTS OF SIGNIFICANCE

For concreteness in this section and the next we shall frequently refer to a numerical example based on Table 54.1, which was formed from

TABLE 54.1

30	19	20	33	28
32	32	38	36	27
28	35	23	29	40
30	30	23	38	29

two-digit random numbers, slightly adjusted for computational convenience. We shall look upon these values as representing observational data for an experiment of type G (one-way classification), with 4 rations (rows) and 5 replicates (columns). We shall focus attention on the fixed model (G1), although the test of significance about to be derived will apply also to the random model.

The null hypothesis is that the means associated with the 4 rows are equal. In terms of the model (53.1) the hypothesis is that $r_1 = \cdots = r_4 = 0$. When this is the case, all 20 values in Table 54.1 are independent values from the normal distribution $N(\mu, \sigma^2)$. The essence of our procedure from this point on is to obtain two estimates of the error variance σ^2, one of which is sensitive to the difference between the rations, the other of which is not. The ratio of these two estimates will be shown in Section 55 to possess the F distribution with known degrees of freedom. If, in an experiment, we obtain a value of this ratio which is beyond a suitable critical value we shall reject the null hypothesis and conclude that the rations are significantly different.

The 4 row means are: $\overline{X}_{1.} = 26$, $\overline{X}_{2.} = 33$, $\overline{X}_{3.} = 31$, $\overline{X}_{4.} = 30$. Each of them is the mean of a sample of 5 values, and under the null hypothesis such means will have the distribution $N(\mu, \sigma^2/5)$. We can thus obtain an estimate of $\sigma^2/5$ by finding the variance of these 4 means (note that $\overline{X}_{..} = 30$ is the grand mean):

$$\tfrac{1}{3}(\Sigma \overline{X}_{i.}^2 - 4\overline{X}_{..}^2) = 8.667.$$

From this we obtain, by multiplying by 5, an estimate of σ^2 which we shall denote by MS_{br}; the MS stands for "mean square," and the subscript for "between rows," terms whose significance will become clear as we proceed. Thus

(54.1) $MS_{br} = \tfrac{5}{3}(\Sigma \overline{X}_{i.}^2 - 4\overline{X}_{..}^2) = 43.33.$

The quantity MS_{br} is called the "between rows mean square," or the "between rows estimate of σ^2."

A second estimate of σ^2, called the "within rows" estimate and denoted by MS_{wr}, can be obtained by finding the variance of each of the 4 rows and averaging these 4 variances:

$$(54.2)\quad MS_{wr} = \tfrac{1}{4}[\tfrac{1}{4}(\Sigma X_{1j}^2 - 5\overline{X}_{1.}^2) + \cdots + \tfrac{1}{4}(\Sigma X_{4j}^2 - 5\overline{X}_{4.}^2)]$$

$$= \tfrac{1}{16}\Sigma X_{ij}^2 - \tfrac{5}{16}\Sigma \overline{X}_{i.}^2 = 32.12.$$

Under the present null hypothesis the ratio of these two estimates obeys the F distribution with 3 and 16 d.f., as will be proved in the next section. We find

$$(54.3)\qquad\qquad F = \frac{MS_{br}}{MS_{wr}} = \frac{43.33}{32.12} = 1.35.$$

At the 5% level of significance this value of F is not significant, not a surprising result in view of the manner of constructing Table 54.1. The estimate MS_{br} will be sensitive to differences between rations, because it is based upon the variances of the means for the 4 rations. Consequently we shall expect it to be larger than σ^2 if the null hypothesis is false. On the other hand, MS_{wr} is so constructed that it is totally insensitive to variation between the rows since it is simply an average of 4 within-row estimates of σ^2. [See Theorem (54.11).] These rather heuristic considerations make it plausible that F, as defined by (54.3), is a suitable critical statistic for the null hypothesis. A rigorous justification for this choice of statistic can be provided by the likelihood ratio method.

It is customary to present the foregoing analysis in the following form, known as an analysis of variance table:

ANALYSIS OF VARIANCE

	Sum of Squares	Degrees of Freedom	Mean Square
Between rows	$SS_{br} = 130$	$\text{d.f.}_{br} = 3$	$MS_{br} = 130/3 = 43.33$
Within rows	$SS_{wr} = 514$	$\text{d.f.}_{wr} = 16$	$MS_{wr} = 514/16 = 32.12$

For our purposes a somewhat preferable form of analysis is that shown in Table 54.2.

TABLE 54.2

	Sum of Squares	Degrees of Freedom	Mean Square
Mean	$SS_m = 18{,}000$	$\text{d.f.}_m = 1$	$MS_m = 18{,}000/1 = 18{,}000$
Between rows	$SS_{br} = 130$	$\text{d.f.}_{br} = 3$	$MS_{br} = 130/3 = 43.33$
Within rows	$SS_{wr} = 514$	$\text{d.f.}_{wr} = 16$	$MS_{wr} = 514/16 = 32.12$
Total	$SS_t = 18{,}644$	$\text{d.f.}_t = 20$	

Although the row labeled "mean" is rarely used in routine analysis, it has certain theoretical values which will be evident as we proceed. We note, first of all, that the quantity SS_t, called the *total sum of squares*, is simply the sum of squares of the 20 values in Table 54.1. The essence of the procedure lies in the partition of SS_t into portions SS_m, SS_{br}, SS_{wr}, and the total degrees of freedom into corresponding portions. The actual calculations of SS_m, SS_{br}, and SS_{wr} are most conveniently carried out using the row totals $X_{i.}$ and the grand total $X_{..}$. In the general case with h rows and k columns, formulas for the sums of squares and degrees of freedom are:

$$SS_m = hk\overline{X}_{..}^2 = \frac{X_{..}^2}{hk} \qquad\qquad \text{d.f.}_m = 1$$

$$(54.4) \quad SS_{br} = k\Sigma(\overline{X}_{i.} - \overline{X}_{..})^2 = \frac{\Sigma X_{i.}^2}{k} - \frac{X_{..}^2}{hk} \quad \text{d.f.}_{br} = h - 1$$

$$SS_{wr} = \Sigma(X_{ij} - \overline{X}_{i.})^2 = \Sigma X_{ij}^2 - \frac{\Sigma X_{i.}^2}{k} \quad \text{d.f.}_{wr} = h(k - 1)$$

These formulas are readily derived by generalizing the expressions obtained above for the sums of squares and the degrees of freedom in the case of Table 54.1 and by using the relations $\overline{X}_{i.} = X_{i.}/k$, $\overline{X}_{..} = X_{..}/hk$. The reader should verify that these formulas yield the quantities exhibited in Table 54.2.

The significance of the partition of the sum of squares and of the degrees of freedom will become more apparent in Section 55, where we shall use orthogonal transformations to derive the distributions associated with the simpler forms of analysis of variance. A number of important features of this partition turn out to be rather simple consequences of the following identity:

$$(54.5) \qquad X_{ij} = \overline{X}_{..} + (\overline{X}_{i.} - \overline{X}_{..}) + (X_{ij} - \overline{X}_{i.}).$$

The partition (54.5) may be applied to *each member* of Table 54.1. For example, the upper left member of Table 54.1 is $X_{11} = 30$. To complete the breakdown (54.5), we need the values $\bar{X}_{1.} = 26$, and $\bar{X}_{..} = 30$. Substituting these values, we find: $30 = 30 + (-4) + 4$. The result of carrying out this partition for all 20 members of Table 54.1 may be conveniently exhibited in tabular form, as is done in Table 54.3.

TABLE 54.3

PARTITION OF TABLE 54.1

	Table X_{ij}					=	Mean $\bar{X}_{..}$					+	Between Rows $(\bar{X}_{i.} - \bar{X}_{..})$					+	Within Rows $(X_{ij} - \bar{X})$				
	30	19	20	33	28		30	30	30	30	30		−4	−4	−4	−4	−4		4	−7	−6	7	2
	32	32	38	36	27	=	30	30	30	30	30	+	3	3	3	3	3	+	−1	−1	5	3	−6
	28	35	23	29	40		30	30	30	30	30		1	1	1	1	1		−3	4	−8	−2	9
	30	30	23	38	29		30	30	30	30	30		0	0	0	0	0		0	0	−7	8	−1
Sums of squares	SS_t					=	SS_m					+	SS_{br}					+	SS_{wr}				
	18,644					=	18,000					+	130					+	514				
Degrees of freedom	d.f.$_t$					=	d.f.$_m$					+	d.f.$_{br}$					+	d.f.$_{wr}$				
	20					=	1					+	3					+	16				

We may verify, in Table 54.3, a number of consequences of Equation (54.5):

(a) We may say that the subtable on the upper left, consisting of the original 20 values, is the sum of the 3 subtables on the right, in the sense that each entry in the left-hand table is the sum of the 3 corresponding entries in the 3 right-hand tables.

(b) The 3 tables on the right are *mutually orthogonal* in the sense that, if each member of any one of these tables is multiplied by each corresponding member of any other and the 20 products added, the sum will be zero. It may be shown that this orthogonality is based on Equation (54.5).

(c) The orthogonality has the consequence that, if we square both sides of (54.5) and sum over all 20 values of X_{ij}, we obtain

$$(54.6) \quad \Sigma X_{ij}^2 = hk\bar{X}_{..}^2 + k\,\Sigma(\bar{X}_{i.} - \bar{X}_{..})^2 + \Sigma(X_{ij} - \bar{X}_{i.})^2.$$

The square of the trinomial on the right of (54.5) will involve 3 cross-product terms; the orthogonality referred to under (b) implies that the summations of these 3 terms will vanish, which is essential for the truth of (54.6). Equation (54.6) gives the basic partition of the sum of squares, corresponding to the partition in Table 54.3. It may be verified that each of the quantities SS_t, SS_m, SS_{br}, SS_{wr} is actually the sum of squares of the 20 values in the corresponding subtable of Table 54.3.

(*d*) We can define the *degrees of freedom* for each subtable as the number of elements in the table, minus the number of independent restrictions to which the table is subject. Thus the X_{ij} subtable contains 20 numbers, subject to no restrictions, and its d.f. is therefore 20. The "mean" subtable has only 1 d.f., since its 20 values are subject to the 19 restrictions that all the values shall be equal. The "between rows" table is subject to 17 restrictions: the column totals are all zero (5 restrictions); in each row there are 5 identical values (4 restrictions per row); all of these 21 restrictions are not independent, for the first 5, together with the 12 restrictions associated with the first 3 rows, imply that the last row must contain identical values. Since there are 17 independent restrictions, the "between rows" table has 3 d.f. The "within rows" table is subject to the 4 independent restrictions that each row totals to zero; it has therefore 16 d.f.

Example 54.1. In a quality control experiment with standard clock springs, 4 springs of the same type from the same manufacturer were cut into sections. The strength of each section was measured by determining the deflection in inches when a standard weight was applied to the end of the spring. Table 54.4*a* gives the deflection values X_{ij} for 3 sections from each spring. In

TABLE 54.4

		(*a*)			(*b*)		
		Values of X_{ij}			Values of $Y_{ij} =$ $1000X_{ij} - 50$		
	1	.053	.055	.043	3	5	−7	1
Spring	2	.055	.055	.052	5	5	2	12
	3	.061	.057	.061	11	7	11	29
	4	.055	.050	.050	5	0	0	5
					24	17	6	47

Table 54.4*b* the values have been coded by multiplying each by 1000 and subtracting 50. This linear transformation will have the effect of multiplying all variance estimates by 10^6 and leaving unaltered the *F* ratio of any pair of these variance estimates. Hence we may just as well carry out the analysis of variance with the more convenient values in Table 54.4*b*. The row totals and the grand total will be used in this example; the column totals will be used in Example 54.2. The null hypothesis for the fixed model (G1) is that the populations means corresponding to the 4 springs (4 rows) are the same. That is, the 4 springs are not distinguishable as to strength. In accordance with (54.4) we calculate

$$\Sigma Y_{ij}^2 = 453, \quad \sum \frac{Y_{i.}^2}{3} = 337.33, \quad \frac{Y_{..}^2}{12} = 184.08,$$

$$SS_{br} = 337.33 - 184.08 = 153.25, \quad \text{d.f.}_{br} = 3,$$
$$SS_{wr} = 453.00 - 337.33 = 115.67, \quad \text{d.f.}_{wr} = 8.$$

The analysis of variance thus takes the form:

	Sum of Squares	Degrees of Freedom	Mean Square
Between springs	153.25	3	$153.25/3 = 51.08$
Within springs	115.67	8	$115.67/8 = 14.46$
			$F = 51.08/14.46 = 3.53$

With 3 and 8 d.f. and a significance level of .01, the critical value is $F = 27.49$. Since the sample value of F does not exceed the critical value, we shall accept the null hypothesis at the 1% level of significance. Our conclusion is that the 4 springs have not been demonstrated to differ in strength by this experiment.

We now extend the analysis to a two-way classification. Using the notation $X_{.j}$ for column sum and $\overline{X}_{.j}$ for column mean, we shall insert another term in Equation (54.5) corresponding to the variation between columns, namely, $\overline{X}_{.j} - \overline{X}_{..}$. We subtract the "between columns" term from the "within rows" term and obtain a new term which we designate as "residual":

$$(X_{ij} - \overline{X}_{i.}) - (\overline{X}_{.j} - \overline{X}_{..}) = (X_{ij} - \overline{X}_{i.} - \overline{X}_{.j} + \overline{X}_{..}).$$

In Equation (54.5) we now replace the previous "within rows" term by the sum of the "between columns" and "residual" terms, obtaining the identity:

(54.7)

$$X_{ij} = \overline{X}_{..} + (\overline{X}_{i.} - \overline{X}_{..}) + (\overline{X}_{.j} - \overline{X}_{..}) + (X_{ij} - \overline{X}_{i.} - \overline{X}_{.j} + \overline{X}_{..}).$$

This partition of X_{ij} leads to a more detailed breakdown of the original Table 54.1 than that shown in Table 54.3. The "within rows" subtable is replaced by two others, as shown in Table 54.5.

TABLE 54.5

PARTITION OF TABLE 54.1

	Mean					Between Rows					Between Columns					Residual				
	30	30	30	30	30	−4	−4	−4	−4	−4	0	−1	−4	4	1	4	−6	−2	3	1
Table =	30	30	30	30	30	3	3	3	3	3	0	−1	−4	4	1	−1	0	9	−1	−7
54.1	30	30	30	30	30	1	1	1	1	1	0	−1	−4	4	1	−3	5	−4	−6	3
	30	30	30	30	30	0	0	0	0	0	0	−1	−4	4	1	0	1	−3	4	−2
SS: 18,644 =	18,000				+	130				+	136				+	378				
d.f. 20 =	1				+	3				+	4				+	12				

The formulas for SS_m and SS_{br}, d.f.$_m$ and d.f.$_{br}$, given in (54.4), will still apply, and in addition we shall have the following formulas for SS_{bc}, SS_r, d.f.$_{bc}$, d.f.$_r$ (here the subscripts bc and r are for "between columns" and "residual"):

$$SS_{bc} = h\Sigma(\overline{X}_{.j} - \overline{X}_{..})^2 = \frac{\Sigma X_{.j}{}^2}{h} - \frac{X_{..}{}^2}{hk},$$

$$\text{d.f.}_{bc} = k - 1,$$

$$SS_r = \Sigma(X_{ij} - \overline{X}_{i.} - \overline{X}_{.j} + \overline{X}_{..})^2$$

(54.8)

$$= \Sigma X_{ij}{}^2 - \frac{\Sigma X_{i.}{}^2}{k} - \frac{\Sigma X_{.j}{}^2}{h} + \frac{X_{..}{}^2}{hk},$$

$$\text{d.f.}_r = (h - 1)(k - 1).$$

It can be verified that the 4 subtables on the right are mutually orthogonal in the sense previously specified. This orthogonality has the consequence that, when we square both sides of (54.7) and sum, we obtain the following equation, analogous to (54.6):

(54.9) $$\Sigma X_{ij}{}^2 = hk\overline{X}_{..}{}^2 + k\Sigma(\overline{X}_{i.} - \overline{X}_{..})^2$$

$$+ h\Sigma(\overline{X}_{.j} - \overline{X}_{..})^2 + \Sigma(X_{ij} - \overline{X}_{i.} - \overline{X}_{.j} + \overline{X}_{..})^2.$$

We summarize the computations for Table 54.1, regarded as a two-way classification, in the analysis of variance in Table 54.6.

We began the discussion for a one-way classification by suggesting, largely on heuristic grounds, two estimates of σ^2 whose ratio would give a reasonable test of the hypothesis that the row means are equal. It will turn out that for a two-way classification the quantities MS_{br},

TABLE 54.6

	Sum of Squares	Degrees of Freedom	Mean Square
Mean	18,000	1	18,000
Between rows	130	3	43.33
Between columns	136	4	34.00
Residual	378	12	31.50
Total	18,644	20	

MS_{bc}, and MS_r of Table 54.6 provide estimates leading to appropriate tests of significance. In fact, we shall show in Section 55 that:

(a) If we use the model (H1) and the null hypothesis $r_1 = \cdots = r_4 = 0$, the quantities MS_{br} and MS_r are both estimates of the variance σ^2, and the ratio $F = MS_{br}/MS_r$ possesses the F distribution with 3 and 12 d.f.

(b) If we use the model (H1) and the null hypothesis $c_1 = \cdots = c_5 = 0$, the quantities MS_{bc} and MS_r are both estimates of the variance σ^2, and the ratio $F = MS_{bc}/MS_r$ possesses the F distribution with 4 and 12 d.f.

The suitability of the ratios MS_{br}/MS_r and MS_{bc}/MS_r as critical statistics is supported by the following facts, which we shall proceed to prove:

(c) The quantity $SS_{br} = k\Sigma(\overline{X}_{i.} - \overline{X}_{..})^2$ is sensitive to variations between the rows but insensitive to variations between the columns.

(d) The quantity $SS_{bc} = h\Sigma(\overline{X}_{.j} - \overline{X}_{..})^2$ is sensitive to variations between the columns but insensitive to variations between the rows.

(e) The quantity $SS_r = \Sigma(X_{ij} - \overline{X}_{i.} - \overline{X}_{.j} + \overline{X}_{..})^2$ is insensitive to variations between the rows, and to variations between the columns.

To verify statements c, d, and e, let the quantity a_1 be added to each element in row 1, a_2 to each element in row 2, etc. That is, we shall define a new variable Y_{ij} by the equation $Y_{ij} = X_{ij} + a_i$. Then the row means, the column mean, and the grand mean of Y_{ij} will be

$$\overline{Y}_{i.} = \overline{X}_{i.} + a_i, \quad \overline{Y}_{.j} = \overline{X}_{.j} + \bar{a}, \quad \overline{Y}_{..} = \overline{X}_{..} + \bar{a},$$

where $\bar{a}$ is the mean of the a's. If we now perform an analysis of variance using the variable Y_{ij}, we shall find, for the sums of squares,

$$SS_{bc}' = h\Sigma(\overline{Y}_{.j} - \overline{Y}_{..})^2 = h\Sigma(\overline{X}_{.j} - \overline{X}_{..})^2,$$

$$(54.10) \quad SS_{br}' = k\Sigma(\overline{Y}_{i.} - \overline{Y}_{..})^2 = k\Sigma(\overline{X}_{i.} - \overline{X}_{..} + a_i - \bar{a})^2,$$

$$SS_r' = \Sigma(Y_{ij} - \overline{Y}_{i.} - \overline{Y}_{.j} + \overline{Y}_{..})^2$$

$$= \Sigma(X_{ij} - \overline{X}_{i.} - \overline{X}_{.j} + \overline{X}_{..})^2,$$

where SS_{bc}', SS_{br}', and SS_r' denote the sums of squares calculated for the Y's. This shows that SS_{bc} and SS_r are unaffected by the transformation $Y_{ij} = X_{ij} + a_i$, while SS_{br} is affected unless all the a_i are equal. A similar argument with the transformation $Y_{ij} = X_{ij} + b_j$ will complete the demonstration.

The result just proved will be needed several times in Section 55. Accordingly we restate it as a theorem:

(54.11) THEOREM.   *Let the values X_{ij} of a two-way table be increased by constants a_i: $Y_{ij} = X_{ij} + a_i$. Let SS_{bc} and SS_r be defined as in (54.4) and (54.8), and let SS_{bc}' and SS_r' denote the corresponding quantities computed from the Y_{ij} instead of the X_{ij}. Then $SS_{bc}' = SS_{bc}$ and $SS_r' = SS_r$. Similarly, if the values X_{ij} are increased by constants b_j: $Y_{ij} = X_{ij} + b_j$ and if SS_{br}' and SS_r' are computed from the Y_{ij}, then $SS_{br}' = SS_{br}$ and $SS_r' = SS_r$.*

The foregoing considerations suggest that the ratios $F = MS_{br}/MS_r$ and $F = MS_{bc}/MS_r$ will, respectively, provide suitable tests of the hypotheses that the row means are equal and that the column means are equal.

Example 54.2.   In the data of Example 54.1 the values in the first column of Table 54.4a were actually samples from the outside sections of the 4 springs, the values in the second column were from the middle sections of the springs, and the values in the third column were from the inside sections of the springs. Thus, if we regard Table 54.4a as a two-way table, we have an opportunity to test the additional hypothesis that there is no difference in the strength of the springs as one proceeds from the outside to the inside. We again use the coding transformation of Example 54.1, which will not affect the F-values. The necessary totals are supplied in Table 54.4b. In accordance with (54.8) we need to calculate the additional quantities:

$$\sum \frac{X_{.j}^2}{4} = 225.25, \quad SS_{bc} = 225.25 - 184.08 = 41.17, \quad \text{d.f.}_{bc} = 2,$$

$$SS_r = 453.00 - 337.33 - 225.25 + 184.08 = 74.50, \quad \text{d.f.}_r = 6.$$

We then have the analysis of variance:

	Sum of Squares	Degrees of Freedom	Mean Square
Between springs	153.25	3	51.08
Between positions	41.17	2	20.58
Residual	74.50	6	12.42

The ratios $F = 51.08/12.42 = 4.11$ and $F = 20.58/12.42 = 1.66$ are computed. Since both of these values are below the 1% level of significance of F, we accept both the hypothesis that there is no difference in strength between the springs and the hypothesis that there is no difference in strength between the 3 positions.

EXERCISE 54

54.1.   When an individual is placed in a dark room and observes a small light, he will perceive it to move; this is called the "autokinetic effect." In an experiment to test the effect of the judgment of another person on this phenomenon, 12 persons viewed the light under 2 conditions. In condition A each subject viewed the light alone. In condition B the same subjects viewed the light in small groups, with discussion of what they saw. In each group an accomplice of the experimenter was present who deliberately claimed to perceive movements smaller than those reported by the subjects under condition A. The results for the 12 subjects were as follows; the values are perceived motion in inches:

Subject	1	2	3	4	5	6	7	8	9	10	11	12
A	15.2	4.7	4.5	4.0	3.3	3.1	.2	1.3	1.3	1.5	2.0	2.5
B	.6	1.0	2.6	1.7	.8	1.6	1.2	2.1	1.2	1.3	1.0	2.1

Analyze these data in 2 ways (use $\alpha = .05$):
  (a) As a paired comparison experiment.
  (b) As a two-way classification.
If method (a) yields a value t, and method (b) a value $F = MS_{br}/MS_r$, verify that $F = t^2$.

54.2. Show, algebraically, that the relation $F = t^2$ of Exercise 54.1 will always hold true for an experiment of the kind described.

54.3. Derive Formulas (54.4) for SS_m, SS_{br}, and SS_{wr}.

*55. DISTRIBUTION THEORY

We are now in a position to round out our discussion of analysis of variance by showing that each of the following quantities possesses an F distribution under the indicated models and hypotheses:

  (a) The ratio $F = MS_{br}/MS_{wr}$, for the model (G1) (one-way classification, fixed), and the null hypothesis $r_1 = r_2 = \cdots = 0$.
  (b) The ratio $F = MS_{br}/MS_r$, for the model (H1) (two-way classification, fixed), and the null hypothesis $r_1 = r_2 = \cdots = 0$.
  (c) The ratio $F = MS_{bc}/MS_r$, for the model (H1) (two-way classification, fixed), and the null hypothesis $c_1 = c_2 = \cdots = 0$.

We may also show (see Exercise 55.1) that

  (d) Under the indicated hypotheses the quantities MS_{br}, MS_{bc}, MS_{wr}, MS_r are estimates of the error variance σ^2.

For convenience we shall give the proofs for the case of a table of 4 rows and 5 columns, such as Table 54.1. But everything we shall do will be immediately capable of generalization to the case of a table of h rows and k columns.

The proof will consist in exhibiting an orthogonal transformation relating the observed values X_{ij} to 20 quantities $u_1, \cdots, u_{20}$ which, under the indicated models and hypotheses, will be independently and normally distributed. The sums of squares SS_{br}, SS_{bc}, SS_{wr}, SS_r are all simply expressible in terms of the u's, and as a consequence each of these sums of squares may be shown to possess a chi-square distribution. As a result the ratios mentioned above are shown to possess the F distribution with appropriate degrees of freedom.

Consider first the fixed model (G1) under the null hypothesis $r_1 = r_2 = r_3 = r_4 = 0$. Then the X_{ij} are independent values from $N(\mu, \sigma^2)$. It is convenient to deal with the quantities $Y_{ij} = X_{ij} - \mu$, which will be independently distributed according to $N(0, \sigma^2)$. The quantities Y_{ij}, arranged in a two-way table, appear as shown in Table 55.1. The

TABLE 55.1

Y_{11}	$\cdots$	Y_{15}	$Y_{1.}$
.	$\cdots$	.	.
.	$\cdots$	.	.
.	$\cdots$	.	.
Y_{41}	$\cdots$	Y_{45}	$Y_{4.}$
$Y_{.1}$	$\cdots$	$Y_{.5}$	$Y_{..}$

marginal totals are also shown, using the "dot" notation. Let us now define quantities $u_1, \cdots, u_{20}$ by the linear transformation

$$u_1 = (20)^{-1/2}(Y_{11} + \cdots + Y_{15} + \cdots + Y_{41} + \cdots + Y_{45})$$

$$u_2 = (10)^{-1/2}(Y_{11} + \cdots + Y_{15} - Y_{21} - \cdots - Y_{25})$$

$$u_3 = (30)^{-1/2}(Y_{11} + \cdots + Y_{15} + Y_{21} + \cdots + Y_{25}$$
$$- 2Y_{31} - \cdots - Y_{35})$$

$$(55.1) \quad u_4 = (60)^{-1/2}(Y_{11} + \cdots + Y_{15} + Y_{21} + \cdots + Y_{25} + Y_{31}$$
$$+ \cdots + Y_{35} - 3Y_{41} - \cdots - 3Y_{45})$$

$$u_5 = \cdots$$
$$\vdots$$
$$u_{20} = \cdots$$

Only the first 4 equations of the linear transformation are written out explicitly. A little later we shall exhibit the complete transformation.

TABLE 55.2

	Mult.	Y_{11}	Y_{12}	Y_{13}	Y_{14}	Y_{15}	Y_{21}	Y_{22}	Y_{23}	Y_{24}	Y_{25}	Y_{31}	Y_{32}	Y_{23}	Y_{34}	Y_{35}	Y_{41}	Y_{42}	Y_{43}	Y_{44}	Y_{45}
u_1	$(20)^{-1/2}$	1	1	1	1	1	1	1	1	1	1	1	1	1	1	1	1	1	1	1	1
u_2	$(10)^{-1/2}$	1	1	1	1	1	-1	-1	-1	-1	-1										
u_3	$(30)^{-1/2}$	1	1	1	1	1	1	1	1	1	1	-2	-2	-2	-2	-2					
u_4	$(60)^{-1/2}$	1	1	1	1	1	1	1	1	1	1	1	1	1	1	1	-3	-3	-3	-3	-3
u_5	. . . .																				
.																						
.																						
u_{20}	. . . .																					

In verifying that the first 4 equations of (55.1) actually fulfill the conditions of orthogonality, it is convenient to set up the matrix of the transformation, as is done in Table 55.2. In order to make the table as compact as possible we use a column headed "Mult.", which gives a factor by which each element in the corresponding row must be multiplied in order that the transformation be orthogonal. For the moment we shall assume that the remaining 16 rows of the matrix, not written out, also fulfill the conditions of orthogonality.

Note that the orthogonality conditions (39.16) require that the sum of the coefficients in each row shall be unity. This determines the value in the "Mult." column. Note also that the sums of products of corresponding elements in each pair of rows is zero and that this is true whatever the values in the "Mult." column.

The first 4 equations of the transformation (55.1) are readily expressible in terms of the row totals of Table 55.1:

(55.2)
$$u_1 = (20)^{-1/2}(Y_{1.} + Y_{2.} + Y_{3.} + Y_{4.})$$
$$u_2 = (10)^{-1/2}(Y_{1.} - Y_{2.})$$
$$u_3 = (30)^{-1/2}(Y_{1.} + Y_{2.} - 2Y_{3.})$$
$$u_4 = (60)^{-1/2}(Y_{1.} + Y_{2.} + Y_{3.} - 3Y_{4.})$$

It will be seen that the transformation equations, written in the form (55.2), follow a definite pattern; compare these equations with those of Example 39.4 and with Equations (39.20). We observe, in fact, that the system (55.2) defines an orthogonal transformation from the 4 variables $Y_{1.}/\sqrt{5}$, $Y_{2.}/\sqrt{5}$, $Y_{3.}/\sqrt{5}$, $Y_{4.}/\sqrt{5}$ to the 4 variables u_1, u_2, u_3, u_4. This observation leads to the conclusion that

$$u_1{}^2 + u_2{}^2 + u_3{}^2 + u_4{}^2 = \tfrac{1}{5}\Sigma Y_i{}^2.$$

Furthermore $u_1 = Y_{..}/\sqrt{20}$. Thus

$$u_2{}^2 + u_3{}^2 + u_4{}^2 = \Sigma \frac{Y_{i.}{}^2}{5} - \frac{Y_{..}{}^2}{20}.$$

Let us denote the quantity on the right of the above equation by SS_{br}'. It is of the same form as the expression for SS_{br} in (54.4), with Y replacing X. In view of the relation $Y_{ij} = X_{ij} - \mu$, (54.11) implies that $SS_{br}' = SS_{br}$. Hence

(55.3) $$u_2{}^2 + u_3{}^2 + u_4{}^2 = SS_{br}.$$

Again, since the transformation (55.1) is orthogonal, it follows that $u_1{}^2 + \cdots + u_{20}{}^2 = \Sigma Y_{ij}{}^2$. Thus

$$u_5{}^2 + \cdots + u_{20}{}^2 = \Sigma Y_{ij}{}^2 - (u_1{}^2 + \cdots + u_4{}^2)$$

$$= \Sigma Y_{ij}{}^2 - \Sigma Y_{.j}{}^2/5 = SS_{wr}',$$

where SS_{wr}' denotes the quantity obtained from SS_{wr} by replacing the X's by Y's. According to (54.11) we must have $SS_{wr}' = SS_{wr}$. Thus

(55.4) $$u_5{}^2 + \cdots + u_{20}{}^2 = SS_{wr}.$$

Under the null hypothesis $r_1 = r_2 = r_3 = r_4 = 0$ the 20 quantities $Y_{11}, \cdots, Y_{45}$ are independently distributed according to $N(0, \sigma^2)$. By (39.19) the 20 quantities $u_1, \cdots, u_{20}$ defined by the orthogonal transformation (55.1) are likewise independently distributed according to $N(0, \sigma^2)$. Hence, from (55.3) and (55.4) SS_{br}/σ^2 and SS_{wr}/σ^2 are independently distributed according to CS(3) and CS(16), respectively. We may finally conclude (using (41.7)) that $F = MS_{br}/MS_{wr} = (16SS_{br})/(3SS_{wr})$ possesses the F distribution with 3 and 16 d.f. This proves the first of the assertions made at the beginning of this section.

We now consider the two-way classification (H1) and the null hypothesis $r_1 = r_2 = r_3 = r_4 = 0$. Referring to Section 53, we note that with this model and hypothesis the X_{ij} are independently distributed and that X_{ij} possesses the distribution $N(\mu + c_j, \sigma^2)$. Hence the quantities $Y_{ij} = X_{ij} - \mu - c_j$ are likewise independently distributed according to $N(0, \sigma^2)$. Letting SS_{br}', SS_{bc}' and SS_r' represent, as before, the "between rows," "between columns," and "residual" sums of squares computed from the Y_{ij}, we may conclude from (54.11) that $SS_{br}' = SS_{br}$, $SS_r' = SS_r$ but that $SS_{bc}' \neq SS_{bc}$ unless we make the additional assumption that $c_1 = c_2 = c_3 = c_4 = c_5 = 0$.

Our strategy, as in the case of the one-way classification, is to exhibit an orthogonal transformation by means of which we can relate the distributions of MS_{br} and MS_r to those of the Y_{ij}. The complete matrix of the transformation is exhibited in Table 55.3, which is an extension of Table 55.2. It is readily verified that the rows of the table

TABLE 55.3

	Mult.	Y_{11}	Y_{12}	Y_{13}	Y_{14}	Y_{15}	Y_{21}	Y_{22}	Y_{23}	Y_{24}	Y_{25}	Y_{31}	Y_{32}	Y_{33}	Y_{34}	Y_{35}	Y_{41}	Y_{42}	Y_{43}	Y_{44}	Y_{45}
u_1	$20^{-1/2}$	1	1	1	1	1	1	1	1	1	1	1	1	1	1	1	1	1	1	1	1
u_2	$10^{-1/2}$	1	1	1	1	1	-1	-1	-1	-1	-1										
u_3	$30^{-1/2}$	1	1	1	1	1	1	1	1	1	1	-2	-2	-2	-2	-2					
u_4	$60^{-1/2}$	1	1	1	1	1	1	1	1	1	1	1	1	1	1	1	-3	-3	-3	-3	-3
u_5	$8^{-1/2}$	1	-1				1	-1				1	-1				1	-1			
u_6	$24^{-1/2}$	1	1	-2			1	1	-2			1	1	-2			1	1	-2		
u_7	$48^{-1/2}$	1	1	1	-3		1	1	1	-3		1	1	1	-3		1	1	1	-3	
u_8	$80^{-1/2}$	1	1	1	1	-4	1	1	1	1	-4	1	1	1	1	-4	1	1	1	1	-4
u_9	$4^{-1/2}$	1	-1				-1	1													
u_{10}	$12^{-1/2}$	1	1	-2			-1	-1	2												
u_{11}	$24^{-1/2}$	1	1	1	-3		-1	-1	-1	3											
u_{12}	$40^{-1/2}$	1	1	1	1	-4	-1	-1	-1	-1	4										
u_{13}	$12^{-1/2}$	1	-1				1	-1				-2	2								
u_{14}	$36^{-1/2}$	1	1	-2			1	1	-2			-2	-2	4							
u_{15}	$72^{-1/2}$	1	1	1	-3		1	1	1	-3		-2	-2	-2	6						
u_{16}	$120^{-1/2}$	1	1	1	1	-4	1	1	1	1	-4	-2	-2	-2	-2	8					
u_{17}	$24^{-1/2}$	1	-1				1	-1				1	-1				-3	3			
u_{18}	$72^{-1/2}$	1	1	-2			1	1	-2			1	1	-2			-3	-3	6		
u_{19}	$144^{-1/2}$	1	1	1	-3		1	1	1	-3		1	1	1	-3		-3	-3	-3	9	
u_{20}	$240^{-1/2}$	1	1	1	1	-4	1	1	1	1	-4	1	1	1	1	-4	-3	-3	-3	-3	12

are mutually orthogonal and that the sum of the elements in each row is unity. It is interesting to note how the numerical pattern of the coefficients first observed in Example 39.4 is repeated many times in this matrix.

In the above transformation the equations for u_1, u_5, u_6, u_7, and u_8 may be conveniently expressed in terms of the column totals $Y_{.1}, \cdots, Y_{.5}$:

$$u_1 = 20^{-1/2}(Y_{.1} + \cdots + Y_{.5})$$

$$u_5 = 8^{-1/2}(Y_{.1} - Y_{.2})$$

(55.5)
$$u_6 = 24^{-1/2}(Y_{.1} + Y_{.2} - 2Y_{.3})$$

$$u_7 = 48^{-1/2}(Y_{.1} + Y_{.2} + Y_{.3} - 3Y_{.4})$$

$$u_8 = 80^{-1/2}(Y_{.1} + Y_{.2} + Y_{.3} + Y_{.4} - 4Y_{.5})$$

Just as Equations (55.2) give an orthogonal transformation from $Y_1./\sqrt{5}, \cdots, Y_4./\sqrt{5}$ to $u_1, \cdots, u_4$, so Equations (55.5) give an orthogonal transformation from $Y_{.1}/2, \cdots, Y_{.5}/2$ to $u_1, u_5, \cdots, u_8$. As a result,

$$(55.6) \qquad u_1^2 + u_5^2 + u_6^2 + u_7^2 + u_8^2 = \Sigma Y_{.j}^2/4.$$

Furthermore, since the first 4 rows of the matrix in Table 55.3 are identical with the first 4 rows of the matrix in Table 55.2, it follows that we shall have, as before,

$$\Sigma Y_{ij}^2 = u_1^2 + \cdots + u_{20}^2, \quad \Sigma \frac{Y_{i.}^2}{5} = u_1^2 + \cdots + u_4^2,$$

$$(55.7)$$

$$\frac{Y_{..}^2}{20} = u_1^2, \quad SS_{br}' = SS_{br} = u_2^2 + u_3^2 + u_4^2.$$

Now by analogy with (54.8), SS_r' is defined by

$$SS_r' = \Sigma Y_{ij}^2 - \Sigma \frac{Y_{i.}^2}{5} - \Sigma \frac{Y_{.j}^2}{4} + \frac{Y_{..}^2}{20}.$$

Using (55.6) and (55.7), we may express SS_r' entirely in terms of the u's:

$$(55.8) \qquad SS_r' = SS_r = u_9^2 + u_{10}^2 + \cdots + u_{20}^2.$$

Under the model and hypothesis which we have assumed the quantities Y_{ij} are independently distributed according to $N(0, \sigma^2)$. Since the transformation from the Y's to the u's is orthogonal, it follows that the quantities $u_1, \cdots, u_{20}$ are independently distributed according to $N(0, \sigma^2)$. Thus $SS_{br} = SS_{br}' = u_2^2 + u_3^2 + u_4^2$ and $SS_r = SS_r' = u_9^2 + \cdots + u_{20}^2$ are independently distributed according to CS(3) and CS(12), respectively. Finally, $F = MS_{br}/MS_r = 12SS_{br}/3SS_r$ has the F distribution with 3 and 12 d.f., as was to be proved.

The distribution of $F = MS_{bc}/MS_r$, under the appropriate model and hypothesis, is derived in an entirely analogous manner. The details are suggested as an exercise.

EXERCISE 55

*55.1. Show that, if $u_1, \cdots, u_{20}$ are defined by (55.1), with $r_1 = r_2 = r_3 = r_4 = 0$, then $E(u_i^2) = \sigma^2$, $i = 1, \cdots, 20$. Hence conclude that $E(MS_{br}) = E(MS_{wr}) = E(MS_r) = \sigma^2$.

*55.2. Let SS_{bc} be defined, for data such as those in Table 54.1, by (54.8) Let $Y_{ij} = X_{ij} - \mu$, and let $u_1, \cdots, u_{20}$ be related to the Y_{ij} by the linear transformation whose matrix is given in Table 55.3. Show that $SS_{bc} = u_5^2$ $+ u_6^2 + u_7^2 + u_8^2$. Under the model (H1) and the null hypothesis $c_1 = c_2$ $= c_3 = c_4 = c_5 = 0$, show that SS_{bc} and SS_r are independently distributed according to CS(4) and CS(12), respectively, and hence that $F = 12SS_{bc}/4SS_r$ has the F distribution with 4 and 12 d.f.

Appendix: Matrices

A rectangular array of quantities,

$$\begin{bmatrix} a_{11} & \cdots & a_{1n} \\ \cdot & & \cdot \\ \cdot & & \cdot \\ \cdot & & \cdot \\ a_{m1} & \cdots & a_{mn} \end{bmatrix}$$

is known as a *matrix*. The above matrix is often abbreviated by using a single letter A or by the notation $[a_{ij}]$. A matrix with only one row, or with only one column, is called a *vector*. Thus the elements of a sample $(x_1, \cdots, x_n)$ form a vector. The coefficients of the linear transformation (39.9) form a *square matrix:*

$$(A.1) \qquad A = \begin{bmatrix} a_n & \cdots & a_{1n} \\ \cdot & & \cdot \\ \cdot & & \cdot \\ \cdot & & \cdot \\ a_{n1} & \cdots & a_{nn} \end{bmatrix}.$$

Note that the first subscript of each element gives its row, the second subscript its column. The *order* of a square matrix is the number of rows and columns; the matrix A of (A.1) is of order n. The elements a_{11}, $a_{22}, \cdots, a_{nn}$ are said to form the main diagonal of the matrix.

If each element of a matrix is multiplied by the same constant, we say that the matrix is multiplied by that constant. Thus

$$k \begin{bmatrix} a_{11} & \cdots & a_{1n} \\ \cdot & & \cdot \\ \cdot & & \cdot \\ a_{n1} & \cdots & a_{nn} \end{bmatrix} = \begin{bmatrix} ka_{11} & \cdots & ka_{1n} \\ \cdot & & \cdot \\ \cdot & & \cdot \\ ka_{n1} & \cdots & ka_{nn} \end{bmatrix}.$$

The basic algebraic operations on matrices are defined in the following way. If two matrices A and B have the same number of rows and also the same number of columns, their sum is the matrix whose elements are the sums of corresponding elements of A and B. Thus

$$\begin{bmatrix} a & b & c \\ d & e & f \end{bmatrix} + \begin{bmatrix} p & q & r \\ x & y & z \end{bmatrix} = \begin{bmatrix} a+p & b+q & c+r \\ d+x & e+y & f+z \end{bmatrix}.$$

This definition of addition extends to the addition of row vectors:

$$[a \quad b \quad c] + [p \quad q \quad r] = [a+p \quad b+q \quad c+r],$$

or to column vectors:

$$\begin{bmatrix} a \\ b \\ c \end{bmatrix} + \begin{bmatrix} p \\ q \\ r \end{bmatrix} = \begin{bmatrix} a+p \\ b+q \\ c+r \end{bmatrix}.$$

Similarly the difference of matrices is defined by subtracting corresponding elements.

Two matrices A and B may be multiplied to form the product AB if the number of columns of A is equal to the number of rows of B. Each element in the product is formed by selecting a row of A and a column of B, multiplying corresponding elements, and adding these products.

$$\text{ith row} \rightarrow \begin{bmatrix} & & \\ a_{i1} & \cdots & a_{in} \\ & & \end{bmatrix} \cdot \begin{bmatrix} & b_{1j} & \\ & \vdots & \\ & b_{nj} & \end{bmatrix} = \begin{bmatrix} & & \\ & \sum_h a_{ih}b_{hj} & \\ & & \end{bmatrix}.$$

jth column $\downarrow$ element in ith row and jth column $\downarrow$

In the illustration we have selected the ith row of the first matrix and the jth column of the second matrix. By combining this row and this column in the indicated way, we obtain the element in the ith row and jth column of the product AB. We illustrate the process by finding the product of two second-order matrices:

$$\begin{bmatrix} a & b \\ c & d \end{bmatrix} \cdot \begin{bmatrix} e & f \\ g & h \end{bmatrix} = \begin{bmatrix} ae+bg & af+bh \\ ce+dg & cf+dh \end{bmatrix}.$$

Let us define column matrices X and U as follows:

(A.2)
$$X = \begin{bmatrix} x_1 \\ \vdots \\ x_n \end{bmatrix} \quad U = \begin{bmatrix} u_1 \\ \vdots \\ u_n \end{bmatrix}.$$

Then the linear transformation (39.9) can be compactly written in matrix form

(A.3)
$$U = AX,$$

where A is defined by (A.1).

The unit matrix of order n, denoted by I (or sometimes by I_n when we wish to emphasize the order) has "1" in each main diagonal position, zeros elsewhere. Thus the unit matrix of order 2 is

$$I_2 = \begin{bmatrix} 1 & 0 \\ 0 & 1 \end{bmatrix}.$$

It is readily verified that, if A is any matrix of order n, then $AI = IA = A$. Thus the matrix I behaves in matrix algebra as the number "1" does in the number system.

The notation $\det A = \det [a_{ij}]$ will be used to designate the determinant

$$\begin{vmatrix} a_{11} & \cdots & a_{1n} \\ \vdots & & \vdots \\ a_{n1} & \cdots & a_{nn} \end{vmatrix}.$$

It is assumed that the reader is familiar with the determinants of order 2 or 3. The definition of determinants of higher order will not be discussed here. If $\det [a_{ij}] \neq 0$, then the system of equations (39.9) or equivalently (A.3) may be solved in the form (39.10). To write (39.10) in matrix form, we define

$$B = \begin{bmatrix} b_{11} & \cdots & b_{1n} \\ \vdots & & \vdots \\ b_{n1} & \cdots & b_{nn} \end{bmatrix}.$$

Then (39.10) becomes

(A.4) $X = BU.$

Let us substitute $U = AX$ from (A.3) in (A.4). We obtain

(A.5) $X = B(AX) = (BA)X.$

We are here assuming that matrix multiplication is associative. Comparing (A.5) with the equation $X = IX$, we see that $BA = I$. In a similar way, by substituting $X = BU$ for X in the equation $U = AX$, we find $AB = I$.

Given a square matrix A for which det $A \neq 0$, we can always find a matrix B such that $AB = BA = I$. B is called the *inverse* of A and is usually written A^{-1}. The operation of finding the inverse of a given matrix A corresponds in matrix algebra to the operation of finding the reciprocal a^{-1} of a given number a.

Example A.1. For $U = AX$ we shall take the simple case

$$u_1 = 3x_1 + 2x_2$$
$$u_2 = 2x_1 + 5x_2.$$

Here the matrix

$$A = \begin{bmatrix} 3 & 2 \\ 2 & 5 \end{bmatrix}.$$

If we solve for the variables x_1, x_2 in terms of u_1, u_2, we find

$$x_1 = \frac{5}{11} u_1 - \frac{2}{11} u_2$$

$$x_2 = \frac{-2}{11} u_1 + \frac{3}{11} u_2.$$

Thus the inverse matrix of A is

$$A^{-1} = \begin{bmatrix} 5/11 & -2/11 \\ -2/11 & 3/11 \end{bmatrix}.$$

The reader should verify that $AA^{-1} = A^{-1}A = I$.

We are assuming, without proof, that Equations (39.9) or $U = AX$ can always be solved provided that det $A \neq 0$. If n is greater than 3 the actual solution of this system may involve much computation, even when methods requiring a minimum of arithmetic are used.

The *transpose* A^{T} of a matrix A is the matrix whose rows are the columns of A and whose columns are the rows of A. Thus the transpose of

$$A = \begin{bmatrix} a & b \\ c & d \end{bmatrix}$$

is

$$A^\mathsf{T} = \begin{bmatrix} a & c \\ b & d \end{bmatrix}.$$

It may be shown, without difficulty, that the transpose of a product of matrices is the product of their transposes in *reverse order*, i.e., $(AB)^\mathsf{T} = B^\mathsf{T}A^\mathsf{T}$.

Let X and Y be column vectors with the same number of elements, n:

$$X = \begin{bmatrix} x_1 \\ \vdots \\ x_n \end{bmatrix}, \quad Y = \begin{bmatrix} y_1 \\ \vdots \\ y_n \end{bmatrix}.$$

Their transposes X^T and Y^T will be row vectors. If we form the matrix products $X^\mathsf{T}Y$ and $Y^\mathsf{T}X$, we find

(A.6) $$X^\mathsf{T}Y = Y^\mathsf{T}X = x_1y_1 + \cdots + x_ny_n.$$

The numerical quantity associated with the vectors X and Y, defined by (A.6), is called the *inner product* of X and Y.

We define the *length* of a vector X, denoted by $|X|$, as follows:

(A.7) $$|X| = \sqrt{X^\mathsf{T}X} = \sqrt{x_1^2 + \cdots + x_n^2}.$$

A vector whose length is unity is called a *unit vector*.

The linear transformation $U = AX$ will be called an *orthogonal transformation*, and the matrix A will be called an *orthogonal matrix*, if for every n-component vector X we have $|U| = |X|$ so that the transformation preserves the length of every vector. Such transformations are analogous to rotations and reflections in two and three dimensions. The transpose of $U = AX = U^\mathsf{T} = X^\mathsf{T}A^\mathsf{T}$. Hence

$$|U| = \sqrt{U^\mathsf{T}U} = \sqrt{X^\mathsf{T}A^\mathsf{T}AX}.$$

Since for an orthogonal transformation we have $|U| = |X|$, it follows that, if A is orthogonal,

$$X^\mathsf{T}A^\mathsf{T}AX = X^\mathsf{T}X = X^\mathsf{T}IX,$$

which will be the case if and only if

(A.8) $$A^\mathsf{T}A = I.$$

If we multiply both members of (A.8) on the right by A^{-1} we find

$$(A.9) \qquad\qquad A^\mathsf{T} = A^{-1},$$

so that the transpose A^T of an orthogonal matrix is also its inverse. As a result (A.8) may be extended:

$$(A.10) \qquad\qquad A^\mathsf{T}A = AA^\mathsf{T} = I.$$

By making use of the definition (A.1) of A, (A.10) becomes

$$\begin{bmatrix} a_{11} & \cdots & a_{n1} \\ \cdot & & \cdot \\ \cdot & & \cdot \\ \cdot & & \cdot \\ a_{1n} & \cdots & a_{nn} \end{bmatrix} \begin{bmatrix} a_{11} & \cdots & a_{1n} \\ \cdot & & \cdot \\ \cdot & & \cdot \\ \cdot & & \cdot \\ a_{n1} & \cdots & a_{nn} \end{bmatrix}$$

$$= \begin{bmatrix} a_{11} & \cdots & a_{1n} \\ \cdot & & \cdot \\ \cdot & & \cdot \\ \cdot & & \cdot \\ a_{n1} & \cdots & a_{nn} \end{bmatrix} \begin{bmatrix} a_{11} & \cdots & a_{n1} \\ \cdot & & \cdot \\ \cdot & & \cdot \\ \cdot & & \cdot \\ a_{1n} & \cdots & a_{nn} \end{bmatrix} = \begin{bmatrix} 1 & 0 & \cdots & 0 \\ 0 & 1 & \cdots & 0 \\ \cdot & \cdot & & \cdot \\ \cdot & \cdot & & \cdot \\ \cdot & \cdot & & \cdot \\ 0 & 0 & \cdots & 1 \end{bmatrix}.$$

By using the definition of matrix multiplication, these matrix equations turn out to be identical with the conditions (39.16) and (39.18) for an orthogonal transformation.

When we are dealing with vectors X and Y in two or three dimensions, it is not difficult to verify that the vectors are perpendicular if and only if $X^\mathsf{T}Y = 0$. By generalizing, two vectors X and Y in n dimensions (i.e., with n components) are said to be *orthogonal* (or perpendicular) if $X^\mathsf{T}Y = 0$.

Let us speak of the row vectors of a matrix to refer to the vectors each of which has the elements of a row of the matrix as its components; we similarly speak of the column vectors of a matrix. In these terms the conditions for orthogonality of a matrix A, (39.16) and (39.18), or (A.10), may be expressed:

(A.11)   *The row vectors of an orthogonal matrix A form a set of n mutually orthogonal unit vectors.   The column vectors of A form a set of n mutually orthogonal unit vectors.*

The second result is of great assistance in constructing orthogonal transformations, for it implies that we need only obtain a set of n mutually orthogonal unit vectors and use them as the rows of the transformation matrix.

Example A.2.   The matrix

$$\begin{bmatrix} 1/\sqrt{3} & 1/\sqrt{3} & 1/\sqrt{3} \\ 1/\sqrt{6} & 1/\sqrt{6} & -2/\sqrt{6} \\ 1/\sqrt{2} & -1/\sqrt{2} & 0 \end{bmatrix}$$

is orthogonal. It is easily verified that the 3 row vectors are mutually orthogonal unit vectors and that likewise the three column vectors are mutually orthogonal unit vectors.

Note, in connection with Example A.2, that the row vectors $X = [1 \quad 1 \quad 1]$ and $Y = [1 \quad 1 \quad -2]$ are orthogonal. Given a pair of orthogonal vectors, such as these, they may be converted into a pair of orthogonal *unit* vectors simply by dividing each component of each vector by the length of that vector. The length of X is $|X| = \sqrt{3}$, and we obtain the unit vector $[1/\sqrt{3} \quad 1/\sqrt{3} \quad 1/\sqrt{3}]$; the length of Y is $|Y| = \sqrt{6}$, and we obtain the unit vector $[1/\sqrt{6} \quad 1/\sqrt{6} \quad -2/\sqrt{6}]$; and these two new vectors are orthogonal.

These considerations reduce the problem of finding orthogonal transformations to the simpler problem of finding a set of mutually orthogonal vectors; these vectors can then be converted into unit vectors by the process outlined above.

The most useful tool available for purposes of building a set of mutually orthogonal vectors is the Gram-Schmidt process. It may be based on the following theorem:

(A.12)   THEOREM.   *Let* $A_1, \cdots, A_k$ *be a set of mutually orthogonal vectors, and let B be any vector. Then, if the vector*

$$\tilde{B} = B - \frac{B^{\mathsf{T}}A_1}{A_1{}^{\mathsf{T}}A_1} A_1 - \frac{B^{\mathsf{T}}A_2}{A_2{}^{\mathsf{T}}A_2} A_2 - \cdots - \frac{B^{\mathsf{T}}A_k}{A_k{}^{\mathsf{T}}A_k} A_k$$

is not zero, it is orthogonal to each of the vectors $A_1, \cdots, A_k$.

Proof.   Let A_i be any one of the vectors $A_1, \cdots, A_k$. We shall prove that $\tilde{B}$ is orthogonal to A_i. We have

$$\tilde{B}^{\mathsf{T}}A_i = B^{\mathsf{T}}A_i - \frac{B^{\mathsf{T}}A_1}{A_1{}^{\mathsf{T}}A_1} A_1{}^{\mathsf{T}}A_i - \frac{B^{\mathsf{T}}A_2}{A_2{}^{\mathsf{T}}A_2} A_2{}^{\mathsf{T}}A_i$$

$$- \cdots - \frac{B^{\mathsf{T}}A_i}{A_i{}^{\mathsf{T}}A_i} A_i{}^{\mathsf{T}}A_i - \cdots - \frac{B^{\mathsf{T}}A_k}{A_k{}^{\mathsf{T}}A_k} A_k{}^{\mathsf{T}}A_i$$

But the inner products of A_i with the vectors $A_1, \cdots, A_k$ will all vanish except $A_i{}^{\mathsf{T}}A_i$. Hence all terms on the right of the above equation are zero except $B^{\mathsf{T}}A_i$ and $-(B^{\mathsf{T}}A_i/A_i{}^{\mathsf{T}}A_i)A_i{}^{\mathsf{T}}A_i$, which cancel each other. Thus $\tilde{B}^{\mathsf{T}}A_i = 0$, and the theorem is proved.

The vector B which is used as a basis for the construction of a new vector $\tilde{B}$ we shall call the *working vector*.

Example A.3. Let us find a vector orthogonal to the 3 mutually orthogonal vectors

$$A_1 = [3, 0, 1, 2, 5]$$

$$A_2 = [1, -1, 1, -2, 0]$$

$$A_3 = [1, 6, 1, -2, 0]$$

For the working vector B let us use $[1, 0, 0, 0, 0]$. The required inner products are: $A_1{}^{\mathsf{T}}A_1 = 39$, $A_2{}^{\mathsf{T}}A_2 = 7$, $A_3{}^{\mathsf{T}}A_3 = 42$, $B^{\mathsf{T}}A_1 = 3$, $B^{\mathsf{T}}A_2 = 1$, $B^{\mathsf{T}}A_3 = 1$.
Hence from Theorem (A.12)

$$\tilde{B} = B - \tfrac{1}{13}A_1 - \tfrac{1}{7}A_2 - \tfrac{1}{42}A_3$$

$$= \tfrac{1}{546}\{546\,B - 42A_1 - 78A_2 - 13A_3\}$$

$$= \tfrac{1}{546}\{[546, 0, 0, 0, 0] - [126, 0, 42, 84, 210] - [78, -78, 78, -156, 0]$$

$$- [13, 78, 13, -26, 0]\}$$

$$= \tfrac{1}{546}[329, 0, -133, 98, -210]$$

It is easily verified that B is orthogonal to each of A_1, A_2, and A_3.

As a final illustration of the use of the Gram-Schmidt process, let us form a set of 4 mutually orthogonal vectors, beginning with the vector $A_1 = [1, 1, 1, 1]$. As our first working vector let us use $B_2 = [1, 0, 0, 0]$. To apply Theorem (A.12), we need $A_1{}^{\mathsf{T}}A_1 = 4$ and $B_2{}^{\mathsf{T}}A_1 = 1$. Hence we have

$$\tilde{B}_2 = B_2 - \tfrac{1}{4}A_1 = \tfrac{1}{4}\{4B_2 - A_1\}$$

$$= \tfrac{1}{4}\{[4, 0, 0, 0] - [1, 1, 1, 1]\} = \tfrac{1}{4}[3, -1, -1, -1].$$

It is readily verified that $\tilde{B}_2$ is orthogonal to A_1. But any multiple of $\tilde{B}_2$ will also be orthogonal to A_1. For convenience we shall multiply the vector B_2 by 4 to clear of fractions and use the result as the second vector A_2 of the orthogonal set we are building. Thus $A_2 = [3, -1, -1, -1]$.

We now use $B_3 = [0, 1, 0, 0]$ as our second working vector. We find $B_3{}^{\mathsf{T}}A_1 = 1$, $B_3{}^{\mathsf{T}}A_2 = -1$, and $A_2{}^{\mathsf{T}}A_2 = 12$. Hence

$$\tilde{B}_3 = B_3 - \tfrac{1}{4}A_1 + \tfrac{1}{12}A_2 = \tfrac{1}{12}\{12B_3 - 3A_1 + A_2\}$$

$$= \tfrac{1}{12}[0, 8, -4, -4] = \tfrac{1}{3}[0, 2, -1, -1]$$

We shall hence use $A_3 = [0, 2, -1, -1]$ as our third vector.

Finally, using $B_4 = [0, 0, 1, 0]$ as a working vector, we obtain

$$\tilde{B}_4 = B_4 - \tfrac{1}{4}A_1 + \tfrac{1}{12}A_2 + \tfrac{1}{6}A_3$$

$$= \tfrac{1}{12}\{12B_4 - 3A_1 + A_2 + 2A_3\} = \tfrac{1}{2}[0, 0, 1, -1].$$

Thus our final vector is $A_4 = [0, 0, 1, -1]$.

The set of 4 mutually orthogonal vectors we have obtained is:

$$A_1 = [1, 1, 1, 1]$$

$$A_2 = [3, -1, -1, -1]$$

$$A_3 = [0, 2, -1, -1]$$

$$A_4 = [0, 0, 1, -1]$$

If we convert each of these into a unit vector by dividing by its length, we obtain the set:

$$U_1 = [1/2, 1/2, 1/2, 1/2]$$

$$U_2 = [3/\sqrt{12}, -1/\sqrt{12}, -1/\sqrt{12}, -1/\sqrt{12}]$$

$$U_3 = [0, 2/\sqrt{6}, -1/\sqrt{6}, -1/\sqrt{6}]$$

$$U_4 = [0, 0, 1/\sqrt{2}, -1/\sqrt{2}].$$

Thus we have the orthogonal matrix

$$\begin{bmatrix} 1/2 & 1/2 & 1/2 & 1/2 \\ 3/\sqrt{12} & -1/\sqrt{12} & -1/\sqrt{12} & -1/\sqrt{12} \\ 0 & 2/\sqrt{6} & -1/\sqrt{6} & -1/\sqrt{6} \\ 0 & 0 & 1/\sqrt{2} & -1/\sqrt{2} \end{bmatrix},$$

and the corresponding orthogonal transformation

$$u_1 = \frac{1}{2}(x_1 + x_2 + x_3 + x_4)$$

$$u_2 = \frac{1}{\sqrt{12}}(3x_1 - x_2 - x_3 - x_4)$$

$$u_3 = \frac{1}{\sqrt{6}} (2x_2 - x_3 - x_4)$$

$$u_4 = \frac{1}{\sqrt{2}} (x_3 - x_4).$$

This differs from the orthogonal transformation of Example 39.4 only in that the variables have been rearranged.

Bibliography

(1) Brunk, H. D., *An Introduction to Mathematical Statistics*, Prentice-Hall, 1960.
(2) Cramér, H., *The Elements of Probability Theory and Some of Its Applications*, John Wiley and Sons, 1955.
(3) Cramér, H., *Mathematical Methods of Statistics*, Princeton University Press, 1946.
(4) Dixon, W. J., and Massey, F. J., *Introduction to Statistical Analysis*, Second Edition, McGraw-Hill Book Company, 1957.
(5) Feller, W., *An Introduction to Probability Theory and Its Applications*, Second Edition, John Wiley and Sons, 1957.
(6) Fraser, D. A. S., *Statistics, an Introduction*, John Wiley and Sons, 1958.
(7) Fry, T. C., *Probability and Its Engineering Uses*, D. Van Nostrand Company, 1929.
(8) Goldberg, S., *Probability, an Introduction*, Prentice-Hall, 1960.
(9) Hoel, P. G., *Introduction to Mathematical Statistics*, Second Edition, John Wiley and Sons, 1954.
(10) Hogg, R. V., and Craig, A. T., *Introduction to Mathematical Statistics*, The Macmillan Company, 1959.
(11) Kolmogorov, A. N., *Foundations of the Theory of Probability*, Chelsea Publishing Company, 1950.
(12) Mood, A. M., *Introduction to the Theory of Statistics*, McGraw-Hill Book Company, 1950.
(13) Munroe, M. E., *Theory of Probability*, McGraw-Hill Book Company, 1951.
(14) Pearson, K., "On the criterion that a given system of deviations from the probable in the case of a correlated system is such that it can be reasonably supposed to have arisen from random sampling," *Philosophical Magazine*, Series 5, Vol. 50 (1900), p. 156.
(15) Wilks, S. S., *Mathematical Statistics*, Princeton University Press, 1944.

Comments on the Bibliography

1. Six of the listed books deal primarily with probability theory, and only secondarily with statistics: Cramér (2), Feller (5), Fry (7), Goldberg (8), Kolmogorov (11), and Munroe (13). Of these, Cramér (2), Goldberg (8), and Munroe (13) are intended for the beginning student of probability. Feller (5) is the definitive reference for probability theory in the discrete case. Fry (7) is a pioneering work on engineering applications of probability, still a basic reference for the serious student. Kolmogorov (11) deals with the postulational or axiomatic approach to

probability and is a standard reference in this area. It is extremely compact and in its entirety is accessible only to the advanced student. However, the first chapter is quite readable and rewarding to the serious beginner in mathematics.

2. An excellent elementary introduction to the theory of sets will be found in the first chapter of Goldberg (8).

3. The following books are introductions to mathematical statistics, which presuppose only an acquaintance with beginning calculus: Brunk (1), Fraser (6), Hoel (9), and Hogg and Craig (10). Mood (12) demands a bit more mathematical maturity than the books mentioned in the preceding sentence but rewards the persistent student in proportion to his effort.

4. Cramér (3) and Wilks (15) are thorough treatises in mathematical statistics and fundamental references for the student who wishes to pursue the subject. Cramér (3) includes, in the first section of the book, an encyclopedic survey of the mathematical tools necessary for the pursuit of advanced mathematical statistics: set theory, measure theory, Lebesgue integration, matrix theory, and a variety of special integrals and formulas.

5. Dixon and Massey (4) is an elementary textbook on statistical methods but exceptionally broad in its coverage and remarkable for its collection of tables.

6. Pearson (13) is the basic reference for Section 40 of this book. It is one of the earliest papers in which the essential nature of the problem of statistical inference is clearly set forth.

Tables

TABLE 1

RANDOM NUMBERS

```
15 77 01 64 69   69 58 40 81 16   60 20 00 84 22   28 26 46 66 36   86 66 17 34 49
85 40 51 40 10   15 33 94 11 65   57 62 94 04 99   05 57 22 71 77   99 68 12 11 14
47 69 35 90 95   16 17 45 86 29   16 70 48 02 00   59 33 93 28 58   34 32 24 34 07
13 26 87 40 20   40 81 46 08 09   74 99 16 92 99   85 19 01 23 11   74 00 79 41 69
10 55 33 20 47   54 16 86 11 16   59 34 71 55 84   03 48 17 60 13   38 71 23 91 83

05 06 67 26 77   14 85 40 52 68   60 41 94 98 18   62 20 94 03 71   60 26 45 17 92
65 50 89 18 74   42 07 50 15 69   86 97 40 25 88   14 17 73 92 07   93 11 93 45 15
59 68 53 31 55   73 47 16 49 79   69 80 76 16 60   58 53 07 04 53   66 94 94 18 13
31 31 05 36 48   75 16 00 21 11   42 44 84 46 84   83 20 49 17 12   21 93 34 61 16
91 59 46 44 45   49 25 36 12 07   25 90 89 55 25   83 47 17 23 93   99 56 14 39 16

63 59 73 21 67   80 00 25 58 25   72 06 12 86 74   54 79 70 85 88   71 58 21 98 48
89 72 47 46 94   78 56 10 65 97   84 79 42 31 49   94 15 31 13 09   45 43 03 82 81
70 51 21 03 18   50 21 99 49 73   06 99 19 24 96   39 43 10 14 12   94 08 55 54 70
14 15 99 60 44   62 72 38 18 36   63 92 61 55 93   77 66 82 10 91   81 51 67 01 47
92 46 90 39 99   64 08 00 97 27   54 96 63 40 54   34 70 27 48 18   68 59 91 83 32

81 23 17 13 01   37 57 92 16 34   15 80 90 25 64   67 77 29 95 84   80 84 84 87 22
87 54 42 46 56   28 89 02 06 98   59 90 74 13 38   98 66 23 20 23   90 55 31 83 48
74 73 84 98 13   11 48 25 33 39   27 36 08 99 57   60 42 88 68 25   22 89 67 83 16
94 55 14 00 97   32 51 92 47 03   92 33 73 20 21   29 77 37 06 98   64 63 34 31 43
69 21 94 26 20   73 90 70 92 76   49 14 60 34 43   90 51 72 11 07   75 94 19 49 40

82 36 36 89 29   87 70 08 71 98   49 00 89 89 99   29 08 02 72 32   68 16 29 82 19
25 06 22 30 87   87 44 48 90 91   38 53 10 60 29   40 07 58 97 84   09 04 33 56 72
82 37 97 60 92   76 39 17 84 34   67 65 52 89 90   62 97 04 33 81   91 27 56 46 35
83 71 07 22 15   17 55 56 82 62   88 83 86 38 14   63 89 39 81 90   25 62 58 68 87
73 13 79 15 12   18 34 22 24 75   56 47 45 22 81   30 82 38 34 52   57 48 30 34 17

91 28 00 57 30   92 12 38 95 21   15 70 78 50 88   01 07 90 72 77   99 53 04 34 73
33 47 55 62 57   08 21 77 31 05   64 74 04 93 42   20 19 09 71 46   37 32 69 69 89
56 66 25 32 38   64 70 26 27 67   77 40 04 34 63   98 99 89 31 16   12 90 50 28 96
88 40 52 02 29   82 69 34 50 21   74 00 91 27 52   98 72 03 45 65   30 89 71 45 91
87 63 88 23 62   51 07 69 59 02   89 49 14 98 53   41 92 36 07 76   85 37 84 37 47

32 25 21 15 08   82 34 57 57 35   22 03 33 48 84   37 37 29 38 37   89 76 25 09 69
44 61 88 23 13   01 59 47 64 04   99 59 96 20 30   87 31 33 69 45   58 48 00 83 48
94 44 08 67 79   41 61 41 15 60   11 88 83 24 82   24 07 78 61 89   42 58 88 22 16
13 24 40 09 00   65 46 38 61 12   90 62 41 11 59   85 18 42 61 29   88 76 04 21 80
78 27 84 05 99   85 75 67 80 05   57 05 71 70 21   31 99 99 06 96   53 99 25 13 63

42 39 30 02 34   99 46 68 45 15   19 74 15 50 17   44 80 13 86 38   40 45 82 13 44
04 52 43 96 38   13 83 80 72 34   20 84 56 19 49   59 14 85 42 99   71 16 34 33 79
82 85 77 30 16   69 32 46 46 30   84 20 68 72 98   94 62 63 59 44   00 89 06 15 87
38 48 84 88 24   55 46 48 60 06   90 08 83 83 98   40 90 88 25 26   85 74 55 80 85
91 19 05 68 22   58 04 63 21 16   23 38 25 43 32   98 94 65 35 35   16 91 07 12 43

54 81 87 21 31   40 46 17 62 63   99 71 14 12 64   51 68 50 60 78   22 69 51 98 37
65 43 75 12 91   20 36 25 57 92   33 65 95 48 75   00 06 65 25 90   16 29 34 14 43
49 98 71 31 80   59 57 32 43 07   85 06 64 75 27   29 17 06 11 30   68 70 97 87 21
03 98 68 89 39   71 87 32 14 99   42 10 25 37 30   08 27 75 43 97   54 20 69 93 50
56 04 21 34 92   89 81 52 15 12   84 11 12 66 87   47 21 06 86 08   35 39 52 28 09

48 09 36 95 36   20 82 53 32 89   92 68 50 88 17   37 92 02 23 43   63 24 69 80 91
23 97 10 96 57   74 07 95 26 44   93 08 43 30 41   86 45 74 33 78   84 33 38 76 73
43 97 55 45 98   35 69 45 96 80   46 26 39 96 33   60 20 73 30 79   17 19 03 47 28
40 05 08 50 79   89 58 19 86 48   27 98 99 24 08   94 19 15 81 29   82 14 35 88 03
66 97 10 69 02   25 36 43 71 76   00 67 56 12 69   07 89 55 63 31   50 72 20 33 36
```

These random numbers are from Table XIX in *Statistical Tables and Formulas* by A. Hald, John Wiley and Sons, 1952.

TABLE 1 (*continued*)

```
15 62 38 72 92   03 76 09 30 75   77 80 04 24 54   67 60 10 79 26   21 60 03 48 14
77 81 15 14 67   55 24 22 20 55   36 93 67 69 37   72 22 43 46 32   56 15 75 25 12
18 87 05 09 96   45 14 72 41 46   12 67 46 72 02   59 06 17 49 12   73 28 23 52 48
08 58 53 63 66   13 07 04 48 71   39 07 46 96 40   20 86 79 11 81   74 11 15 23 17
16 07 79 57 61   42 19 68 15 12   60 21 59 12 07   04 99 88 22 39   75 16 69 13 84

54 13 05 46 17   05 51 24 53 57   46 51 14 39 17   21 39 89 07 35   47 87 44 36 62
95 27 23 17 39   80 24 44 48 93   75 94 77 09 23   48 75 91 69 03   55 51 09 74 47
22 39 44 74 80   25 95 28 63 90   41 19 48 46 72   51 12 97 39 83   35 83 23 17 29
69 95 21 30 11   98 81 38 00 53   41 40 04 16 78   67 29 83 41 18   30 90 44 37 64
75 75 63 97 12   11 57 05 86 52   82 72 47 72 14   37 72 69 75 48   72 21 52 51 81

08 74 79 30 80   70 11 66 79 25   88 01 94 52 31   38 57 98 71 62   12 56 61 01 54
04 88 45 98 60   90 92 74 77 87   40 18 65 87 37   08 68 62 39 52   84 74 90 68 18
97 35 74 05 75   42 13 49 48 38   74 19 06 42 60   20 79 90 81 77   18 51 71 27 27
53 09 93 28 29   80 19 68 30 45   94 49 49 71 21   93 93 71 30 34   52 65 83 40 13
26 36 68 48 09   37 69 26 22 80   23 34 10 45 70   83 51 07 37 44   62 96 74 42 64

49 16 57 15 79   56 63 22 94 28   11 39 69 55 38   53 06 97 20 42   09 14 90 43 48
03 51 79 78 74   75 23 73 75 98   47 85 07 26 02   61 28 01 22 16   14 12 15 67 22
21 88 87 28 48   23 44 03 03 80   53 89 07 87 93   30 17 84 17 74   16 53 31 39 01
56 41 73 33 41   59 16 59 50 98   24 24 87 06 75   99 52 09 88 05   86 25 43 50 94
72 39 19 70 17   01 04 01 22 33   04 84 63 27 65   84 39 45 55 31   95 88 93 90 37

97 28 25 81 49   71 69 22 04 51   56 46 56 15 10   69 59 99 50 29   33 50 16 93 09
18 87 02 72 08   74 52 16 03 82   20 19 66 23 62   37 51 04 89 31   32 19 59 85 57
53 40 11 75 45   13 56 85 31 37   09 17 71 96 79   39 50 79 27 62   71 14 95 53 03
60 49 03 41 56   78 33 77 28 92   21 90 10 62 01   97 06 45 01 19   95 12 24 18 52
09 16 12 75 04   39 69 95 00 48   26 85 28 73 08   66 92 10 66 75   62 61 27 82 57

64 20 19 87 54   88 15 12 54 24   06 99 57 07 28   51 34 54 98 50   70 88 02 86 48
31 28 07 58 77   03 98 26 76 09   10 44 57 61 28   60 29 85 70 79   80 29 19 98 92
80 04 28 47 76   35 73 67 78 28   09 39 88 63 74   41 26 92 42 33   06 80 06 33 84
24 60 22 51 19   34 54 08 24 73   86 72 11 44 69   76 90 81 17 85   57 47 35 16 84
59 16 11 26 29   18 97 78 44 43   58 92 78 70 80   09 65 32 68 26   65 73 90 50 46

58 54 29 98 27   40 51 92 07 13   58 41 59 56 94   16 32 51 42 54   77 37 13 85 19
20 18 34 22 73   57 40 67 17 28   63 57 74 36 18   65 55 25 50 68   35 90 00 03 38
53 90 46 56 19   50 58 33 84 53   14 74 17 40 73   86 11 04 02 04   02 28 49 62 36
97 16 93 94 65   70 95 95 83 20   91 42 57 95 63   00 86 29 02 53   02 27 86 70 95
72 55 71 70 92   04 22 53 19 29   67 29 13 56 70   45 73 45 05 04   32 43 30 93 41

99 19 72 58 35   49 09 26 00 74   26 42 94 52 02   83 31 85 65 66   31 97 67 52 15
48 21 49 72 97   79 19 64 81 82   78 92 51 96 51   28 79 13 20 82   34 81 39 46 86
52 37 68 15 53   22 98 30 16 31   83 24 87 69 29   24 85 44 25 50   75 62 83 95 41
97 50 52 53 52   26 78 21 68 69   57 79 42 40 89   55 81 75 24 52   51 32 79 97 05
36 05 09 18 11   71 01 63 17 60   11 65 19 43 07   44 86 19 58 92   23 71 32 96 19

20 79 70 09 30   81 14 53 80 93   71 94 10 18 14   83 69 76 53 25   27 36 65 65 05
13 07 89 72 08   00 37 75 14 94   83 85 06 72 66   07 47 30 17 11   16 02 63 97 30
94 26 82 37 43   34 23 00 14 50   96 85 41 17 71   69 20 15 98 82   79 69 68 50 31
13 55 88 38 43   75 37 43 83 85   53 74 54 62 99   68 93 74 43 95   06 26 79 78 87
02 44 24 97 71   97 93 12 70 89   42 52 33 24 91   05 87 53 15 77   49 92 83 97 80

34 90 96 63 54   22 84 36 38 99   85 36 25 03 27   49 24 72 10 50   95 14 18 26 64
13 67 06 34 98   04 20 80 12 54   01 18 54 20 76   92 10 47 04 65   54 45 82 42 90
18 75 55 82 66   34 77 27 71 79   67 65 85 92 68   16 43 83 18 74   12 48 68 87 22
91 25 52 57 15   21 54 40 05 50   67 51 66 45 69   84 72 74 32 30   17 70 40 90 24
76 24 00 14 92   14 29 12 17 73   77 46 44 24 30   48 50 36 30 24   93 08 01 39 37
```

TABLE 2

AREAS UNDER THE UNIT NORMAL CURVE: $\int_0^z \frac{1}{\sqrt{2\pi}} e^{-t^2/2}\, dt$

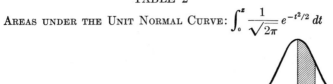

z	.00	.01	.02	.03	.04	.05	.06	.07	.08	.09
0.0	.0000	.0040	.0080	.0120	.0160	.0199	.0239	.0279	.0319	.0359
0.1	.0398	.0438	.0478	.0517	.0557	.0596	.0636	.0675	.0714	.0753
0.2	.0793	.0832	.0871	.0910	.0948	.0987	.1026	.1064	.1103	.1141
0.3	.1179	.1217	.1255	.1293	.1331	.1368	.1406	.1443	.1480	.1517
0.4	.1554	.1591	.1628	.1664	.1700	.1736	.1772	.1808	.1844	.1879
0.5	.1915	.1950	.1985	.2019	.2054	.2088	.2123	.2157	.2190	.2224
0.6	.2257	.2291	.2324	.2357	.2389	.2422	.2454	.2486	.2517	.2549
0.7	.2580	.2611	.2642	.2673	.2703	.2734	.2764	.2794	.2823	.2852
0.8	.2881	.2910	.2939	.2967	.2995	.3023	.3051	.3078	.3106	.3133
0.9	.3159	.3186	.3212	.3238	.3264	.3289	.3315	.3340	.3365	.3389
1.0	.3413	.3438	.3461	.3485	.3508	.3531	.3554	.3577	.3599	.3621
1.1	.3643	.3665	.3686	.3708	.3729	.3749	.3770	.3790	.3810	.3830
1.2	.3849	.3869	.3888	.3907	.3925	.3944	.3962	.3980	.3997	.4015
1.3	.4032	.4049	.4066	.4082	.4099	.4115	.4131	.4147	.4162	.4177
1.4	.4192	.4207	.4222	.4236	.4251	.4265	.4279	.4292	.4306	.4319
1.5	.4332	.4345	.4357	.4370	.4382	.4394	.4406	.4418	.4429	.4441
1.6	.4452	.4463	.4474	.4484	.4495	.4505	.4515	.4525	.4535	.4545
1.7	.4554	.4564	.4573	.4582	.4591	.4599	.4608	.4616	.4625	.4633
1.8	.4641	.4649	.4656	.4664	.4671	.4678	.4686	.4693	.4699	.4706
1.9	.4713	.4719	.4726	.4732	.4738	.4744	.4750	.4756	.4761	.4767
2.0	.4772	.4778	.4783	.4788	.4793	.4798	.4803	.4808	.4812	.4817
2.1	.4821	.4826	.4830	.4834	.4838	.4842	.4846	.4850	.4854	.4857
2.2	.4861	.4864	.4868	.4871	.4875	.4878	.4881	.4884	.4887	.4890
2.3	.4893	.4896	.4898	.4901	.4904	.4906	.4909	.4911	.4913	.4916
2.4	.4918	.4920	.4922	.4925	.4927	.4929	.4931	.4932	.4934	.4936
2.5	.4938	.4940	.4941	.4943	.4945	.4946	.4948	.4949	.4951	.4952
2.6	.4953	.4955	.4956	.4957	.4959	.4960	.4961	.4962	.4963	.4964
2.7	.4965	.4966	.4967	.4968	.4969	.4970	.4971	.4972	.4973	.4974
2.8	.4974	.4975	.4976	.4977	.4977	.4978	.4979	.4979	.4980	.4981
2.9	.4981	.4982	.4982	.4983	.4984	.4984	.4985	.4985	.4986	.4986
3.0	.4987	.4987	.4987	.4988	.4988	.4989	.4989	.4989	.4990	.4990

From *Elementary Statistics*, by Paul G. Hoel, John Wiley and Sons, 1960.

TABLE 3

Selected Percentiles of the Chi-Square Distribution

u \ n	.005	.010	.025	.050	.100	.250	.500	.750	.900	.950	.975	.990	.995
1	$.0^4393$	$.0^3157$	$.0^3982$	$.0^3393$	$.0^2158$	.102	.455	1.32	2.71	3.84	5.02	6.63	7.88
2	.0100	.0201	.0506	.103	.211	.575	1.39	2.77	4.61	5.99	7.38	9.21	10.6
3	.0717	.115	.216	.352	.584	1.21	2.37	4.11	6.25	7.81	9.35	11.3	12.8
4	.207	.297	.484	.711	1.06	1.92	3.36	5.39	7.78	9.49	11.1	13.3	14.9
5	.412	.554	.831	1.15	1.61	2.67	4.35	6.63	9.24	11.1	12.8	15.1	16.7
6	.676	.872	1.24	1.64	2.20	3.45	5.35	7.84	10.6	12.6	14.4	16.8	18.5
7	.989	1.24	1.69	2.17	2.83	4.25	6.35	9.04	12.0	14.1	16.0	18.5	20.3
8	1.34	1.65	2.18	2.73	3.49	5.07	7.34	10.2	13.4	15.5	17.5	20.1	22.0
9	1.73	2.09	2.70	3.33	4.17	5.90	8.34	11.4	14.7	16.9	19.0	21.7	23.6
10	2.16	2.56	3.25	3.94	4.87	6.74	9.34	12.5	16.0	18.3	20.5	23.2	25.2
11	2.60	3.05	3.82	4.57	5.58	7.58	10.3	13.7	17.3	19.7	21.9	24.7	26.8
12	3.07	3.57	4.40	5.23	6.30	8.44	11.3	14.8	18.5	21.0	23.3	26.2	28.3
13	3.57	4.11	5.01	5.89	7.04	9.30	12.3	16.0	19.8	22.4	24.7	27.7	29.8
14	4.07	4.66	5.63	6.57	7.79	10.2	13.3	17.1	21.1	23.7	26.1	29.1	31.3
15	4.60	5.23	6.26	7.26	8.55	11.0	14.3	18.2	22.3	25.0	27.5	30.6	32.8
16	5.14	5.81	6.91	7.96	9.31	11.9	15.3	19.4	23.5	26.3	28.8	32.0	34.3
17	5.70	6.41	7.56	8.67	10.1	12.8	16.3	20.5	24.8	27.6	30.2	33.4	35.7
18	6.26	7.01	8.23	9.39	10.9	13.7	17.3	21.6	26.0	28.9	31.5	34.8	37.2
19	6.84	7.63	8.91	10.1	11.7	14.6	18.3	22.7	27.2	30.1	32.9	36.2	38.6
20	7.43	8.26	9.59	10.9	12.4	15.5	19.3	23.8	28.4	31.4	34.2	37.6	40.0
21	8.03	8.90	10.3	11.6	13.2	16.3	20.3	24.9	29.6	32.7	35.5	38.9	41.4
22	8.64	9.54	11.0	12.3	14.0	17.2	21.3	26.0	30.8	33.9	36.8	40.3	42.8
23	9.26	10.2	11.7	13.1	14.8	18.1	22.3	27.1	32.0	35.2	38.1	41.6	44.2
24	9.89	10.9	12.4	13.8	15.7	19.0	23.3	28.2	33.2	36.4	39.4	43.0	45.6
25	10.5	11.5	13.1	14.6	16.5	19.9	24.3	29.3	34.4	37.7	40.6	44.3	46.9
26	11.2	12.2	13.8	15.4	17.3	20.8	25.3	30.4	35.6	38.9	41.9	45.6	48.3
27	11.8	12.9	14.6	16.2	18.1	21.7	26.3	31.5	36.7	40.1	43.2	47.0	49.6
28	12.5	13.6	15.3	16.9	18.9	22.7	27.3	32.6	37.9	41.3	44.5	48.3	51.0
29	13.1	14.3	16.0	17.7	19.8	23.6	28.3	33.7	39.1	42.6	45.7	49.6	52.3
30	13.8	15.0	16.8	18.5	20.6	24.5	29.3	34.8	40.3	43.8	47.0	50.9	53.7

Let $F(x|n)$ denote the chi-square distribution function with n degrees of freedom, and let $F^{-1}(u|n)$ denote its inverse. The table gives the values of $F^{-1}(u|n)$ for selected values of u and n.

This table is reproduced from A. M. Mood, *Introduction to the Theory of Statistics*, McGraw-Hill Book Company, 1950. It is abridged from "Tables of the incomplete beta function and of the chi-square distribution," *Biometrika*, Vol. 32 (1941). It is published here with the permission of the Biometrika Trustees, and of A. M. Mood and the McGraw-Hill Book Company.

TABLE 4

Selected Percentiles of the t Distribution

n \ u	.75	.90	.95	.975	.99	.995	.9995
1	1.000	3.078	6.314	12.706	31.821	63.657	636.619
2	.816	1.886	2.920	4.303	6.965	9.925	31.598
3	.765	1.638	2.353	3.182	4.541	5.841	12.941
4	.741	1.533	2.132	2.776	3.747	4.604	8.610
5	.727	1.476	2 015	2.571	3.365	4.032	6.859
6	.718	1.440	1.943	2.447	3.143	3.707	5.959
7	.711	1.415	1.895	2.365	2.998	3.499	5.405
8	.706	1.397	1.860	2.306	2.896	3.355	5.041
9	.703	1.383	1.833	2.262	2.821	3.250	4.781
10	.700	1.372	1.812	2.228	2.764	3.169	4.587
11	.697	1.363	1.796	2.201	2.718	3.106	4.437
12	.695	1.356	1.782	2.179	2.681	3.055	4.318
13	.694	1.350	1.771	2.160	2.650	3.012	4.221
14	.692	1.345	1.761	2.145	2.624	2.977	4.140
15	.691	1.341	1.753	2.131	2.602	2.947	4.073
16	.690	1.337	1.746	2.120	2.583	2.921	4.015
17	.689	1.333	1.740	2.110	2.567	2.898	3.965
18	.688	1.330	1.734	2.101	2.552	2.878	3.922
19	.688	1.328	1.729	2.093	2.539	2.861	3.883
20	.687	1.325	1.725	2.086	2.528	2.845	3.850
21	.686	1.323	1.721	2.080	2.518	2.831	3.819
22	.686	1.321	1.717	2.074	2.508	2.819	3.792
23	.685	1.319	1.714	2.069	2.500	2.807	3.767
24	.685	1.318	1.711	2.064	2.492	2.797	3.745
25	.684	1.316	1.708	2.060	2.485	2.787	3.725
26	.684	1.315	1.706	2.056	2.479	2.779	3.707
27	.684	1.314	1.703	2.052	2.473	2.771	3.690
28	.683	1.313	1.701	2.048	2.467	2.763	3.674
29	.683	1.311	1.699	2.045	2.462	2.756	3.659
30	.683	1.310	1.697	2.042	2.457	2.750	3.646
40	.681	1.303	1.684	2.021	2.423	2.704	3.551
60	.679	1.296	1.671	2.000	2.390	2.660	3.460
120	.677	1.289	1.658	1.980	2.358	2.617	3.373
∞	.674	1.282	1.645	1.960	2.326	2.576	3.291

Let $F(x|n)$ denote the t distribution function with n degrees of freedom, and let $F^{-1}(u|n)$ denote its inverse. The table gives the values of $F^{-1}(u|n)$ for selected values of u and n.

This table is reproduced from A. M. Mood, *Introduction to the Theory of Statistics*, McGraw-Hill Book Company, 1950. It is abridged from the *Statistical Tables* of R. A. Fisher and Frank Yates published by Oliver & Boyd, Ltd., Edinburgh and London, 1938. It is published here with the permission of the authors and their publishers.

TABLE 5

Selected Percentiles of the F Distribution

n	u	1	2	3	4	5	6	7	8	9	10	12	15	20	30	60	120	∞
1	.90	39.9	49.5	53.6	55.8	57.2	58.2	58.9	59.4	59.9	60.2	60.7	61.2	61.7	62.3	62.8	63.1	63.3
	.95	161	200	216	225	230	234	237	239	241	242	244	246	248	250	252	253	254
	.975	648	800	864	900	922	937	948	957	963	969	977	985	993	1000	1010	1010	1020
	.99	4,050	5,000	5,400	5,620	5,760	5,860	5,930	5,980	6,020	6,060	6,110	6,160	6,210	6,260	6,310	6,340	6,370
	.995	16,200	20,000	21,600	22,500	23,100	23,400	23,700	23,900	24,100	24,200	24,400	24,600	24,800	25,000	25,000	25,000	25,500
2	.90	8.53	9.00	9.16	9.24	9.29	9.33	9.35	9.37	9.38	9.39	9.41	9.42	9.44	9.46	9.47	9.48	9.49
	.95	18.5	19.0	19.2	19.2	19.3	19.3	19.4	19.4	19.4	19.4	19.4	19.4	19.5	19.5	19.5	19.5	19.5
	.975	38.5	39.0	39.2	39.2	39.3	39.3	39.4	39.4	39.4	39.4	39.4	39.4	39.4	39.5	39.5	39.5	39.5
	.99	98.5	99.0	99.2	99.2	99.3	99.3	99.4	99.4	99.4	99.4	99.4	99.4	99.4	99.5	99.5	99.5	99.5
	.995	199	199	199	199	199	199	199	199	199	199	199	199	199	199	199	199	199
3	.90	5.54	5.46	5.39	5.34	5.31	5.28	5.27	5.25	5.24	5.23	5.22	5.20	5.18	5.17	5.15	5.14	5.13
	.95	10.1	9.55	9.28	9.12	9.01	8.94	8.89	8.85	8.81	8.79	8.74	8.70	8.66	8.62	8.57	8.55	8.53
	.975	17.4	16.0	15.4	15.1	14.9	14.7	14.6	14.5	14.5	14.4	14.3	14.3	14.2	14.1	14.0	13.9	13.9
	.99	34.1	30.8	29.5	28.7	28.2	27.9	27.7	27.5	27.3	27.2	27.1	26.9	26.7	26.5	26.3	26.2	26.1
	.995	55.6	49.8	47.5	46.2	45.4	44.8	44.4	44.1	43.9	43.7	43.4	43.1	42.8	42.5	42.1	42.0	41.8
4	.90	4.54	4.32	4.19	4.11	4.05	4.01	3.98	3.95	3.93	3.92	3.90	3.87	3.84	3.82	3.79	3.78	3.76
	.95	7.71	6.94	6.59	6.39	6.26	6.16	6.09	6.04	6.00	5.96	5.91	5.86	5.80	5.75	5.69	5.66	5.63
	.975	12.2	10.6	9.98	9.60	9.36	9.20	9.07	8.98	8.90	8.84	8.75	8.66	8.56	8.46	8.36	8.31	8.26
	.99	21.2	18.0	16.7	16.0	15.5	15.2	15.0	14.8	14.7	14.5	14.4	14.2	14.0	13.8	13.7	13.6	13.5
	.995	31.3	26.3	24.3	23.2	22.5	22.0	21.6	21.4	21.1	20.7	20.7	20.4	20.2	19.9	19.6	19.5	19.3
5	.90	4.06	3.78	3.62	3.52	3.45	3.40	3.37	3.34	3.32	3.30	3.27	3.24	3.21	3.17	3.14	3.12	3.11
	.95	6.61	5.79	5.41	5.19	5.05	4.95	4.88	4.82	4.77	4.74	4.68	4.62	4.56	4.50	4.43	4.40	4.37
	.975	10.0	8.43	7.76	7.39	7.15	6.98	6.85	6.76	6.68	6.62	6.52	6.43	6.33	6.23	6.12	6.07	6.02
	.99	16.3	13.3	12.1	11.4	11.0	10.7	10.5	10.3	10.2	10.1	9.89	9.72	9.55	9.38	9.20	9.11	9.02
	.995	22.8	18.3	16.5	15.6	14.9	14.5	14.2	14.0	13.8	13.6	13.4	13.1	12.9	12.7	12.4	12.3	12.1
6	.90	3.78	3.46	3.29	3.18	3.11	3.05	3.01	2.98	2.96	2.94	2.90	2.87	2.84	2.80	2.76	2.74	2.72
	.95	5.99	5.14	4.76	4.53	4.39	4.28	4.21	4.15	4.10	4.06	4.00	3.94	3.87	3.81	3.74	3.70	3.67
	.975	8.81	7.26	6.60	6.23	5.99	5.82	5.70	5.60	5.52	5.46	5.37	5.27	5.17	5.07	4.96	4.90	4.85
	.99	13.7	10.9	9.78	9.15	8.75	8.47	8.26	8.10	7.98	7.87	7.72	7.56	7.40	7.23	7.06	6.97	6.88
	.995	18.6	14.5	12.9	12.0	11.5	11.1	10.8	10.6	10.4	10.2	10.0	9.81	9.59	9.36	9.12	9.00	8.88
7	.90	3.59	3.26	3.07	2.96	2.88	2.83	2.78	2.75	2.72	2.70	2.67	2.63	2.59	2.56	2.51	2.49	2.47
	.95	5.59	4.74	4.35	4.12	3.97	3.87	3.79	3.73	3.68	3.64	3.57	3.51	3.44	3.38	3.30	3.27	3.23
	.975	8.07	6.54	5.89	5.52	5.29	5.12	4.99	4.90	4.82	4.76	4.67	4.57	4.47	4.36	4.25	4.20	4.14
	.99	12.2	9.55	8.45	7.85	7.46	7.19	6.99	6.84	6.72	6.62	6.47	6.31	6.16	5.99	5.82	5.74	5.65
	.995	16.2	12.4	10.9	10.1	9.52	9.16	8.89	8.68	8.51	8.38	8.18	7.97	7.75	7.53	7.31	7.19	7.08
8	.90	3.46	3.11	2.92	2.81	2.73	2.67	2.62	2.59	2.56	2.54	2.50	2.46	2.42	2.38	2.34	2.31	2.29
	.95	5.32	4.46	4.07	3.84	3.69	3.58	3.50	3.44	3.39	3.35	3.28	3.22	3.15	3.08	3.01	2.97	2.93
	.975	7.57	6.06	5.42	5.05	4.82	4.65	4.53	4.43	4.36	4.30	4.20	4.10	4.00	3.89	3.78	3.73	3.67
	.99	11.3	8.65	7.59	7.01	6.63	6.37	6.18	6.03	5.91	5.81	5.67	5.52	5.36	5.20	5.03	4.95	4.86
	.995	14.7	11.0	9.60	8.81	8.30	7.95	7.69	7.50	7.34	7.21	7.01	6.81	6.61	6.40	6.18	6.06	5.95

n	u	1	2	3	4	5	6	7	8	9	10	12	15	20	30	60	120	∞
9	.90	3.36	3.01	2.81	2.69	2.61	2.55	2.51	2.47	2.44	2.42	2.38	2.34	2.30	2.25	2.21	2.18	2.16
	.95	5.12	4.26	3.86	3.63	3.48	3.37	3.29	3.23	3.18	3.14	3.07	3.01	2.94	2.86	2.79	2.75	2.71
	.975	7.21	5.71	5.08	4.72	4.48	4.32	4.20	4.10	4.03	3.96	3.87	3.77	3.67	3.56	3.45	3.39	3.33
	.99	10.6	8.02	6.99	6.42	6.06	5.80	5.61	5.47	5.35	5.26	5.11	4.96	4.81	4.65	4.48	4.40	4.31
	.995	13.6	10.1	8.72	7.96	7.47	7.13	6.88	6.69	6.54	6.42	6.23	6.03	5.83	5.62	5.41	5.30	5.19
10	.90	3.29	2.92	2.73	2.61	2.52	2.46	2.41	2.38	2.35	2.32	2.28	2.24	2.20	2.15	2.11	2.08	2.06
	.95	4.96	4.10	3.71	3.48	3.33	3.22	3.14	3.07	3.02	2.98	2.91	2.84	2.77	2.70	2.62	2.58	2.54
	.975	6.94	5.46	4.83	4.47	4.24	4.07	3.95	3.85	3.78	3.72	3.62	3.52	3.42	3.31	3.20	3.14	3.08
	.99	10.0	7.56	6.55	5.99	5.64	5.39	5.20	5.06	4.94	4.85	4.71	4.56	4.41	4.25	4.08	4.00	3.91
	.995	12.8	9.43	8.08	7.34	6.87	6.54	6.30	6.12	5.97	5.85	5.66	5.47	5.27	5.07	4.86	4.75	4.64
12	.90	3.18	2.81	2.61	2.48	2.39	2.33	2.28	2.24	2.21	2.19	2.15	2.10	2.06	2.01	1.96	1.93	1.90
	.95	4.75	3.89	3.49	3.26	3.11	3.00	2.91	2.85	2.80	2.75	2.69	2.62	2.54	2.47	2.38	2.34	2.30
	.975	6.55	5.10	4.47	4.12	3.89	3.73	3.61	3.51	3.44	3.37	3.28	3.18	3.07	2.96	2.85	2.79	2.72
	.99	9.33	6.93	5.95	5.41	5.06	4.82	4.64	4.50	4.39	4.30	4.16	4.01	3.86	3.70	3.54	3.45	3.36
	.995	11.8	8.51	7.23	6.52	6.07	5.76	5.52	5.35	5.20	5.09	4.91	4.72	4.53	4.33	4.12	4.01	3.90
15	.90	3.07	2.70	2.49	2.36	2.27	2.21	2.16	2.12	2.09	2.06	2.02	1.97	1.92	1.87	1.82	1.79	1.76
	.95	4.54	3.68	3.29	3.06	2.90	2.79	2.71	2.64	2.59	2.54	2.48	2.40	2.33	2.25	2.16	2.11	2.07
	.975	6.20	4.77	4.15	3.80	3.58	3.41	3.29	3.20	3.12	3.06	2.96	2.86	2.76	2.64	2.52	2.46	2.40
	.99	8.68	6.36	5.42	4.89	4.56	4.32	4.14	4.00	3.89	3.80	3.67	3.52	3.37	3.21	3.05	2.96	2.87
	.995	10.8	7.70	6.48	5.80	5.37	5.07	4.85	4.67	4.54	4.42	4.25	4.07	3.88	3.69	3.48	3.37	3.26
20	.90	2.97	2.59	2.38	2.25	2.16	2.09	2.04	2.00	1.96	1.94	1.89	1.84	1.79	1.74	1.68	1.64	1.61
	.95	4.35	3.49	3.10	2.87	2.71	2.60	2.51	2.45	2.39	2.35	2.28	2.20	2.12	2.04	1.95	1.90	1.84
	.975	5.87	4.46	3.86	3.51	3.29	3.13	3.01	2.91	2.84	2.77	2.68	2.57	2.46	2.35	2.22	2.16	2.09
	.99	8.10	5.85	4.94	4.43	4.10	3.87	3.70	3.56	3.46	3.37	3.23	3.09	2.94	2.78	2.61	2.52	2.42
	.995	9.94	6.99	5.82	5.17	4.76	4.47	4.26	4.09	3.96	3.85	3.68	3.50	3.32	3.12	2.92	2.81	2.69
30	.90	2.88	2.49	2.28	2.14	2.05	1.98	1.93	1.88	1.85	1.82	1.77	1.72	1.67	1.61	1.54	1.50	1.46
	.95	4.17	3.32	2.92	2.69	2.53	2.42	2.33	2.27	2.21	2.16	2.09	2.01	1.93	1.84	1.74	1.68	1.62
	.975	5.57	4.18	3.59	3.25	3.03	2.87	2.75	2.65	2.57	2.51	2.41	2.31	2.20	2.07	1.94	1.87	1.79
	.99	7.56	5.39	4.51	4.02	3.70	3.47	3.30	3.17	3.07	2.98	2.84	2.70	2.55	2.39	2.21	2.11	2.01
	.995	9.18	6.35	5.24	4.62	4.23	3.95	3.74	3.58	3.45	3.34	3.18	3.01	2.82	2.63	2.42	2.30	2.18
60	.90	2.79	2.39	2.18	2.04	1.95	1.87	1.82	1.77	1.74	1.71	1.66	1.60	1.54	1.48	1.40	1.35	1.29
	.95	4.00	3.15	2.76	2.53	2.37	2.25	2.17	2.10	2.04	1.99	1.92	1.84	1.75	1.65	1.53	1.47	1.39
	.975	5.29	3.93	3.34	3.01	2.79	2.63	2.51	2.41	2.33	2.27	2.17	2.06	1.94	1.82	1.67	1.58	1.48
	.99	7.08	4.98	4.13	3.65	3.34	3.12	2.95	2.82	2.72	2.63	2.50	2.35	2.20	2.03	1.84	1.73	1.60
	.995	8.49	5.80	4.73	4.14	3.76	3.49	3.29	3.13	3.01	2.90	2.74	2.57	2.39	2.19	1.96	1.83	1.69
120	.90	2.75	2.35	2.13	1.99	1.90	1.82	1.77	1.72	1.68	1.65	1.60	1.54	1.48	1.41	1.32	1.26	1.19
	.95	3.92	3.07	2.68	2.45	2.29	2.18	2.09	2.02	1.96	1.91	1.83	1.75	1.66	1.55	1.43	1.35	1.25
	.975	5.15	3.80	3.23	2.89	2.67	2.52	2.39	2.30	2.22	2.16	2.05	1.94	1.82	1.69	1.53	1.43	1.31
	.99	6.85	4.79	3.95	3.48	3.17	2.96	2.79	2.66	2.56	2.47	2.34	2.19	2.03	1.86	1.66	1.53	1.38
	.995	8.18	5.54	4.50	3.92	3.55	3.28	3.09	2.93	2.81	2.71	2.54	2.37	2.19	1.98	1.75	1.61	1.43
∞	.90	2.71	2.30	2.08	1.94	1.85	1.77	1.72	1.67	1.63	1.60	1.55	1.49	1.42	1.34	1.24	1.17	1.00
	.95	3.84	3.00	2.60	2.37	2.21	2.10	2.01	1.94	1.88	1.83	1.75	1.67	1.57	1.46	1.32	1.22	1.00
	.975	5.02	3.69	3.12	2.79	2.57	2.41	2.29	2.19	2.11	2.05	1.94	1.83	1.71	1.57	1.39	1.27	1.00
	.99	6.63	4.61	3.78	3.32	3.02	2.80	2.64	2.51	2.41	2.32	2.18	2.04	1.88	1.70	1.47	1.32	1.00
	.995	7.88	5.30	4.28	3.72	3.35	3.09	2.90	2.74	2.62	2.52	2.36	2.19	2.00	1.79	1.53	1.36	1.00

Let $F(x|m,n)$ denote the F distribution function with m and n degrees of freedom, that is, the distribution function of the ratio nY/mX, where X and Y are chi-square distributed quantities whose degrees of freedom are n and m, respectively. Let $F^{-1}(u|m,n)$ denote the inverse of the distribution function $F'(x|m,n)$.

The table gives the values of $F^{-1}(u|m,n)$ for selected values of u, m, and n.

This table is reproduced from A. M. Mood, *Introduction to the Theory of Statistics*, McGraw-Hill Book Company, 1950. It is abridged from "Tables of percentage points of the inverted beta distribution," *Biometrika*, Vol. 33 (1943). It is published here with the permission of the Biometrika Trustees, and of A. M. Mood and the McGraw-Hill Book Company.

TABLE 6

LOGARITHMS OF FACTORIALS

n	log n!	n	log n!	n	log n!	n	log n!	n	log n!	n	log n!
1	0·0000	51	66·1906	101	159·9743	151	264·9359	201	377·2001		
2	0·3010	52	67·9066	102	161·9829	152	267·1177	202	379·5054		
3	0·7782	53	69·6309	103	163·9958	153	269·3024	203	381·8129		
4	1·3802	54	71·3633	104	166·0128	154	271·4899	204	384·1226		
5	2·0792	55	73·1037	105	168·0340	155	273·6803	205	386·4343		
6	2·8573	56	74·8519	106	170·0593	156	275·8734	206	388·7482		
7	3·7024	57	76·6077	107	172·0887	157	278·0693	207	391·0642		
8	4·6055	58	78·3712	108	174·1221	158	280·2679	208	393·3822		
9	5·5598	59	80·1420	109	176·1595	159	282·4693	209	395·7024		
10	6·5598	60	81·9202	110	178·2009	160	284·6735	210	398·0246		
11	7·6012	61	83·7055	111	180·2462	161	286·8803	211	400·3489		
12	8·6803	62	85·4979	112	182·2955	162	289·0898	212	402·6752		
13	9·7943	63	87·2972	113	184·3485	163	291·3020	213	405·0036		
14	10·9404	64	89·1034	114	186·4054	164	293·5168	214	407·3340		
15	12·1165	65	90·9163	115	188·4661	165	295·7343	215	409·6664		
16	13·3206	66	92·7359	116	190·5306	166	297·9544	216	412·0009		
17	14·5511	67	94·5619	117	192·5988	167	300·1771	217	414·3373		
18	15·8063	68	96·3945	118	194·6707	168	302·4024	218	416·6758		
19	17·0851	69	98·2333	119	196·7462	169	304·6303	219	419·0162		
20	18·3861	70	100·0784	120	198·8254	170	306·8608	220	421·3587		
21	19·7083	71	101·9297	121	200·9082	171	309·0938	221	423·7031		
22	21·0508	72	103·7870	122	202·9945	172	311·3293	222	426·0494		
23	22·4125	73	105·6503	123	205·0844	173	313·5674	223	428·3977		
24	23·7927	74	107·5196	124	207·1779	174	315·8079	224	430·7480		
25	25·1906	75	109·3946	125	209·2748	175	318·0509	225	433·1002		
26	26·6056	76	111·2754	126	211·3751	176	320·2965	226	435·4543		
27	28·0370	77	113·1619	127	213·4790	177	322·5444	227	437·8103		
28	29·4841	78	115·0540	128	215·5862	178	324·7948	228	440·1682		
29	30·9465	79	116·9516	129	217·6967	179	327·0477	229	442·5281		
30	32·4237	80	118·8547	130	219·8107	180	329·3030	230	444·8898		
31	33·9150	81	120·7632	131	221·9280	181	331·5606	231	447·2534		
32	35·4202	82	122·6770	132	224·0485	182	333·8207	232	449·6189		
33	36·9387	83	124·5961	133	226·1724	183	336·0832	233	451·9862		
34	38·4702	84	126·5204	134	228·2995	184	338·3480	234	454·3555		
35	40·0142	85	128·4498	135	230·4298	185	340·6152	235	456·7265		
36	41·5705	86	130·3843	136	232·5634	186	342·8847	236	459·0994		
37	43·1387	87	132·3238	137	234·7001	187	345·1565	237	461·4742		
38	44·7185	88	134·2683	138	236·8400	188	347·4307	238	463·8508		
39	46·3096	89	136·2177	139	238·9830	189	349·7071	239	466·2292		
40	47·9116	90	138·1719	140	241·1291	190	351·9859	240	468·6094		
41	49·5244	91	140·1310	141	243·2783	191	354·2669	241	470·9914		
42	51·1477	92	142·0948	142	245·4306	192	356·5502	242	473·3752		
43	52·7811	93	144·0632	143	247·5860	193	358·8358	243	475·7608		
44	54·4246	94	146·0364	144	249·7443	194	361·1236	244	478·1482		
45	56·0778	95	148·0141	145	251·9057	195	363·4136	245	480·5374		
46	57·7406	96	149·9964	146	254·0700	196	365·7059	246	482·9283		
47	59·4127	97	151·9831	147	256·2374	197	368·0003	247	485·3210		
48	61·0939	98	153·9744	148	258·4076	198	370·2970	248	487·7154		
49	62·7841	99	155·9700	149	260·5808	199	372·5959	249	490·1116		
50	64·4831	100	157·9700	150	262·7569	200	374·8969	250	492·5096		

From *Statistical Tables and Formulas*, by A. Hald, John Wiley and Sons, 1952.

TABLE 6 (*continued*)

n	log n!	n	log n!	n	log n!	n	log n!	n	log n!
251	494·9093	301	616·9644	351	742·6373	401	871·4096	451	1002·8931
252	497·3107	302	619·4444	352	745·1838	402	874·0138	452	1005·5482
253	499·7138	303	621·9258	353	747·7316	403	876·6191	453	1008·2043
254	502·1186	304	624·4087	354	750·2806	404	879·2255	454	1010·8614
255	504·5252	305	626·8930	355	752·8308	405	881·8329	455	1013·5194
256	506·9334	306	629·3787	356	755·3823	406	884·4415	456	1016·1783
257	509·3433	307	631·8659	357	757·9349	407	887·0510	457	1018·8383
258	511·7549	308	634·3544	358	760·4888	408	889·6617	458	1021·4991
259	514·1682	309	636·8444	359	763·0439	409	892·2734	459	1024·1609
260	516·5832	310	639·3357	360	765·6002	410	894·8862	460	1026·8237
261	518·9999	311	641·8285	361	768·1577	411	897·5001	461	1029·4874
262	521·4182	312	644·3226	362	770·7164	412	900·1150	462	1032·1520
263	523·8381	313	646·8182	363	773·2764	413	902·7309	463	1034·8176
264	526·2597	314	649·3151	364	775·8375	414	905·3479	464	1037·4841
265	528·6830	315	651·8134	365	778·3997	415	907·9660	465	1040·1516
266	531·1079	316	654·3131	366	780·9632	416	910·5850	466	1042·8200
267	533·5344	317	656·8142	367	783·5279	417	913·2052	467	1045·4893
268	535·9625	318	659·3166	368	786·0937	418	915·8264	468	1048·1595
269	538·3922	319	661·8204	369	788·6608	419	918·4486	469	1050·8307
270	540·8236	320	664·3255	370	791·2290	420	921·0718	470	1053·5028
271	543·2566	321	666·8320	371	793·7983	421	923·6961	471	1056·1758
272	545·6912	322	669·3399	372	796·3689	422	926·3214	472	1058·8498
273	548·1273	323	671·8491	373	798·9406	423	928·9478	473	1061·5246
274	550·5651	324	674·3596	374	801·5135	424	931·5751	474	1064·2004
275	553·0044	325	676·8715	375	804·0875	425	934·2035	475	1066·8771
276	555·4453	326	679·3847	376	806·6627	426	936·8329	476	1069·5547
277	557·8878	327	681·8993	377	809·2390	427	939·4633	477	1072·2332
278	560·3318	328	684·4152	378	811·8165	428	942·0948	478	1074·9127
279	562·7774	329	686·9324	379	814·3952	429	944·7272	479	1077·5930
280	565·2246	330	689·4509	380	816·9749	430	947·3607	480	1080·2742
281	567·6733	331	691·9707	381	819·5559	431	949·9952	481	1082·9564
282	570·1235	332	694·4918	382	822·1379	432	952·6307	482	1085·6394
283	572·5753	333	697·0143	383	824·7211	433	955·2672	483	1088·3234
284	575·0287	334	699·5380	384	827·3055	434	957·9047	484	1091·0082
285	577·4835	335	702·0631	385	829·8909	435	960·5431	485	1093·6940
286	579·9399	336	704·5894	386	832·4775	436	963·1826	486	1096·3806
287	582·3977	337	707·1170	387	835·0652	437	965·8231	487	1099·0681
288	584·8571	338	709·6460	388	837·6540	438	968·4646	488	1101·7565
289	587·3180	339	712·1762	389	840·2440	439	971·1071	489	1104·4458
290	589·7804	340	714·7076	390	842·8351	440	973·7505	490	1107·1360
291	592·2443	341	717·2404	391	845·4272	441	976·3949	491	1109·8271
292	594·7097	342	719·7744	392	848·0205	442	979·0404	492	1112·5191
293	597·1766	343	722·3097	393	850·6149	443	981·6868	493	1115·2119
294	599·6449	344	724·8463	394	853·2104	444	984·3342	494	1117·9057
295	602·1147	345	727·3841	395	855·8070	445	986·9825	495	1120·6003
296	604·5860	346	729·9232	396	858·4047	446	989·6318	496	1123·2958
297	607·0588	347	732·4635	397	861·0035	447	992·2822	497	1125·9921
298	609·5330	348	735·0051	398	863·6034	448	994·9334	498	1128·6893
299	612·0087	349	737·5479	399	866·2044	449	997·5857	499	1131·3874
300	614·4858	350	740·0920	400	868·8064	450	1000·2389	500	1134·0864

Answers to Exercises

1.1. (a) Discrete. (b) {Ala., $\cdots$, Wyo.}. (c) The student body of the university. (d) Put Alabama = 1, Alaska = 2, $\cdots$, Wyoming = 50.

1.3. (a) {emission, no emission}. (b) {1, 0}. (c) The results of an infinite sequence of trials.

1.5. (a) A: {no fish, one or more fish}. B: {0, 1, 2, 3, $\cdots$}. (b) Both discrete. (c) A: {0, 1} B: {0, 1, 2, 3, $\cdots$}.

1.7. (a) Continuous. (b) Weight: {$0 < X < 5$} in pounds. Spec. gr: {$2 < x < 8$}.

1.9. (a) Not random. This plan will favor students who regularly leave the building at noon. (b) Random. The shuffling will present difficulties. (c) Not random. This plan favors students presently taking English. It will also favor students in a certain classification (freshman, soph., jun., sen.) depending on the level of the course. (d) Random, provided that the first name is randomly selected.

SECTION 2

2.1. (a) {(0, 0), (0, 1), (1, 0), (1, 1)}.   (b)

(c)

2.3. (a), (b)

0	9	18	27	36	45	54	63	72	81
0	8	16	24	32	40	48	56	64	72
0	7	14	21	28	35	42	49	56	63
0	6	12	18	24	30	36	42	48	54
0	5	10	15	20	25	30	35	40	45
0	4	8	12	16	20	24	28	32	36
0	3	6	9	12	15	18	21	24	27
0	2	4	6	8	10	12	14	16	18
0	1	2	3	4	5	6	7	8	9
0	0	0	0	0	0	0	0	0	0

(c) 10.

2.5. (a) Good. (b) Not random. The number 5 would be much more likely than either 0 or 10. (c) Not random. The likeliest sum would be 7. (See Figure 2.3.) (d) Good. (e) Good, if it is used so infrequently that no "learning" can occur. (f) Good, provided that this final digit is not systematically assigned when the plates are made and given out. (g) Not quite random. The likeliest number is 1. (h) Good.

2.7. (a) Segment joining $(0, 0)$ and $(1, 1)$. (b) Interior of the triangle joining $(0, 0)$, $(1, 1)$, $(1, 0)$.

2.9. Arrange the sample points in a rect. array as follows:

$$(1, 1, 1), (1, 2, 1), (1, 3, 1), \cdots, (6, 6, 1)$$

$$(1, 1, 2), (1, 2, 2), (1, 3, 0), \cdots, (6, 6, 2)$$

$$\cdots \cdots \cdots \cdots \cdots \cdots \cdots \cdots \cdots$$

$$(1, 1, 6), (1, 2, 6), (1, 3, 6), \cdots, (6, 6, 6)$$

By the argument in Example 2.2, all the points in any row must be regarded as equally likely. Since only the third die varies in any column, all sample points in any column must be regarded as equally likely. Hence all 216 points are equally likely.

SECTION 3

3.1.

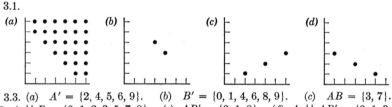

3.3. (a) $A' = \{2, 4, 5, 6, 9\}$. (b) $B' = \{0, 1, 4, 6, 8, 9\}$. (c) $AB = \{3, 7\}$. (d) $A \cup B = \{0, 1, 2, 3, 5, 7, 8\}$. (e) $AB' = \{0, 1, 8\}$. (f) $A \cup AB' = \{0, 1, 3, 7, 8\}$. (g) $A \cup A'B = \{0, 1, 2, 3, 5, 7, 8\}$.

3.5. (a) $A' = (0, .2) \cup (.5, 1)$. (b) $B' = (0, .3] \cup [.7, 1)$. (c) $AB = (.3, .5]$. (d) $A \cup B = [.2, .7)$. (e) $AB' = [.2, .3]$.

SECTION 4

4.1. (a)

X	3	4	5	6	7	8	9	10	11	12	13	14	15
f	1	1		3	5	11	15	23	11	12	11	5	2
cf	1	2		5	10	21	36	59	70	82	93	98	100

(b) Prop. $< 10 = .36$, Prop. $> 10 = .31$.

4.3. (a)

X	1	2	3	4	5	6
f	20	43	53	86	70	54

(b)

f/n	.0500	.1075	.1325	.2150	.1750	.1350

(a)

X	7	8	9	10	11	12
f	37	18	10	5	2	2 /400

(b)

f/n	.0925	.0450	.0250	.0125	.0050	.0050/1.000

SECTION 5

5.1. (a) .02560. (b) .01048.

5.3. (a) .229. (b) .120. (c) .880.

5.5. (a) $P(5 < x < 11) = .566$. (b) $P(2 < x < 7.2) = .421$.

5.7. (a) $A \cup B$: The card is red or even-numbered or both. $P = 36/52 = 9/13$. (b) $A \cap B$: A red, even-numbered card. $P = 10/52 = 5/26$. (c) $A \cup C$: The card is red or numbered less than 9, or both. $P = 42/52 = 21/26$. (d) $A \cap C$: A red card numbered less than 9. $P = 16/52 = 4/13$. (e) $A \cup B \cup C$: The card is red or even numbered less than 9. $P = 44/52 = 11/13$. (f) $A \cap (B \cup C)$: The card is red, and numbered 1, 2, 3, 4, 5, 6, 7, 8, 10. $P = 18/52 = 9/26$. (g) $B' \cap C$: The card is numbered 1, 3, 5, 7. $P = 16/52 = 4/13$.

5.9. 22/64.

SECTION 6

6.1. (a)

$x + y$	2	3	4	5	6
p	.06	.23	.35	.27	.09

(b)

$x^2 + y^2$	2	5	8	10	13	18
p	.06	.23	.20	.15	.27	.09

6.3. (b), (c).

SECTION 7

7.1. 2,522,520. 7.3 (a) .003968. (b) .3968. (c) .007936. (d) .3175.

7.5. .008816, $f(x_1, x_2, x_3, x_4) = \binom{52}{13}^{-1} \binom{13}{x_1} \binom{13}{x_2} \binom{13}{x_3} \binom{13}{x_4}$.

7.7. (a) $f(x) = \binom{5}{x}(.7)^x(.3)^{5-x}$. (b) $f(x) = \dfrac{\binom{7}{x}\binom{3}{5-x}}{\binom{10}{5}}$.

7.11. $p = .001$ 7.13. $p = .01$

7.15. .20183.

7.19. $p = .000617$.

7.21. Using binomial distribution with $p = .1$ (a) .348678 (b) .387420 (c) .193710 (d) .05739.

7.23. $p = .7113$.

7.25. $p = .0922$.

7.27. (a) 120/286. (b) 135/286. (c) 30/286. (d) 1/286.

7.29. 3/5.

SECTION 8

8.1. $\bar{X} = 10$, rms$(X) = 11.20$, var$(X) = 25.33$, $D(X) = 5.032$, $s_x^2 = 30.4$, $s_x = 5.514$.

8.9. $t = \bar{X}$ in both cases.

8.11. Mean $= \dfrac{(n\bar{X} + a)}{n + 1}$, Variance $= \dfrac{1}{n}\left[(n - 1)s_x^2 + n\bar{X}^2 + a^2 - \dfrac{(n\bar{X} + a)^2}{n + 1} \right]$.

8.13. $\bar{X} = 10.21$, $s_x^2 = 5.26$, $s_x = 2.29$.

8.15. $\bar{X} = 4.68$, $s_x^2 = 4.47$, $s_x = 2.11$.

8.17. $\bar{X} = 980.10556$, $s_x = .01003$.
8.19. $\bar{X} = 3.53$, $s_x = 1.48$.

SECTION 9

9.1. $\sigma^2 = (n + 1)/(12n)$.
9.3. (a) $a > \sqrt{200}$. (b) $a > 20$.

SECTION 10

10.3.

$\bar{x}$	1	1.5	2	2.5	3	3.5	4	4.5	5	5.5	6
p	1/36	2/36	3/36	4/36	5/36	6/36	5/36	4/36	3/36	2/36	1/36

10.5.

$\bar{x}$	1	2	3	4	5	6
f	16	40	52	52	40	16

SECTION 11

11.1. $E(X) = 3.5$, $E(X^2) = 91/6$, $\sigma^2 = 35/12$, $E(X^3) = 73.5$, $E(\log_{10} X) = .4762$, $E(1/X) = 49/120$.
11.3. $m_1' = 0$, $m_2' = 10.4$, $m_3' = 0$, $m_2 = 10.4$, $m_3 = 0$, $g_1 = 0$.
11.7. (a) $E(Y) = am_2' + b$, $D^2(Y) = a^2(m_4' + (m_2')^2)$. (b) $E(Z) = am_2' + bm_1' + c$, $D^2(Z) = a^2(m_4' - m_2'^2) + 2ab(m_3' - m_1'm_2') + b^2(m_2' - m_1'^2)$.
11.9. Expand $(X + 1)^r$ by the binomial theorem.

SECTION 12

12.1. (a) g.f. $= (1/6)(t + t^2 + t^3 + t^4 + t^5 + t^6)$, m.g.f. $= (1/6)(e^t + e^{2t} + e^{3t} + e^{4t} + e^{5t} + e^{6t})$. (b) g.f. $= (1/10)(t + \cdots + t^{10})$. m.g.f. $= (1/10)(e^t + e^{2t} + \cdots + e^{9t})$. (c) g.f. $= .2 + .4t + .3t^2 + .1t^3$, m.g.f. $= .2 + .4e^t + .3e^{2t} + .1e^{3t}$.
12.5. $\mu = np$, $\sigma^2 = npq$.
12.7. $G(t) = e^{\mu(t-1)}$, $M(t) = e^{\mu(e^t - 1)}$.

SECTION 13

13.1. $\bar{X} = 20.42$, $s_x = 1.72$.
13.3. Using the system of intervals 38.80–38.89, 38.90–38.99, $\cdots$, we find $\bar{X} = 39.320$, $s_x = .205$.

SECTION 14

14.1. $Q_3 = 21.56$, $P_{20} = 18.96$, $P_{65} = 21.12$, $P_{95} = 23.07$.
14.3. Interpolation: 2.93; by (10.2): 3.0.

SECTION 15

15.1. (a) $F(x) = 0$, $x < 1$; $F(x) = x - 1$, $1 \leq x \leq 2$; $F(x) = 1$, $x > 2$.

(b) $P(1.5 \leq x \leq 1.7) = .2$. (c)

.RN	.908	.326	.316
X	1.908	1.326	1.316

15.3. (a) $F(x) = 0, x < 0; F(x) = 1 - e^{-x}, x \geqq 0.$ (b) .00674.

(c)

.RN	.505	.181	.443	.728	.406
X	.703	.200	.585	1.302	.521

15.7.

.RN	.644	.367	.665	.025	.073
X	203.7	196.6	204.3	180.4	185.5

15.9. From $\log y = a - bx^2$, we find $y = 10^{a-bx^2} = e^{2.303a}e^{-2.303bx^2}$, hence $k_1 = e^{2.303a}\sqrt{2\pi}, k_2 = \sqrt{4.604b}.$

SECTION 16

16.1.

x^2	1	4	9	16		$1/x$	1	1/2	1/3	1/4
p	.1	.3	.2	.4		p	.1	.3	.2	.4

16.3. Density of $y = 3y/2\sqrt{y}, 0 \leqq y \leqq 1.$
16.5. Density of $y = 1/2\sqrt{y}, 0 \leqq y \leqq 1.$

SECTION 17

17.1. Yes, provided that $n > 2.$
17.3. 157.96961.

SECTION 18

18.1. $k = 12, F(x) = 3x^4 - 8x^3 + 6x^2, 0 \leqq x \leqq 1.$
18.3. $k = 15/8, F(x) = \frac{1}{8}(3x^5 - 10x^3 + 15x), 0 \leqq x \leqq 1.$
18.5. Not a density.
18.7. $k = 1/\pi, F(x) = \frac{1}{\pi}(\sin x - x \cos x + x), 0 \leqq x \leqq \pi.$
18.9 $k = [(\log 4) - 1.25]^{-1}, F(x) = 3.668x(4 - x)\log x, 1 \leqq x \leqq 2.$
18.11. $k = \beta/\pi, F(x) = \frac{1}{\pi}\left[\arctan\left(\frac{x-\alpha}{\beta}\right) + \frac{\pi}{2}\right], -\infty < x < \infty.$

SECTION 19

19.1. $\mu_n' = n!, \mu = 1, \sigma^2 = 1.$
19.3. $\mu_1' = 0, \mu_2' = 1/3, \mu_3' = 0.$
19.5. $\mu_1' = 4/5, \mu_2' = 2/3, \mu_3' = 4/7, M_x(t) = \frac{4e^t}{t^4}(t^3 - 3t^2 + 6t - 6 + 24e^{-t}).$
19.7. $\mu_1' = 0, \mu_2' = 1/6.$
19.9. $\mu_n' = 0$ if n is odd; $\mu_n' = (1)(3)(5) \cdots (n - 1)$, if n is even.
19.17. $M_x(t) = 1 + t + t^2 + \cdots.$

SECTION 20

20.1.   Frequency table: Probability table:

x \ y	1	2	3	
1	4	10	6	20
2	10	25	15	50
3	6	15	9	30
	20	50	30	100

x \ y	1	2	3	
1	.04	.10	.06	.2
2	.10	.25	.15	.5
3	.06	.15	.09	.3
	.2	.5	.3	1.0

The marginal and conditional distributions all reduce to those of the original urn.

20.3.

x	2	3	4	5
p	3/13	8/13	1/13	1/13

20.5. $k = 1/\pi, f_1(x) = (2/\pi)\sqrt{1 - x^2}, f_2(y) = (2/\pi)\sqrt{1 - y^2}, f(x|y) = (1/2)(1 - y^2), f(y|x) = (1/2)(1 - x^2)$.

20.7. $k = 6, f_1(x) = 3(1 - x)^2, f_2(y) = 3(1 - y)^2, f(x|y) = 2/(1 - y)^2, f(y|x) = 2/(1 - x)^2, P(x + y \leq .5) = 1/2$.

20.9. $k = (2/\pi)\sqrt{1 - x^2}, \ f_1(x) = (8/3\pi)(1 - x^2)^{3/2}, \ f_2(y) = (8/3\pi)(1 - y^2)^{3/2}, f(x|y) = (3/4)(1 - x^2 - y^2)(1 - y^2)^{-3/2}, f(y|x) = (3/4)(1 - x^2 - y^2)(1 - x^2)^{-3/2}$.

20.11. $f_1(x) = 6x(1 - x); f_2(y) = 6y(1 - y); f(x|y) = x/(y(1 - y)), 0 \leq x \leq y; f(x|y) = 1/(1 - y), y \leq x \leq 1 - y, 0 \leq y \leq 1/2; f(x|y) = 1/y, y \leq x \leq 1 - y, 1/2 \leq y \leq 1; f(x|y) = (1 - x)/(y(1 - y)), 1 \leq y \leq x \leq 1$.

20.13. 3/7.

20.15. (a) .08.   (b) .56.   (c) 2/9.

SECTION 21

21.1.

x + y	1	2	3	4	5	6
p	.12	.30	.19	.17	.19	.03

21.3. $G_1 = .4t + .2t^2 + .4t^3, G_2 = .16t^2 + .16t^3 + .36t^4 + .16t^5 + .16t^6, G_3 = .064t^3 + .096t^4 + .240t^5 + .200t^6 + .240t^7 + .096t^8 + .064t^9, G_4 = .0256t^4 + .0512t^5 + .1408t^6 + .1664t^7 + .2320t^8 + .1664t^9 + .1408t^{10} + .0512t^{11} + .0256t^{12}$.

21.5. $P = .1043$.

SECTION 22

22.3. $\tilde{d}_1 = .1732, \tilde{d}_2 = .0833, \tilde{d}_3 = .0487$.

SECTION 23

23.1. (a) .1757.   (b) .2617.

23.3. .0065.   (b) .0071.

23.5. 1, 10, 45, 120, 252, 210, 120, 45. 10, 1.

23.7.

x	p	p' (Normal approx)	Absolute Error $p - p'$	Per Cent Error
0	.1074	.0937	+.0137	12.8
1	.2684	.2285	+.0399	14.9
2	.3020	.3064	−.0044	14.6
3	.2013	.2285	−.0272	13.5
4	.0881	.0937	−.0056	6.4
5	.0264	.0212	+.0052	19.7
6	.0055	.0026	+.0029	52.7
7	.0008	.0002	+.0006	75
8	.0001	.0000	+.0001	100
9	0	0		
10	0	0		

23.9. (a) .0000.   (b) .0000.
23.11. (a) .1715.   (b) .4036.

SECTION 24

24.1. $f(x_1, x_2) = (1/24\pi)e^{-[(x_1-5)^2/18]-[(x_2-2)^2/32]}$.
24.3. .1714.
24.5. .2013.
24.7. .0224.

SECTION 25

25.1. (a) .1165.   (b) .1197.

SECTION 26

26.3. 310.56, 319.84.
26.5. .726.

SECTION 27

27.1. (a) $E(X) = 1.94$.   (b) $E(Y) = 1.95$.   (c) $E(X^2) = 4.42$.   (d) $E(Y^2) = 4.35$.
(e) $\sigma_x^2 = .6564$.   (f) $\sigma_y^2 = .5475$.   (g) $E(XY) = 3.82$.   (h) $\text{cov}(X, Y) = .0370$.
(i) $E(2X + 3Y) = 9.73$.   (j) $E(X^2Y) = 8.66$.   (k) $\rho = .0617$.
27.3. (a) 2/3. (b) 2/3. (c) 1/2. (d) 1/2. (e) 1/18. (f) 1/18. (g) 4/9. (h) 0.
(i) 10/3. (j) 1/3. (k) 0.
27.5. $f_1(x) = \frac{3}{2}x(2 - x)$, $f_2(y) = \frac{3}{2}y(2 - y)$, $E(x) = E(y) = \frac{5}{8}$, $\sigma_x^2 = \sigma_y^2 = \frac{19}{320}$, $\rho = \frac{3}{19}$.
27.9. $\mu_x = 0$, $\sigma_x^2 = 2c/(4ac - b^2)$, $\mu_y = 0$, $\sigma_y^2 = 2a/(4ac - b^2)$, $\rho = -b/(2\sqrt{ac})$.
27.17. $M_x(t) = a/(a - t)$, $M_y(t) = b/(b - t)$, $M_z(t) = M_x(t)\, M_y(t)$.
27.19. $1/\sqrt{2(1 - t^2)}$.

SECTION 28

28.1. X has the binomial distribution with $n = 200$, $p = 1/6$. The approximating normal distribution is $N(33.33, 27.78)$. X' is the 95th percentile of this distribution, that is, 42.00.

SECTION 29

29.1. H_0: $p = .95$; H_1: $p < .95$; $n = 200$; crit. stat. $= X =$ number of seeds germinating in a sample of 200. Crit. value $= 180.5$; i.e., the lot is rejected if the sample contains more than 180 non-germinating seeds.

29.3. H_0: $p = .5$; H_1: $p > .5$; crit. stat. $= X =$ number of voters favoring candidate in a sample of 1000; crit. value $= 526.01$; i.e., candidate will be supported if more than 526 of the sample favor him.

29.5. H_0: $\mu = 173.9$; H_1: $\mu > 173.9$; crit. stat. $= Z$, with distribution $N(0, 1)$. Crit. value: with $\alpha = .05$, $z_{.95} = 1.645$; with $\alpha = .01$, $z_{.99} = 2.326$. Sample value $Z = 3.744$; reject H_0.

29.7. H_0: $\mu_1 = \mu_2$; H_1: $\mu_1 \neq \mu_2$ (two-sided); crit. stat. $= t = Z$ [see (29.3)]. Crit. value: with $\alpha = .05$, $t_{.975} = z_{.975} = 1.960$; with $\alpha = .01$, $t_{.995} = z_{.995} = 2.576$. Sample value $t = 2.48$; accept H_0 at 5% level, reject H_0 at 1% level.

SECTION 30

30.7. Graphically, $n = 24$; by interpolation, $n = 23.7$.

SECTION 31

31.1. $(-.006, 5.220)$.

31.5. Using (31.5), $(.8436, .9496)$; using Exercise 31.3, $(.8579, .9621)$.

SECTION 32

32.1. The parameter p may vary over the interval $(0, 1)$. 32.3$\mu = x$.

SECTION 35

35.1.

x	0	1	2	3	4	5	6	7	8	9
$f(x)$	.1353	.2706	.2706	.1804	.0902	.0361	.0120	.0034	.0008	.0002

35.7. $f(x_1, \cdots, x_n) = \dfrac{k^{\Sigma x} e^{-nk}}{x_1! \cdots x_n!}$, $\hat{k} = \bar{X}$.

35.9.

x	0	1	2	3	4	5	6	7	8	9
rel f	0	.0013	.0037	.0064	.0152	.0296	.0525	.0741	.1007	.1113
$f(x)$	.0000	.0004	.0018	.0062	.0159	.0328	.0562	.0825	.1061	.1212

x	10	11	12	13	14	15	16	17	18	19
rel f	.1228	.1153	.1100	.0954	.0583	.0386	.0290	.1052	.0114	.0043
$f(x)$	.1246	.1165	.0998	.0790	.0580	.0398	.0255	.0155	.0088	.0048

x	20	21	22
rel f	.0017	.0021	.0008 , $\bar{X} = 10.2826$.
$f(x)$	.0025	.0012	.0005

SECTION 36

36.1. $\phi(u) = e^{-u/3} - e^{-u/2}$.

36.3. $\phi(u) = 3/2$ for $0 \leq u \leq 1/2$; $\phi(u) = (1 - u^2)/2u^2$ for $1/2 \leq u \leq 1$.

SECTION 37

37.1. .019.

37.3. .213.

37.5. H_0: $\sigma^2 = 29.7$; H_1: $\sigma^2 \neq 29.7$; crit. stat. s^2/σ^2; crit. values: 5.629, 26.119; sample value = 1.75; reject H_0.

SECTION 38

38.1. $f(x_1, x_2, x_3) = 2^{-1/2}\pi^{-3/2}e^{-(1/32)[4(x_1-2)^2+4(x_2+3)^2+(x_3-10)^2]}$.

38.3. $f(x_1, \cdots, x_n) = (\sigma_1 \cdots \sigma_n)^{-1}(2\pi)^{-3/2}e^{-[(x_1-\mu_1)^2/2\sigma_1^2+\cdots+(x_n-\mu_n)^2/2\sigma_n^2]}$.

SECTION 39

39.1. $\theta = \arctan 3$.

SECTION 40

40.1 $\chi^2 = .4056$, with 2 d.f.   Accept H_0.

40.3. $\chi^2 = 6.352$ with 11 d.f.   Accept H_0.

40.5. $\chi^2 = 6.09$, with 16 d.f.   Accept H_0.

SECTION 41

41.1. $P(Y/X > 3) = .1024$; $P(Y > 3X) = .5$.

41.5. .211.

41.7. H_0: $\sigma_1^2 = \sigma_2^2$; H_2: $\sigma_1^2 > \sigma_2^2$; crit. stat $= F = s_1^2/s_2^2$, which has the F distribution with 9, 9 d.f.; crit. value $= F_{.99} = 5.35$, sample value: $F = 1.53$; accept H_0.

SECTION 42

42.1. $X_1 = 4$, $X_3 = 7$, $X_5 = 8$, $X_9 = 12$, $X_{10} = 14$.

42.3. (a) Use the critical statistic X = number of values in the sample which are less than 6. With $\alpha = .0123$ the critical region is $X < 3$. Since the sample value is $X = 1$ we reject H_0. (b) .8205.

SECTION 43

43.1. (a) $E(X_1 + X_2)^3 = 2\mu_3' + 6\mu_1'\mu_2'$. (b) $E(X_1 + X_2)^4 = 2\mu_4' + 8\mu_1'\mu_3' + 6\mu_2'^2$. (c) $E(X_1 + X_2)^5 = 2\mu_5' + 10\mu_1'\mu_4' + 20\mu_2'\mu_3'$. (d) $E(X_1 + X_2 + X_3)^3 = 3\mu_2'^3 + 18\mu_1'\mu_2' + 6\mu_1'^3$. (e) $E(X_1 + X_2 + X_3)^4 = 3\mu_4' + 24\mu_1'\mu_3' + 18\mu_2'^2 + 36\mu_1'^2\mu_2'$.

SECTION 45

45.1. Regression.

45.3. Correlation.

45.5. Regression.

45.7. Correlation.

SECTION 47

47.1. $Y' = 999.39772 + .03417x$.

47.7. $Y' = 3.19507 + .44314X - .76591x^2$.

47.9. $\Sigma Y = na_0 + a_1\Sigma u_1 + \cdots + a_k\Sigma u_k$

$\Sigma u_1 Y = a_0\Sigma u_1 + a_1\Sigma u_1^2 + \cdots + a_k\Sigma u_1 u_k$

. . . .

$\Sigma u_k Y = a_0\Sigma u_k + a_1\Sigma u_1 u_k + \cdots + a_k\Sigma u_k^2$

SECTION 48

48.1. $\Sigma(Y - \overline{Y})^2 = 86$, $\Sigma(Y - Y')^2 = 1.9$, $\Sigma(Y' - \overline{Y})^2 = 84.1$.

SECTION 49

49.5. (b) $Y' = 60.721 + .28500x$. (c) $r = .4147$.

SECTION 51

51.1. $b = -.2422$, $s_{y \cdot x}^2 = 9.306$, $t = -.420$; accept H_0.

SECTION 52

52.1. (B).
52.3. (D).
52.5. (A).
52.7. (H3).

SECTION 54

54.1. (a) For a two-sided test the crit. region is $t > 2.201$, $t < -2.201$. Sample value of t is 1.838. Accept H_0. (b) Crit. region: $F > 4.84$. Sample value of F is 3.380. Accept H_0.

Index